Capitalist Dogs

A Financial Fable

By
Jack Katz
M.S., J.D.

Let *Wealth Corgis*, Wall Street's only pedigreed financial advisers, guide and teach you about the dog-eat-dog investing world, in a way never before dreamed possible.

Capitalist Dogs

Jack Katz, M.S., J.D.

Jack Katz

Pentland Press, Inc.
www.pentlandpressusa.com

PUBLISHED BY PENTLAND PRESS, INC.
5122 Bur Oak Circle, Raleigh, North Carolina 27612
United States of America
919-782-0281

ISBN 1-57197-285-4
Library of Congress Control Number: 2001 130321

Printed in the United States of America

For Leslie

I feel very fortunate to have had Barbara Nichols advise me on my first book. Barbara was the editor for the phenomenally successful *Chicken Soup for the Soul* book. *Cherchez la femme*: this book could not have been created without the support and encouragement of my wife Leslie, who also gave me some wonderful ideas for improving my work. The cover photos of Ricky "Don't Lose That Number" and author with Rosie O'Grady were taken by David Swain. Ricky was a generous gift to us from the well-known Corgi doctor, Charles Kruger of dockruger.com. In addition, I wish to specifically thank the following individuals who helped in one way or another to make this book possible:

Suzan R. Wilson M.A., M.F.C.C.
Dr. George Peterfy M.D., F.R.C.P.
Dr. Don Bonnington M.D.
Angela Fay Bellacosa
Kim Runciman
Marlin Vortman, J.D.
John White
Pat Carroll
V. James Gray
Joe West
Merwin Kato
"Money" Penny Edwards
Dr. Gary Palmer D.C.
The staff of Pentland Press

Introduction

My father introduced me to the stock market at an early age. We lived for a time in the far north mining town of Val D'Or (Valley of Gold), Quebec back when many of the prime stocks of the day were mining stocks, as Internet stocks are today. One day on his way to town, he passed by a mine and noticed that the employees were hard at work. When he checked the mine's listing on the stock exchange, he found that the stock of that company had taken heavy losses. He found, furthermore, that it was because of a rumor that the mine had closed. When he told people that the mine was still open for business, no one believed him or bothered to drive out of town and check it out. It would have been easy: the town was only one block long. So my father loaded up on shares of the mine's stock and the stock price skyrocketed the following day when the rumor was laid to rest.

One day, my father took me to the town "stock exchange," a room with rows of bridge chairs and an enormous chalkboard. Runners were rushing about changing the stock prices in white chalk as news came in by phone. On the front seat sat two brothers who had come from Montreal every summer for years to play the market, buying and selling mining stocks based on slight changes in price. They looked for action and patterns of investor behavior without caring what the stock represented or was worth. They were traders rather than investors. Without the luxury of computers, let alone the Internet, these two fellows consistently made enough money to spend the rest of the year in Florida. They were professionals who understood the markets and were highly disciplined about their business, unlike so many of the amateurs today. My father's stock market stories and my childhood observations gave me an appreciation for the importance of psychology and the role of commodities in investing long before I ever understood what these words meant.

For example, when my dad quit his job as a shoe salesman and opened up his first shoe store in Val D'Or, he lacked the capital to buy proper inventory. So, he bought a very small inventory of shoes for sales and to dress the store window. He filled the rest of the store with empty shoeboxes. No one was the wiser when he opened the door for business. The public assumed that the dozens of empty shoeboxes were actually filled with shoes.

This was my first memorable lesson about false assumptions and the power of marketing to create the illusion of content and substance. Those empty shoeboxes bring to mind what is going on in the highly lucrative financial sales education industry. Main Street investors get to see a few basic facts, lots of window dressing, with wall-to-wall boxes of empty sales information manufactured on Wall Street.

I became a stockbroker a few years ago. I had been interested in financial markets since my boyhood and thought my years of teaching experience and background would be of great advantage. My brokerage firm sent me to the World Trade Center in New York for training classes. I was initially excited because the self-study course used to help prepare for the brokers exam seemed to be mainly useful for getting the license and little else. I was filled with anticipation and ready to learn a great deal about the ins and outs of financial markets. Instead, the courses focused primarily on teaching sales techniques for three weeks. This is typical broker education. What distinguishes the top firms from the others is that you just get better sales training.

Towards the end of the training, one lecturer proudly announced to us, "You now know more than 90% of the investing public." I nearly burst out laughing. Assuming that our teacher's statement was correct, the public obviously could not know that much. I have seen little to change my opinion since then. The average broker (brokerage house anointed financial consultant or adviser) receives a financial education comparable to an education in nutrition funded and administered by manufacturers of snack foods and soft drinks. Small investors are then ill served with sugarcoated pabulum.

Study after study, by both the federal government and private industry, indicates that the average investor in charge of a retirement account is "financially illiterate." Actually, the situation is more serious than statistics indicate because the information given to investors often comes from biased sources such as mutual fund companies. The test scores also seem to be getting worse from year to year. An article in the November, 1998 *Research Magazine* entitled "The New Retiree" quotes the president of a financial planning firm: "I would say there's been a tremendous increase in awareness about retirement planning. The number of people who watch CNBC is way up. But folk's savvy has not increased. That's the crazy part."

Actually, it's not crazy at all. It makes perfect sense. The public is not getting a real education so much as it is dished out sales pitches combined with old-hat investment mantras like "buy and hold" and "you can't time the market" from a professional sales industry. It's bad enough that commercial interests are increasingly penetrating the high schools and even lower grades. In the investment world, the commercial interests dominate the educational system. What can one honestly expect for results? The sales industry, in self-defense, responds that financial products are getting more complex. They never question their competency to teach. Nor do they acknowledge their conflicts of interest. More worrisome still is the fact that the public doesn't much question it either. Maybe they will question it after the next economic downturn?

Occasionally, an investment book comes out by a highly touted "expert" who has worked at a leading Wall Street brokerage firm. Readers do not realize how meaningless that kind of background can be. That's why it's so effective. Their expertise usually resides in sales. The book cover may be compelling and the marketing may be outstanding, but the material is often the same old mediocre information distilled for a target audience of women, minorities and novice investors who are treated like children. Target marketing of adult audiences in this way can have the appearance of meeting special needs but is often demeaning. There is a double message: special can also mean second class learning. Niche marketing is too often about cosmetic changes to sell books. I'm waiting to see if such marketing will advance into fringe areas. Why not a book called *Trailer Trash Investing* or *Erotic Wealth Secrets for Lovers* or *Financial Advice for Vegetarians*? Sandwiched between the first class New Age marketing is still flat, unimaginative, low grade quality teaching—golden arched McDodo books with subprime material designed for quick mass consumption. The public deserves better choices than merely more varieties of junk food education.

Before I became involved as a professional in the financial world in the 1990s, I had taught for many years at the college and university level and I still do. My initial interest in writing this book arose in November of 1997. I was shopping in Seattle and saw a picture of Alan Greenspan, Chairman of the Federal Reserve, grinning from ear to ear on the cover of *Time* magazine with the caption, "Why is this man smiling?" *Because he is suffering from irrational exuberance,* I jokingly said to myself.

Greenspan had used the term "irrational exuberance" in 1996 to describe the public's possible overenthusiasm for the stock market or speculative excess as it climbed to heights never seen before. I wrote a one-page essay mocking the *Time* feature article and predicting that Alan Greenspan would not be smiling on the cover of any magazine in a year's time. Approximately eleven months later, there appeared somber pictures of Greenspan dealing with the greatest threat to the global financial system since the Great Depression. The only newspaper willing to print my comments was a paper called *The New Federalist.*

After being "published" for the first time and later experiencing the satisfaction of being correct in my prediction, I naturally became even more enthusiastic about writing financial material. I decided it was time to attempt to offer something significantly better than the 'dummy type' investing books, which probably serve only to contribute to the financial illiteracy problem. Are these books really about the input ability of the public or the output ability of the authors? I suspect it is often the latter. If the market moves significantly in a negative direction, there will likely be a well-deserved backlash against appealing, feel good, simplistic, "dummy" advice approaches. 'Dummy type' books seem to be much more about smart marketing from clever salespeople than wise investing. What I'm trying to do is offer the public genuine choice. It's meaningless to lecture the public about the need to be better educated when the choice is mostly between Tweedledee and Tweedledum investment books. I agree with the financial sales industry that education is important—too important to be learned from them.

My purpose as an educator is to encourage critical thought, provide information not commonly known, share insights and observations, explore areas not generally covered and offer a more rounded comprehensive view of the financial world than is present in typical texts.

As I set out to write this book, I sensed that the reader needed a way to remember the complex information I wanted to present. Facts by themselves tend to be boring and easily forgotten. It occurred to me that financial language is frequently colorful and often refers to animal behavior, such as in the term "dead cat bounce," which is used to describe a mild stock recovery after a steep drop. Taking my lead from those famous Wall Street bulls and bears, I came up with a cast of animal characters to guide you through the financial jungle. I have found that animals afford an easy and entertaining way to remember the concepts presented, and so I have allowed them to present the information in the form of a financial fable.

The main characters are "Wealth Corgis" the capitalist dogs of the title. I am quite familiar with Welsh Corgis since my wife and I have adopted four such dogs that needed a good home. We have found that they are very smart and determined dogs. All through the book one Wealth Corgi or another leads the reader through situations in which other animal characters explain the ins and outs of the financial marketplace.

In *Capitalist Dogs* you will meet many characters. You'll meet a clam that explains insider information, a vulture capitalist, a currency shark, a legal weasel, a financial ferret, a corporate gadfly, a financial albatross, a corporate mole, a financial sloth, a cash cow, a commodity bull and an accounting cheetah. Even famous personalities like legendary super investor *Warren Bassett* and billionaires *Billy Goats* and *H. Ross Parrot* offer sophisticated information not found in conventional investment books. One of my main teaching goals has been to use this fantasy world of animal characters as a door to a better understanding of the real financial and investing jungle; and help empower you to deal with a system that in many respects preys on small investors.

In this book, I include much about psychology, a subject I have taught for many years separately and as part of an interdisciplinary course called Law and Psychology. It's difficult to find good books that cover psychology in the financial world. Behavioral finance, which studies the impact of emotions on investment behavior, has recently become a hot topic in the investment world and in academic circles. But the books available are, for the most part, dry textbooks. Additionally, no books that I am aware of cover all three topics of psychology, law and investing as this one does. *Capitalist Dogs* explores not only psychology, but also how psychoanalytic concepts might explain investment behavior. I believe that *Capitalist Dogs* presents a higher level of information than most books about the financial markets, yet is readable, entertaining, and helpful for those dedicated to creating and preserving wealth.

The story takes place in and around a bakery where all the big dough is made. The capitalist dogs meet and discuss the financial world with a host of zany and informative characters. My intention is for the readers to have their financial cake and eat it too. Sophisticated financial information to empower investors can be presented in a way that is easily and enjoyably digested. Bon appetit!

—Jack Katz
Seattle
October 2000

"The Good, the Bad, and the Corgi"

*You see things, and you say, "Why?" But I dream
things that never were, and I say, "Why not?"*
—George Bernard Shaw

"Tell me, Mr. Catz, isn't it true that the easiest way to make a small fortune is to start off with a really large one?" demanded a husky, male voice which heavily stressed the word "true" to the point where it felt like an annoying ringing sound in Bob's ears. On the final night of the 20th century, Bob Catz slowly awakened to a dream. He could feel his five-foot-three-inch body quickly shrinking to such an extent that he found himself standing up and staring directly into the eyes of a friendly looking red and white haired, fox-like dog with very short legs. The head of this constantly smiling adult dog was so large that it had kind of a teddy bear look. On top of the dog's long back was a very small version of a well-worn, brown leather English riding saddle.

"Greetings," the little dog said sharply in a Welsh accent. "I hope you don't mind, but I do enjoy asking 'isn't it true' type questions after watching all those lawyer programs on late night television. From your stunned look, I have the feeling you have never encountered an 'in your face' type of dog before. Please allow me to introduce myself. My name is Sir Real. I'm a purebred Pembroke Welsh Corgi, which is sometimes known as 'the Queen's dog.' We're the reigning dogs, Mr. Catz."

This made Bob wonder and prompted him to ask, "Are you addressed as 'Sir' because you are a Queen's dog?"

"No," replied Sir Real, "all Corgis are called Queen's dogs. Corgis have been part of the British Royal family for many years. However, only I, Rich Real, have had the distinct privilege of being knighted by Queen Elizabeth II."

This further caused Bob to wonder and inquire, "Why you?"

To which Sir Real replied, "It happened shortly after I explained to the Queen during 'high tea' how the American stock market will probably go to the dogs in the not-too-distant future. During the ceremony on the palace grounds, the Queen remarked how much she valued my dogged skepticism."

"Of course." Bob observed, "You are one of those real rich Welsh Corgis known as 'Wealth Corgis.' I remember reading about you in one of those ostentatious displays of wealth magazines called *Puttin' On The Dog*; or maybe it was in *Is Martha Stewart Really Living?* magazine. I can't be sure. At any rate, why would this subject be of such interest to royalty? The closest I have ever come to royalty have been my contacts with drama queens, student princes and a date long ago with a spoiled American princess."

Sir Real didn't have a tail, but wagged his body rhythmically and responded, "Tech tock. Tech tock. It's about the cyclical clock, which not even rulers of high technology can escape. It's about time—the greatest ruler of all. Her Majesty knows that in good economic times when borrowing is relatively easy, making risk more popular, even the lowliest commoners may treat rich, green cash as paw, white trash. However, the Queen also recognizes that cycles ultimately rule the economic world. What is not supposed to go on forever usually doesn't. Things change. Demand slacks off as markets become saturated. Companies find they have over invested in expansion and technology from over optimism and misplaced fears about competitors and then have to scale back. That's what cycles are about.

"The Queen knows that prosperity often leads to overconfidence and excess, which is followed by economic downturns; and that markets are not only shortsighted but have short memories. She appreciates how stocks of companies crowned with exaggerated worth, and borrowers owing princely sums, can be quickly dethroned as interest rates rise. Her Highness understands far better than her high tech loving subjects how even the high and mighty can be brought to their knees by a price uprising from lowly commodities such as common base metals, crude oil and even the most unrefined food products.

"Her Majesty is deeply concerned that accountants so often cleverly manipulate company earnings reports that the investing public is being subjected to an unprecedented reign of error, which may one day undermine confidence in the financial markets. Most of all, the Queen fully accepts that in tough economic times, cash always becomes King and only companies consistently achieving greater than expected profits will continue to get the royal treatment by investors. You see, it all has to do with royalty."

Bob, who had hung on every word Sir Real had uttered, exclaimed, "My God. What a head she must have to figure all that out."

To which Sir Real commented, "Naturally, it's the Queen's *job* to be a figurehead, not live in a world of make-believe."

Bob perceived that behind Sir Real was a large body of dark black, soupy liquid composed of numbers that moved back and forth with a wave-like sound and was lightly covered with mist. Multicolored certificates marked "stocks" and "bonds" from companies Bob had never heard of such as "As Seen On TV," and "Bubble.Com, Inc." floated on top. Some of the certificates looked freshly minted while others appeared to be much older. Astonished, he could only say, "Why are those certificates floating in that primordial looking soup? Doesn't anyone clean up around here?"

Sir Real explained, "Let me assure you that corporations, lawyers and the capitalist pig investment bankers clean up around here all the time. Those fresh looking ones are new issues of corporate securities made available to the public to buy and sell. Corporations trade their 'securitized paper' created through what are called investment banks to obtain public cash or capital. This is what 'going public' means with one's company. By such means, a company can fund its business either through offering shares of the company to the general public and/or borrowing through bonds.

"The first time a stock is sold to the public it is called an initial public offering, or IPO. Emotions among would-be investors can run high with demand outstripping supply. So prices may be driven up too high in the beginning. That's why IPO has been said to also stand for 'It's Probably Overpriced.' Like any stock, there is no assurance that an IPO price will float, let alone fly. Some flounder after issuance or, like a salmon, swim upstream only to die. The public has the mistaken belief that capitalist pig bankers have this high-quality control system for bringing companies public. That's hogwash. It's all about pigging out on astounding commissions. That's the real screening process. You can check for new offerings to the public at sites such as www.ipomonitor.com. Shares that are offered to the public at later dates from the same company are called secondary offerings. Remember, though, that the more shares there are in circulation, the more diluted the value of existing shares become."

Bob was fascinated. He pursued the subject further by asking, "How common is this need for public money?"

Sir Real was more than happy to respond. "Very common. The public capital or money markets, which include both stocks and bonds, have become more and more important over time as a source of funds rather than getting the money from banks. Bond markets are not only serving the credit needs of companies, but are also serving the needs of banks which convert their loans into securitized debt sold to the public in the form of bonds—allowing them to make even more loans. Banks syndicate, or sell off portions of their loans to the marketplace. You can buy into those corporate loans, as you will learn later when you meet a financial jackass. These general methods of funding by going to the public for money are called 'the float.' The float is about what the public owns and is separate from what the company owns. Once in the marketplace, through a public offering, this paper can swim or sink in value depending on investor interest. No one knows for sure what will happen until some time after a stock or bond issue is floated. Sinking prices aren't necessarily a bad thing. Sometimes they can be quite profitable if you know how to pick up bargains and bet against the market."

Bob commented, "There seems to be quite a few of those Bubble.Com certificates marked 'bond' and 'stock.' What kind of a company is that?"

"I'm not sure," replied Sir Real, "I think it's an Internet company. All I know is that they have never made any profits and if they do one day, it will be probably at the cost of drastically slimming down their operations. They keep floating equity, or shares of the company, and debt, or bonds, to acquire funding to keep operating and expanding. There isn't enough money from profits or internal operations, so money has to come from somewhere. How long this will keep up is anyone's guess. It's all part of a great dream—a dream of future profits with unproven companies. I understand their stock price is currently floating near the bottom of its fifty-two-week price range. In this world, even when something sinks it can still be said to float."

Bob, who was always one to look on the bright side, exclaimed, "After hearing how much the business world is dog-eat-dog, I find it quite refreshing to hear that, even in this day and age, people are still willing to give others a huge amount of credit just for trying!"

Sir Real continued, "Yes, it's kind of a funny thing. Those who invest in the stocks and bonds of such new or relatively new unproven post-public companies are sometimes called 'unknowing venture capitalists.' Real venture capitalists are those who knowingly take high risks while investing in new *pre*-public companies. Small investors don't usually think of themselves as 'unknowing venture capitalists,' but that's how some professionals describe them."

"Cool!" exclaimed Bob. "I've recently started a business called The Two Catz Fabricating Company and expect I'll be rejected by my local commercial bank. Can *I* do one of those float things?"

"I doubt it," sighed Sir Real. "Please understand. It's not just because your company name sounds like a total fabrication and has an underlying sexual tone to it. A company has to be a fairly big or important fish in the pre-public company pond to catch the interest of an investment bank. Then the bank may support or underwrite the pre-public company so that it can become publicly traded. An investment bank is a different breed of bank."

"How so?" inquired Bob.

"Well," explained Sir Real, "an investment bank can't provide commercial loans or accept savings deposits. However, it can help secure loans for a company from the public through a bond offering. An investment bank is where you go to get advice and assistance in going to the public markets for funds. This backing is called 'underwriting' and constitutes some of the most profitable business of investment banks. The banks' fat fees often come to approximately 7% of the money raised. That amounts to a heck of a lot when hundreds of millions and billions are involved per transaction."

"Going public is the way to even greater success, isn't it?" asked Bob.

Seeing that he had an enthusiastic student in Bob, Sir Real was happy to continue his lecture. "Even if you have a highly successful private company, taking it public might be seen as validation of your success, but it doesn't necessarily mean it will be successful as a public company. Moreover, the previously *private* company will be open to all kinds of public as well as governmental scrutiny and demands. Entrepreneurs lose a lot of the control they once enjoyed. It intensifies the pressure to show results. Moreover, company owners have to be prepared to go on the road for months on end performing what is called a 'dog and pony road show,' explaining to potential big investors, like mutual funds, why the company deserves to go public and be invested in."

Not happy at all about his bleak prospects, Bob insisted, "But my company needs money."

Sir Real replied, "Who doesn't? The chief problem for entrepreneurial companies is the need for capital or money to grow. An IPO, however, isn't the only way you can go. If your company has potential and you need funds for expanding, you can approach what is called the private equity market. There you may find private financial supporters such as angel investors and venture capitalists."

Seeing that there was hope, Bob's tone brightened, "What do they do?"

"Well," Sir Real began, "it's about ground floor investing in a company. Angel investors often provide at least $100,000 in what is known as seed capital to help fledgling start-ups get off the ground in return for a share of ownership in a pre-public company. Often the angel investors are friends, neighbors or relatives. Some of the biggest corporations in America were helped initially by angel funds. For angels the devil is in the details of making money with a very high risk investment.

"There are also funds run by deep-pocketed kangaroos called venture capitalists that may fund your enterprise. Venture capitalism involves professional underwriting, but at a much lower level than investment banks. They tend to be involved later in the pre-public process, perhaps after you have demonstrated success with angel money. Venture capitalists invest other people's money—rich people's money—and those of institutions. The objective of venture capitalist investment is often to get a handsome profit later on by "liquefying" the investment in the public markets through an IPO. Wealthy individuals who invest in those kind of funds have to meet net worth requirements of $1 million or more or have an annual income of $200,000 or more— $300,000 or more if married."

"Why?" asked Bob.

"This is a legal requirement," explained Sir Real, "to become an 'accredited' investor in a venture capital fund. There are many opportunities as well as risks involved. That's why there is a legal barrier to entry for these pre-public ventures. Of course, as I mentioned, you can act like a venture capitalist in a post-public company by buying shares in a new company with no long-term track record or any at all. True blue venture capitalists may demand too much of the company for some entrepreneurs, so other methods can be used. This is just another way to go other than a commercial bank loan, which often demands a track record."

"So the next step means my company has to grow big enough to do a big public offering?" asked Bob.

"Not necessarily," responded Sir Real. "Surely you have heard of *Lattesbucks Coffee* in this frothy cappuccino economy of ours?"

"No," replied Bob. "Who's Lattesbucks? Do you go there?"

"Oh no," exclaimed Sir Real, aghast at the very idea. "Being from Wales, Corgis never order lattes, mochas or anything expensive. We only order cheap black coffee with refills, which make us very apprehensive."

"So who's Lattesbucks?" Bob asked. "Well," responded Sir Real, "they are quite common across the nation and are expanding worldwide. You don't get out much, do you? Anyway, there is a little, determined underdog company that is nipping at their heels in Seattle which would enjoy hearing your response. Just about everywhere you see a Lattesbucks in Seattle, this underdog establishes a very competitive coffeehouse practically next door or across the street. It's the first coffee retail service company to challenge Lattesbucks' nationally. They have already set up shop on Wall Street."

To this Bob exclaimed, "Well, this little underdog company can't be that little if they are already in the world's leading financial area."

Sir Real expanded further, "It's actually a coffee shop on Wall Street in downtown Seattle. Unlike regular dogs, Wealth Corgis don't do tricks, they just perform language tricks. One of the lessons you will be learning on your financial journey is the importance of not jumping to conclusions or at least not becoming a top athlete. I won't bother telling you the name, because you don't even know who Lattesbucks is. What I will tell you is that instead of going public at this time, they used another method called a 'small public offering.' With this procedure, a small war chest of money was raised to continue fighting the daily grinding coffee battles in the marketplace without incurring the prohibitive costs of full federal registration."

"I see you like to play with words as well as dough. What do you mean by costly full registration?" asked Bob. "Do you smell something really fishy? I do. It reminds me of the herring you buy in a delicatessen. I think it's pickled herring."

"Most definitely herring," announced Sir Real, "but not pickled and it doesn't smell schmaltzy either. My sense of smell is far more powerful than yours because my nose is padded with extra membranes to soak up smells. It smells smoked to me. That must be Ms. Red Herring you are talking about."

With barely a sound, a red herring the size of a small car bobbed to the surface of the green liquid mass and came to its edge. It opened its dark red colored mouth and began to speak, "Hello, I'm called Red. The expression 'red herring' came about from dragging a smoked herring across a trail to distract hounds. Before you went on your merry way, I wanted to make sure you knew about me and my pals at the SEC."

"What is the SEC?" asked Bob.

"SEC," Red responded, "stands for Securities and Exchange Commission. It is a federal agency, or arm of the government. Agencies are set up to deal with complex technical matters like regulating securities and creating rules that have the effects of laws with powers of enforcement. The SEC is in charge of supervising all investment trading done by exchanges, associations, individuals and companies.

"Accordingly, the government watchdogs of the SEC require that any new issue of shares or bonds going to the public that isn't exempt under law, such as a small public offering, go through a full federal registration process. This is to insure that the investing public is fully informed about the security and the company that issued it. The law requires that a prospectus, a detailed information statement, be given to buyers."

"Why is that important?" Bob inquired.

Red went on to explain, "The initial prospectus contains important material and information designed for full and fair disclosure about the company and the offering. Many investors these days are breezing past the information in prospectuses anxious to get in on the hot new public issues. They can get burned by the hot IPO later on. It's been called the 'crying wolf' phenomenon. Many an investor considers all the legal warnings just cries of wolf, until the wolf comes to their door. As long as the companies have provided proper information, they are the ones who are protected."

"How does this process work?" wondered Bob aloud.

"After a company files its application with the Securities and Exchange Commission," Red explained, "there is a twenty-day cooling off period while the material is being reviewed. The only material a prospective customer can see is this preliminary prospectus."

"Does this have a name?" Bob asked.

"Yes, Red answered, "you are looking at it. The preliminary prospectus is called a 'red herring.' Red herring is about me, Buster. No sales are allowed on the red herring until the SEC gives the final prospectus a green light. It doesn't have a cool name like mine. It's just called final prospectus. What many investors don't understand is how important a prospectus is. It is designed to reveal the heart and guts of the company including expected competition, risk factors, who is backing the company, et cetera. Companies like Venture Wire at www.herring.com can help with information on backers. A prospectus is a really good way to learn about what you may be investing in. You want to see if anything smells fishy. Copies are available from brokers or through www.freedgar.com."

"So the government is guaranteeing what is said?" queried Bob.

"Not at all," retorted Red. "Are you making an assumption? Who said that? I never said that. Did anyone hear me say that? I would remember. The government just reviews the prospectus to ensure that it contains the material facts it deems necessary. It doesn't decide whether the prospectus is fishy or not. The government doesn't guarantee what's said, and doesn't say whether it approves or disapproves of the issue. It simply clears the stock or bond for distribution. Of course, if the company lies about what they say, then they and anyone involved would be answerable to the SEC, as well as individual investors suing them. It often pays to wait weeks or even months later after a new issue comes out to

see how it floats in value over time. It's time for me to float away."
Red Herring then swam backward, slowly sinking in the distance.

Bob was amazed at what he saw. "Why is that liquid mass
made of different consistencies? Am I having some kind of a semi-
solid wet dream? I do feel kind of excited."

"You should be so lucky. It's strictly for financial reasons," Sir
Real responded. "You are merely looking at various forms of
liquidity. Liquidity is about the world of buyers and sellers for all
types of assets. When we talk about liquidity in this world, we are
talking about the ease of change into goods and services or
convertibility. The financial world demands liquidity. It's the
equivalent of a lubricant for the financial system. The near global
meltdown of the financial system in 1998 was actually about a
liquidity crisis.

"The system of buyers and sellers, borrowers and lenders, nearly
seized or froze up like machinery. Many corporate borrowers, for
example, couldn't access new funds because of spreading fear that
drove up borrowing costs or shut them out completely. They
developed liquidity problems, which in turn affected others like a
domino effect because they didn't have the cash or credit to pay
bills. It has been estimated that half the businesses, in general, that
fail each year in good times are profitable. They may be owed a lot
of money, but they don't have cash on hand, proper liquidity, to
meet their needs."

"What about the really clear part?" asked Bob.

Sir Real replied, "The clearest part of this soupy mass behind
me contains liquid assets. Liquid assets are the purest form of
money, a virtual stash—numbers in a financial account listed
under U.S. cash. Cash assets are the purest form of assets because
of their ease of convertibility to other assets, portability and
transferability. The Swiss franc and Dutch guilder for the past
twenty years have been much stronger currencies than the U.S.
dollar. However, when it comes to liquidity, the dollar goes further.
Money is not simply a medium of exchange. It's about liquid asset
power on paper and the ability to change."

"I see," Bob said, "So what about stocks?"

"The liquidity of stocks depends on what you own," Sir Real
replied. "Stocks that are not publicly traded, as in private companies,
have generally very low liquidity, meaning it can be very difficult
to sell them. Publicly traded stocks have much higher liquidity, but

even stocks that are publicly traded can have low liquidity, such as those selling for under a dollar. When you own securities such as stocks and bonds, you have daily paper losses and gains. Until a security is sold, you don't know what the final price will be or even if you can sell it. When you sell a security, you still have to wait several business days to have the proceeds listed in your account. No matter how easy it may be to sell the security for the price you want, there is still a waiting period that affects liquidity. Home real estate, in comparison, is relatively illiquid because it can take days, months or years to convert to cash."

"Why is the liquid mass so choppy?" asked Bob.

Sir Real continued his exposé. "Financial markets are always in a state of flux. Prices are constantly fluctuating—going up or down. Right now, too, there is also a lot of additional liquidity in the moat because bankers are in relatively relaxed moods and loaning lots of money. With worries about the end of the century computer glitches adversely affecting the financial system, the Federal Reserve Bank has opened up credit valves. You'll get a look at them soon.

"That's one of the reasons why you see the liquid occasionally overflowing its banks. The M1 credit valve was opened up so much that the money supply from that valve alone shot up 15% just in December. The central bank has flooded the system with extra credit and money to the extent that interest rates during the last few days of this year have been brought down to 4%. Our central bank wants to make sure that our banking system remains afloat in case anything goes wrong.

"If nothing bad happens, this excess liquidity will probably further feed into the financial markets and have to be drained off later. Investors may end up with access to too much easy low interest rate money. A large spillover into the stock market from all this extra liquidity can drive up stock prices even higher than their current sky-high levels. The problem for investors is that a subsequent fall can become much harder when cloud nine is replaced by storm clouds on the economic horizon."

"How can the economic climate change?" asked Bob, doing his best to follow Sir Real.

"Well," began Sir Real, "the liquidity level can change when the credit cycle swings in the opposite direction and the valves are tightened by orders of the Federal Reserve. The liquid level will then go down considerably. You'll see. Right now, rising tides of liquidity continue to raise corporate boats—even those with holes in them. The abundant liquidity also helps support business theories that can't hold water. However, this kind of financial wealth can evaporate very quickly when liquidity starts to dry up with interest rate increases. A financial drought makes it much harder to make new public offerings for stock and bond sales. All sales require demand.

"The financial process should become clearer when you talk to Cecilia, our corporate seal. Cecilia is unavailable at the moment because she discovered this whole treasure trove of what are called 'underwater options' at the bottom of the moat behind me. They are actually quite worthless, but she is one of those compulsive collectors. Enough talk about business. Why don't you relax and take a good look at our corporate landscape?"

As Sir Real was speaking, the mist continued to roll back like a curtain on command revealing the oddest scenery Bob had ever come across. Bob took out a pen and notepad, which he always brought with him to record what he saw and heard. He then proceeded to ask more questions. "What kind of response are you getting to your opinion about the possible future course of the American stock market?"

"Of course my views are unpopular with the masses," began Sir Real, "especially the masses of American investors where now nearly half of all households, some fifty million, are invested directly or indirectly in the stock market. Never before have the fortunes of so many Americans been tied to the movements of the stock market. At the beginning of 1990, less than 20% of households participated, less than 10% in 1980. Many Americans have become very reliant on the ever-rising success of the stock market for 'the wealth effect' to buy more goods, services and pay for retirement. There is an assumption encouraged by New Era enthusiasts, those who believe new technology and 'free trade' can save us from boom-bust cycles of the past, that the trends of the '90s will simply continue.

"Yet, financial markets rarely ever take the long view for very long. Personal savings rates are currently at their lowest level in recent history—the lowest recorded since the Great Depression. This is not good for what is called personal liquidity: the ability to access an exact amount of cash or liquid assets whenever you need to. Some economic critics have claimed that too many investors are living in a make-believe financial world—sort of like this one."

"Please go on," urged Bob.

"My pleasure," declared Sir Real. "I have talked about the dangers of overreliance on the stock market for savings and that the investing climate, from what will soon be the longest business expansion ever seen in this country, will change. What has been called a virtuous circle of stock market gains feeding into the economy and back again into the stock market, could one day I fear reverse itself; and become a vicious circle—a riches to rags wealth effect in reverse.

"To my surprise, I have been told I have a lot of nerve to say that life is just a bell curve. The bulk is in the middle, the rest at the extremes. That's what it seems. My American lecture series, *Fat Years, Lean Years and Some In Between*, has been labeled obscene for daring to suggest a return to the mean. Critics have claimed that I can do nothing but damage if I continue to preach about the law of the average. Not too long ago, many investors thought high inflation was a permanent state of affairs. Now many think quite the opposite. Things tend to normalize, come full circle, and average out. That's all I'm really barking about."

Chew On This

Bob exclaimed, "I see what you mean by reversion to the mean and how one day it could do a *real number* on me. However, Americans these days are not receptive to that kind of talk. They want to hear rosy New Era economic predictions with dreamy state numbers, not old-fashioned fundamentals. The average American with his average retirement nest egg relying on the statements of the average financial expert, and average market performance—based on what's happened in the market for the past ten years—doesn't want to know about your mean world of statistics. Even though you are a rather handsome little dog with a knighthood, Americans obviously perceive you as not having been brokerage house broken. They rightfully think you are just a big pooper—a party pooper. Queen's dog, my foot. You made a major *faux paw, n'est paw*? Now tell me truthfully, is Sir Real really your name?"

To this Sir Real retorted, "All I can tell you for now is that what I have to say is for real and that the growing gap between the super wealthy and the public is surreal. I also believe real time is certainly the best way to do business. This means I like to do business in the financial markets with no delay whatsoever in receiving price information."

"Although you have ducked my question," said Bob, "why is real time of such importance?"

"You'll see what I'm talking about when I introduce you to Black in the Box," replied Sir Real, "and you'll learn why mutual fund investors are usually in the dark about what they own."

"Is Black in the Box some kind of burger chain?" asked Bob. "Unlike you, I don't have any *e. coli* resistance."

"No," Sir Real answered, "but what Black in the Box has to say might help prevent your investments from turning into ground meat. Hamburger can be made from castrated bulls—even stock market bulls. It's about thinking outside of the box—the mutual fund box. Ms. Box is the name of a notorious black sheep from the mutual fund industry. She has a big beef with them, often complaining about how they pull the wool over the eyes of investors who get fleeced on taxes. I understand that she is currently writing a book called *The Science of the Lambs*, inspired by the recent slaughter of mutual fund investors in Japan, where funds reportedly lost up to 90% of their value. Can you imagine what the results might have been without the benefit of professional money managers in the land of rising losses and setting sums? When an economic downturn happens in the U.S. the public will learn that American fund managers can pick dog stocks, big time losers, just like their Japanese counterparts and amateur investors."

In amazement, Bob asked, "What *are* mutual funds good for?"

Sir Real replied, "There are three basic types of funds: those that deal with stocks, bonds or money market funds. Mutual funds have a number of great advantages such as the need for minimal amounts of money to access professional money management and the financial markets; but it can be at the cost of minimal knowledge about your investments and minimal control over them. Black in the Box will also talk about other, perhaps better, choices."

Bob simply said, "I don't know much about stocks or bonds. I don't know much about mutual funds. I do know that I would like to know more."

"Rest assured, you will likely know far more than many others about investing and related matters by the time I'm finished with you. Any Queen's dog can easily run circles around the dogma the general public is exposed to and run-of-the-puppy mill financial adviser training. Please understand that it is a sensitive issue with us. Corgis, being of small stature, know what it is like to be talked down to; and work hard to offer more than is expected, like any good company."

Bob, eager to learn more, asked, "So what are stocks?" Sir Real, just as eager to teach, began, "For now, just think of stocks as units of ownership or shares in a company with the ability to profit from this relationship; and yet have no day-to-day responsibilities or legal liability. No matter what happens to the company, the most you can lose is your principal—what money you invested. As far as legal liability is concerned, it doesn't make a difference what company your company keeps.

"Stocks are often chosen for their ability to increase in value and achieve what is called capital appreciation. If you hold a stock at least a year before selling it, then any gain in its value is taxed as a capital gain, which is a much lower rate than ordinary income taxes.

"Stocks in general over the past century have provided a higher rate of return than bonds. However, everything is a trade-off. In order to achieve a higher rate of return, you are taking on more risk. These days with the overall stock market in the U.S. achieving double-digit gains year after year, it's difficult for many to see the added risk. A sense of lower risk has been cited as a major reason for the rapid growth of the stock market in recent years."

"And what about bonds?" Bob asked.

"Bonds involve loans to companies and governments," Sir Real replied, "and are considered to be relatively safer, but with less opportunity for profit. There are basically two ways to invest in the markets: become an owner or lender. Bonds in general provide steady income in the form of interest payments, which are taxed as ordinary income tax and tend to be much safer. For example, they are rated for safety with the higher levels being called bank or investment grade bonds and lower levels being below-investment grade or junk as they are sometimes called. In return for higher levels of safety, one tends to get lower rates of return than stocks. Taxes, risk level and rate of return, which is how much you stand to make, generally influence the choice."

"And mutual funds?" asked Bob.

"Mutual funds," Sir Real continued, "are about pooling your money with others through an investment company that selects stocks and other securities like bonds for you. An investment company is a general term to describe companies, which have these pools of money for investing and are traded on the stock market for the general public to buy into. When it comes to mutual fund-type investment companies, different pools of money are used for different purposes, resulting in thousands of mutual funds to choose from. As an investor, you buy and sell shares in one or more of these funds. Since your money is just added to this pool of other money, you can't individually own securities like stocks and bonds."

"I understand a little about stocks and bonds," said Bob, wanting to know more, "but what did you mean by money market funds?"

"Money market funds," said Sir Real, "mean that your money is invested in an extremely stable mutual fund that invests in short-term government and corporate debt, passing the interest to shareholders in the form of dividends. The funds aim to achieve a stable $1 per share value, but they are neither insured nor guaranteed by the U.S. government. There is no guarantee of any kind. It's what is called an 'implied guarantee' to maintain a $1 per share value. The money isn't sitting in a savings account as cash because it's being invested. Shares owned in the money market fund have to be sold to convert to cash. The ease of converting to cash speaks to the degree of liquidity. They are known as cash equivalents.

"Money market funds themselves can have different degrees of liquidity. There are checking accounts with instant access and others that require a three-business day waiting period just like when you sell any other security. Money market funds tend to provide higher interest rates than savings accounts for the extra risk and relatively lower liquidity involved. They also have a floating interest rate that goes up or down depending on general interest rate conditions. That's why they have become so popular."

"What happens if interest rates go up?" asked Bob.

"If the interest rate rises," Sir Real responded, "the money market funds, which involve short term loans, pay a higher rate of interest soon after while your principle still maintains a stable dollar a share in value. These money funds are about loans like bond funds, except that bond funds are riskier. If interest rates rise, longer-term bond funds suffer because they are longer term and paying a lower rate of interest. Since these bond funds are worth less because they pay less interest, their value tends to go down.

"When it comes to providing income and stability, there has been a big shift in the direction of money funds and away from bond funds. Still bond funds are very popular and may be recommended over money funds simply because money funds often don't pay a commission to brokers. There is pressure to get clients to invest in either bonds or stocks. Money funds are excellent funds for providing protection against rising interest rates, which tend to depress stock and bond prices. There are money funds that mention federal insurance. However, a careful reading of the literature probably reveals that it only applies when the money fund does a 'sweep' of cash into your account at the end of the day. During the day, the money is, of course, invested. Not only dogs are good at tricks. Furthermore, the public often wrongly assumes that money funds are basically alike. There are important legal loopholes in the aura of safety net that surrounds them. One day nest eggs could fall through these holes. The safest funds rely on government guarantees mostly or entirely."

"How many investors own mutual funds?" asked Bob.

"Perhaps as many as sixty to eighty million people in the U.S. now own mutual funds, depending on what news report you read," replied Sir Real. "Yes, it can vary that much. Stocks, bonds, and mutual funds are called securities because they can be used as collateral to secure personal loans, for example. You can use them to borrow money to buy more shares or even use them as a down payment on a house through certain brokerage firms without having to sell them."

"Why not just take the money from the sale and use it as a down payment?" asked Bob.

"It may not be advisable," Sir Real responded, "to sell securities if you have made large enough profits, are not anxious to sell and sales would subject you to taxes, which would also decrease the amount you could offer for a down payment. As far as the brokerage firm is concerned, it is able to find out much more information about your assets, who you owe money to, tie you in closer to them, make money on interest payments and build a better information file for selling more financial products. One stop shopping is also convenient for financial institutions.

"A financial albatross will explain this process called borrowing on margin later. By the way, a collection or basket of various portable securities like stocks, bonds and mutual funds is called a portfolio. Let me make it clear that I am doggedly determined to make you aware of not only opportunities, but also dangers in this world of finance and investing. I don't bite, but reality certainly can. Don't think for a moment that you can sit back and rely on 'professional money management' without really understanding what you are dealing with. At the end of the day it all comes down to do-it-to-yourself gains and losses."

"I think I get the picture," observed Bob. "You don't bite; but you are one of those neighborhood alarm-type dogs that can be heard running around in circles and barking all the time."

"Actually," Sir Real remarked, "I kind of like to poop along. Although I have been known to make 'ruff ruff' sounds about areas in the investment world that are rife with riff raff—especially when it comes to accounting gimmickry. Someone has to bark now and then because reality often communicates in silence. I am known in some circles as a card-carrying contrarian—one who believes that the investing pack is right with the trend, but often wrong about the beginning and the beginning of the end. Sometimes with the investing pack, perception is more important than the real. That's how I feel. I believe that you, Mr. Catz, would make an excellent contrarian investor because cats can't be herded."

"So, if I have this right, you believe that it is important to be at the right place at the right time, but also the right place at the wrong time," Bob responded.

"That's right," answered Sir Real. "I'm so contrarian that I even like to spell adviser with a contrary 'e' rather than the common 'o' popular with the Wall Street crowd, because I can. As for my alleged alarmist nature, I do find the growing influence of the financial sales industry on educational matters over time quite alarming. I also think it's high time new methods were developed to deal with the alarming rate of financial illiteracy. Study after study by both the government and private industry indicates that more than half the investors with retirement accounts have been classified as 'financially illiterate.' Not only that, the scores in these studies have been getting lower from year to year. Apparently, investors are learning more and more while knowing less and less. This ignorance has helped create wonderful opportunities for stock promoters and financial product sellers."

"What are retirement accounts?" asked Bob.

"Well," explained Sir Real, "retirement accounts are designed to encourage people to save money for the future. Allowing saved money to be deducted from present taxes in most accounts does this. Moreover, any profits made on savings are to be protected from taxes, which helps the account grow much faster. There are individual retirement accounts, also known as IRAs, and company-related retirement accounts like 401(k) accounts.

"You'll learn more about retirement accounts when you talk to Shelley who specializes in retirement shells and owns a shell business, which is a company in name only. He will explain why it pays to shell out money for these accounts. Many investors and financial advisors don't realize, for example, that retirement shells may be helpful in preventing a financial shellacking from a lawsuit judgment in this, the most litigation prone country in the world. He'll advise you on small company retirement plans. Yours sounds too small for a 401(k)."

"I've heard so much about 401(k). What is it anyway?" Bob wanted to know.

Sir Real expounded from his treasury of knowledge, "A 401(k) is a savings vehicle with special tax treatment provided certain requirements are met as spelled out by the Internal Revenue Code. Congress enacted the Revenue Act of 1978 with a passage called Section 401, paragraph (k). Over the past two decades, there has been a shift from traditional pension funds managed by professionals that paid out a specific monthly benefit to employees after years of service, to the newer 401(k) plans. With 401(k) plans, it is up to the employees to make investment choices; and there are no predictable benefits upon retirement. Unlike traditional pension plans, the Pension Benefit Guarantee Corporation does not insure 401(k) plans, which is a federal agency. More and more investors are facing increasing choices and risks with their retirement savings. Retirement planning experts often advise the public to take advantage of the 401 (k) and not worry about making the wrong choices. The greatest danger, they say, is not investing at all. Sure, and it doesn't make a difference how much you get paid on a job as long as you take advantage of the opportunity to be employed. I think these experts copied the 'Just Do It' advice from the successful ad for athletic shoes and applied it to running up your losses investing."

One thing troubled Bob. "What you said just a moment ago about test scores doesn't make sense to me. Investors have more access to information than ever before with previously undreamed-of low cost technology. That's what I have read in everyday newspapers. There are many thousands of Web sites that deal with financial information. Scores should be getting better not worse." A light sounding female voice could now be heard. The voice cheerfully sang about how her teacher should leave her alone, because she didn't "lack no edyoucayshun." The lyrics sounded like they had been adapted from the Pink Floyd rock album "The Wall." However, no one could be seen.

Fear Of Frying

> *If the facts change, I change my opinion. What do you do, Sir?*
>
> —John Maynard Keynes

Sir Real started sniffing the air and turned his head in the direction of the liquid mass. A familiar looking deep pink colored creature nearly two feet in length with a slender elongated body, long legs and a long spiny projection flipped out of the strange liquid and landed with a thud on the ground. "My name is Barbi Q," it announced with a delicate female accent that was pure New Orleans. It took Bob a few seconds to realize the creature was a giant prawn. "No matter how much I try to grow and change, there are those who will always see me as a shrimp," she continued. "Perceptions are about how you see what you see. The way I see it, you are both missing the point because your attention is focused on the scores. You are not questioning where that information originated. Even if scores were high, what good would they really be if the test were on incomplete and/or slanted information? Financial illiteracy is probably much greater than what the tests are revealing."

"What do you mean?" asked Bob.

"What I mean," gushed Barbi Q, "is that the public relies heavily on the financial industry directly or indirectly for learning about investments. Even financial magazines that supposedly consider the reader audience first are heavily influenced by advertising dollars and hardly unbiased. They are part of the vast financial sales education industry. The whole business is an oxymoron like jumbo shrimp and genuine fake. Sales education is slanted education. And you can't be serious about retirement planning unless you are also serious about the quality of the information you are receiving. You can't be jumbo and a shrimp at the same time. At least that's what I keep telling myself."

This curious creature fascinated Bob. "Could you give me an example or two?" he asked.

Barbi Q went on, "The public repeatedly hears that history shows that over the long, stocks outperform bonds. This is the mantra and banner song of the 'equity culture,' those who preach that you are always better off in the long term with stocks. Since investing in stock is considered riskier than ultra-safe government bonds, it makes sense, so the argument goes, that being provided an extra rate of return— which is called the equity risk premium, would compensate investors. Stocks are more variable and unpredictable in price compared to steady interest paying bonds; and bond investors are at the beginning of the line to get paid if the company goes bankrupt."

"It does seem to make sense," remarked Bob.

"Yes," continued Barbi Q, "but even the word nonsense is made of sense. There are a number of other factors to consider when munching on that juicy tidbit of information. History shows that past performance is no guarantee of future results; and markets don't necessarily make sense. So who's to say for sure that bonds won't at some time outperform stocks in the long term? Or maybe stocks will continue to outperform bonds, but not by as much as in the recent past. There are those who point to the last fifty years of stock investing in the U.S. as exceptionally good years for stocks and bad years for bonds. The next fifty years might be unexceptional or below average for stocks in general and great for bonds. After all, averages include everything: the good, the bad and *il brutto*, the ugly. You don't want your financial security to be another fairy tale."

"Just how big is this extra compensation from stocks on average, anyway?" asked Bob. "It must be at least 15 to 20%."

To this, Barbi Q rattled off the following, "The superior rate of return for investing in stocks versus investing in ultra-safe government bonds over the long term has been estimated to be a difference of approximately 6 to 7 percentage points when taking inflation into account during the past century."

"That's all? What do you mean by inflation?" Bob asked.

Barbi Q was more than happy to oblige and gushed the following, "Inflation is about the general rise in prices for goods and services fueled by the presence of more money in circulation. Inflation means that eventually there will come a time when a quarter buys what previously cost a dime. To figure out your real gains, you have to deduct losses in buying power caused by this rise in prices every year. If you are making 10% interest in a bank account, for example, but inflation is 8%, then your real rate of return is ten minus eight, or 2%. Real interest is what you make after inflation. By figuring out your real interest, you can see whether you really have wealth creation.

"Anyway, you would think perhaps that with all the extra risk and worry associated with stocks, not to mention publicity from legions of stock promoters, that the difference would be much greater than some barely-high single digit number like six or seven. Furthermore, these long-term studies look backward, studying data over the past one hundred years. The last fifty years may have been exceptionally generous to stockholders. Who knows about the future?"

Bob was intrigued by all this startling information. "What do you think the future might have in store?" he asked.

"I have no idea," Barbi Q replied. "That's why it is called the future. Stock proponents don't know either. They are just guessing and acting as if they know. Some critics of this equity culture think that in the future the overall difference of stocks versus bonds could likely be far smaller. If that happens over a long enough period of time then stocks could really suffer, when it registers with the public that general potential benefits are so small as not to be worth the risk of stock ownership. They have as much chance of being right or wrong as those who preach the opposite to the public. My point is that those who sell stock and stock-related products for a living aren't likely to ask you to give consideration to such possibilities before making a decision, let alone mention them. No matter what facts emerge, they will fashion an image of ultimate success through equities, because the equity culture is, deep down, a sales culture. It's about selling investment vehicles.

"If stocks are doing poorly at a given time, the proponents of the equity culture like to point to the past long-term performance of stocks versus bonds. If stocks are doing well, they mention the same historical information to confirm why stocks are now doing well. Either way, you virtually always get the same 'now is a good time to buy stocks' sales response. It's because you are usually hearing from someone involved directly or indirectly with sales of stocks and pocketing money from their comments. It is pocket science, not rocket science."

At this point, Sir Real added his two cents to the conversation. "But why should it make a difference whether they sell you a stock or a bond? A sale is a sale. Isn't that true?"

"No," replied Barbi Q, "it isn't, as you know, Sir Real. Fees and commissions that financial representatives receive for stocks and stock-related financial products are generally far higher than when they market fixed income investments like bonds and bank certificates of deposit. Those marketing financial products don't advertise that they stand to gain far more in commissions in the long run if clients buy equities instead of non-equity products. The public isn't really aware of how the commission is structured. Investment vehicle sales are analogous to car and truck sales. Companies and sales reps make far more profits on certain vehicles, like SUVs, than others."

Bob, not content to just sit and listen to a Corgi and a giant prawn discuss the finer points of high finance, jumped back into the thick of it. "Are you saying that perhaps a higher income potential might influence a seller's presentation of the value of stocks as compared to the value of bonds?"

"Does butter influence the taste of prawns?" challenged Barbi Q. "Absolutely. That's why you can't rely on the sales industry for a proper financial education. You have the recipe and ingredients for disastrous results. The sales industry doesn't belong in the classroom. The public is basically getting a sales presentation inside a narrow frame of education. What you have here is an elaborate illusion. From a marketing standpoint, it's a work of art. However, investors probably won't pay attention until their portfolios are cut down in size—perhaps from jumbo to shrimp."

"I get the bleak picture. What about mutual funds?" inquired Bob.

"What about them, indeed?" exclaimed Barbi Q. "Those who market mutual funds are unlikely to teach about the very significant drawbacks in owning them. For example, are they really going to teach investors the disadvantages of owning bond funds—like loss of control—compared to owning individual bonds?"

"What do you mean?" asked Bob.

Sir Real bounded back into the discussion, "If you go it alone like the lone wolf, you can have much more control in selling off your bonds as you wish than if you run with the pack. In this pooled money fund, the results are either somewhere in the plus or minus range depending on the overall performance of the fund, which has no set maturity or expiration date."

"What do you mean?" Bob interjected. "I don't quite follow, or should I say 'heel.'"

"Well," began Sir Real, "when you buy a bond, it's for a set period of time. At the end of that time, you collect interest plus your principal investment or money spent on the bond. Bond *funds* have no set dates for collecting interest because they are *pools* of bonds maturing at different times. More importantly, you don't have the same guarantees as you do owning your own bonds even if the bond fund invests in the safest bonds of all, U.S. Treasuries. You can learn this information by reading the warning literature or prospectus, but investors often don't bother to read it or they disregard the importance of it. Saying it's in the literature protects the sales industry, but how many go out of their way to explain such points in detail when they are trying to make a sale? Selling and education belong together like a dog and a cat."

"What does it cost to be in a fund?" queried Bob.

"That's an interesting question," replied Sir Real. "Mutual funds don't even properly inform their customers as to what they are paying in services and fees. That's why there has been a government investigation through the General Accounting Office, the investigative arm of Congress. Investors have to calculate actual costs themselves because fees are presented as a percentage of assets, called an 'expense ratio,' rather than simple black and white actual costs. The expense ratio is the annual fee for costs like record keeping and administration."

"Why is it done that way?" asked Bob.

Barbi Q jumped back into the discussion, "Their claim, in general, is that a clear statement of costs would 'confuse' investors as well as be costly for their business, even though their business specializes in numbers and money. Go figure. Meanwhile, in the past ten years, mutual fund assets have grown some seven times greater, yet costs haven't come down very much. In fact, critics point out that they have been inching back up."

"Why don't they just express costs in both dollar terms and percentage of assets—in one of those 'win win' situations?" asked Bob.

"It would be a 'win' for investors, and a 'lose' for them. Investor ignorance is bliss for the mutual fund companies. They're not worried about investors being confused. They're worried about investors being *informed*. Little investors like you have helped mutual fund companies' assets multiply by trillions of dollars. Yet, they have a paternalistic attitude. It doesn't matter how much you have grown in financial importance. In their eyes, you are still a financial shrimp—someone who is undeserving of a simple clearly-stated bill such as you can get from any self-respecting plumber, mechanic, doctor or lawyer.

"Back in 1988, funds were required by government ruling to publish a 'total return' of what investors were making in a fund. This included all the factors relevant to returns such as dividends, interest and increase in value or capital appreciation. They didn't do this voluntarily. They liked their investors to be 'mutually' ignorant. Prior to that ruling, investors had to determine the numbers themselves. Jumbo companies always claim they know what's best for the shrimp.

"Most mutual funds are called open-ended because fund managers can create as many shares as are demanded by the buying public and investors can sell them back to the fund company anytime at a known price, but when it comes to letting investors know what is going on, they can be quite closed-minded and tight-fisted. Americans may be having a love affair with mutual funds, but the feeling doesn't seem to be mutual. I saw your smirk when you first looked at me, Bob. Now, I hope you realize how much we have in common, you little pip-squeak investor. Think pink."

To this Bob retorted, "Is there anything you care to add to your little snide remarks, you big shrimp?"

"Let me say this too," replied Barbi Q. "Everyone knows that the stock market goes down as well as up, but mutual fund companies slant their literature to focus on long-term upward movement with the mantra of 'buy and hold,' meaning at least five years. It makes sense. After all, they make their money from investors buying and holding assets on which they charge fees. Not only that, they are constantly fishing in the markets for new securities or IPOs. So you see, they don't want to encourage people to learn how to bet and make money on stocks going down, especially stocks they are holding. It's not in their interest. Only a small number of funds make money for their clients when the market goes down. You will be meeting one of them later, a bear fund, called 'Bearly Legal.' I understand he hails from Eastern Europe where I'm told their past is even more difficult to predict than their future. Bearly Legal will give you the bear facts. Even if you are a financial shrimp you need to have more than just a 'pretty in pink' education to help you avoid being in the red. Market losses are also about investment gains."

Bob was truly impressed with the expertise that his newfound friend possessed and decided to test her knowledge in another area of high finance. "What about simple concepts like dollar cost averaging that I just heard about?" asked Bob.

"Simple can be more complex than face appearance," responded Barbi Q, who was tickled pink with her student's interest. "Mutual fund companies teach about dollar cost averaging, which means investing the same amount of money on a regular basis no matter what is going on in the market, as one of the best ways to invest. The idea, they say, is to average out your costs, thereby lowering your risk as security prices go up and down all the time. What they don't advertise is that dollar cost averaging is important to them because it helps mutual funds get a constant flow of new money from investors."

"But isn't it true that it reduces risk, too?" Sir Real asked.

"Yes, the strategy can reduce risk for investors. However, the benefits only come if the stock market goes down while you are investing, and up later. It doesn't work well when markets are going up and you've missed the opportunity to put more money in the market. It doesn't work well either when the market goes down and stays down for long stretches of time as has happened in Japan recently.

"In fact there are studies that suggest you can be better off not using dollar cost averaging. The main purpose is psychological. It's about marketing. It's about making the public feel more secure so they will keep investing. The mutual fund industry and brokers are worried about investors getting scared off by bad times. Do you think mutual funds explain all this when they talk about dollar cost averaging? I think not. It's difficult to make an educated choice when you don't have the whole story. And that's the way they want it. There is a common perception that mutual funds are about consumer advocacy. I have news for you: they are in it for the money. The average fund manager makes hundreds of thousands of dollars a year in pay.

"So what if you learn about the upsides of dollar cost averaging and correctly answer the definition on a test? It still doesn't mean you understand what you need to know about dollar cost averaging. Companies selling financial products are giving you their perception of investing, nothing more. Millions of small investors rely on mutual fund companies for information on retirement planning. These are the same companies that can't even explain their costs properly. Expecting them to provide an objective education makes as much sense as jumbo shrimp. You are getting a virtual education, not a real one. Financial shrimps can get thrown on the barbi, fried or skewered, just like I can. I would like to stay and give you more examples, but I'm already late for dinner. Want to see me do a back flip? I can sing too, like that New Wave rock star Cyndi Lauper: Oh, Oh, girls just wannah have funds. They just want . . . they just want . . . accurate funds."

Sounds Like Caw Caw To Me

> *The trouble with people is not that they don't know,*
> *but that they know so much that ain't so.*
>
> —Josh Billings

Before Bob could answer, Barbi Q leaned forward then bounced into the air flipping backwards into the soupy liquid. New sounds could be heard coming from above. A raucous black bird circled over Sir Real, cawing, "Yes, yes, more can be less," while complaining all the while that the world was too filled with 'noise,' what statisticians call irrelevant data. It then spelled its name out in the sky as 'Cawligula,' before landing beside Bob and beginning to speak in a low eerie voice:

> *My heart is black as the night,*
> *But my words are whiter than white.*
>
> *If you want to make your money grow,*
> *There is something you should really know.*

Information is not the same as knowledge,
This is what I learned at Crow Magnon College.

Knowledge involves useful information,
In a sea of trivia and commercialization.

You may rely on those who know,
And even those who don't know.

But beware those who don't even know,
That they don't know.
For they will make you eat crow.

Cawligula then flew away cawing about the horrors of the unknown and unknowable, while spelling the word evil backwards as "live."

The Wheel Of Fortune Tellers

> When I think of Wall Street, I think of the most overrated minds of the 20th century. The people on Wall Street say a crash can't possibly happen again. Well, it might not happen the same way, but it may happen again, globally. We haven't learned from the past.
>
> —Studs Terkel, journalist

Bob watched the sky for some time after Cawligula had departed. *These creatures seem to be making some pretty wild disrespectful comments*, thought Bob. *Surely there are experts someone like little ol' me can rely on. I thought dreams were more self-censored and more self-centered.*

Dirt started flying into the air about two feet to the left of Sir Real and a creature with a long pointed snout, very small eyes and velvety fur popped out of the ground. It had a small magnifying glass attached to a chain around its neck and in its mouth was a *Business Week* cover story page dated 1979, entitled "The Death Of Equities." After dropping the page and urinating on it, the creature announced in a shrill voice that it was the famous pet peeve detective, Nancy Shrew.

"Excuse me for interrupting, Bobby," shrieked the shrew. "I can call you Bobby, can't I? Or do you prefer the new term 'Bobo' a contraction of 'bohemian bourgeois?' Let me tell you a little secret if you want to learn about being a shrewd investor: if anyone really, really knew what was going to happen next, do you really think they would run to tell you or Joe Six-pack, let alone little runts like me? The information would be priceless. It wouldn't make sense to tell us because these fortune tellers would be the richest beings in the universe. They don't make forecasts for the public good. They make them to sell securities and publicize themselves and their companies. You don't need to be a pet detective to know that, but obviously you need a shrew to get through to little old you.

"Virtually none of the experts you see or hear on television and radio predicted the 1998 worldwide financial crisis, which was the most serious threat to global financial stability since the Great Depression. It caught them totally by surprise. They couldn't see the financial forest for the trees. The reason they weren't able to warn in advance is because they simply had no idea what was going to happen next. Even President Clinton and his advisers didn't have a clue when the financial crisis started in the summer of 1997 in some country not much bigger than California called Thailand. The White House called the Southeast Asian crisis nothing more than a 'blip on the radar screen.' Months later, the President was saying that the world was facing 'the worst financial crisis in half a century.' That was a flip-flop—even for him. The public easily forgets but not Nancy Shrew.

"All the president's sources and all the president's men couldn't put their Humpty Dumpty prediction back together again. The government and private experts didn't know then and they are unlikely to know in the future. The flip 'blip on the radar screen' response was just another demonstration of the 'arrogance of ignorance.' What they all count on is that the public regularly falls asleep at the wheel of fortune tellers. They know that no matter how wrong their predictions come next May or November, barely a soul will ever remember. They are only good at acting as wise commentators after an event has already occurred, giving the financial news junkies their next fix of junk news. If someone doesn't know the worst is coming, how could they possibly know when the worst is over? It only makes sense to the sales industry."

"Do you have anything else to add while I'm taking notes, Ms. Shrew?" asked Bob.

To this, Nancy Shrew's beady little eyes became even more beady as they narrowed in scorn, "That's a dumb question, Bobby. I can go on for days, weeks and years if I have to. I even like to argue with lawyers for hours about the color of a wall. You would think some of them would have something better to do. Anyway, many of these so-called financial experts recommended emerging market mutual funds in the early 1990s with holdings in Asia and South America. These funds ended up being submerging market funds when the crisis hit. They are still trying to recover. By the way, emerging markets used to be called third world countries till the marketing boys stepped in.

"In the 1980s, experts were routinely advising the public to have holdings in precious metals to hedge against inflation. Except the inflation they predicted never came and these holdings plunged in value. Economists have typically agreed until just recently that an unemployment rate of 6% or lower would cause prices to start rising. In 1995, unemployment dropped below 6% and below 5%, yet prices kept dropping. Am I getting through to you, Mr. Peewee investor?"

"I think so, Ms. Shrew," said Bob, "but please talk slower."

"As you please, geese are swans and swans are geese," responded Nancy Shrew. "Psychiatrists only have a success rate of 50% in predicting future individual behavior. What chance do you really think some financial twit fortune teller has with mass behavior? You might as well ask an astrologer what is going to happen."

"Are they any good?" asked Bob.

"They really aren't that bad," responded Nancy Shrew. "I understand all major U.S. stock market crashes have happened a day or two before a new moon. I believe those were in the years 1857, 1873, 1929 and 1987 in case you are foolish enough to challenge me. These so-called experts are mostly expert at spinning stories to manipulate public perceptions and investor sentiment—nothing more and nothing less."

Looking Back To The Future

Sir Real joined the discussion, "But isn't it true, Ms. Shrew, that there are those who have made correct predictions too?"

"Even when some fortune teller is right, it can happen just by the laws of chance," said Nancy Shrew. "If you look back on their fortune telling histories, they don't tend to have a consistent record of success. Some of their records are actually quite abysmal. In this business, it can be more important to look good than to be good.

The famed *Dr. Green Spin*, Chairman of the Central Bank, is a prime example. He has been getting it wrong for years, but as long as nothing goes terribly wrong with the economy, he has what psychologists call a 'halo effect' like a teacher's pet. Virtually everything he says or does is wonderful. In his defense, he at least knows he doesn't know."

"So why do so many people pay such close attention to popular commentators if the ability to predict is so poor?" Bob wanted to know.

"What these media fortune tellers have is the ability to project confidence and authority," explained Nancy Shrew. "They are masters of applied psychology. No matter what happens, they keep coming back with more predictions despite the fact that their history and/or theories may have more holes than Swiss cheese. Even when reporters have dug into their unreliable prediction history, the public still goes on listening to them. The public enjoys the entertainment value and longs to believe that someone really knows what is going to happen in the future. It is comforting to have the illusion of control. Psychology is the reason why fantasy can be so much more influential than actual finance. It's also the reason little investors keep returning like homing pigeons to unreliable sources of information that have the comfort of prestige, popularity and familiarity. Financial shows on TV like *See 'N Be Seen* are basically about advertising revenue, while the public watches the blind talk to the blind about financial insight. If you can't take the heat stay out of the fiction. If you really want to know what's going on in the economy by watching TV you would probably learn more keeping track of the number and frequency of ads for headache and stomach medicine. It's important to learn how to read between the lines, but I'm not getting paid enough to explain it to you."

"From what I can tell, some of these people have done quite well for themselves," observed Bob.

"Yes," agreed Nancy Shrew, "some of these fortune tellers have become celebrities with the help of financial media personalities. They are what I call 'I Yah Toll Yahs,' like those religious leaders in the Middle East. They go around with this holier-than-thou attitude saying 'I yah toll yah' this or that was going to happen. 'I yah toll yah. I yah toll yah.' These marketing 'I Yah Toll Yahs' with services to sell to the public use a singsong approach which goes something like this: 'Yah shuddah listened to me. Yah cuddah have done X, Y or Z.

Don't yah see, yah wuddah become financially free? Shuddah, cuddah, wuddah, but you didn't.'"

All they are really doing, though, is predicting what has already happened because, over time, on average, they are no better at predictions than you or I. Only a true prophet can predict with assurance. These fortune tellers are nothing more than false prophets of profits, who over time never fail to fail."

She Deafened Me With Science

"What about computer capabilities," asked Bob, "especially with sorting out large amounts of information?"

"The great irony of the information age is that the information isn't any more reliable than before," observed Nancy Shrew. As you will learn, mutual fund companies, for example, have these wonderful websites to speedily access information, except that the information is usually deliberately out-of-date for small investors like you, Bob. Access to unbelievable amounts of information has created an enormous illusion of knowledge and, consequentially, overconfidence. A Nobel prizewinning formula used for assisting predictability helped create a near financial disaster in 1998. It was used by big hedge funds run by hedgehogs, who are masters at hedging their bets, and the world nearly went over the hedge. The assumption was that extremely rare events are unlikely to occur, except they did occur—in spades. Remember, computer and information futurists once predicted a paperless office. Instead, just the opposite happened. You see, this visionary stuff has little to do with seeing and everything to do with selling. No computer can ever match a great nose, which has evolved over millions of years for detecting opportunity and trouble. The tech worshipers don't believe that yet. It will take greater crises to shake their misplaced faith."

"But I heard that high upward and downward movement of the stock market these days is connected with the unprecedented access to information," observed Bob.

"That's just another sales spin from the marketing buoys and guiles of Wall Street," responded Nancy Shrew. "Some of them are so good they could convince you that a cross is really a plus sign. Large scale volatility is largely about ignorance on a grand scale. With brilliant marketing, simple ignorance has been sold to the public as a sign of complex improvement. There is unprecedented access to poor quality information, young Mr. Bobby Stocks. It doesn't make any difference how sophisticated communication is when hiding critical information is still standard procedure in the financial business. Bad information can spread faster than ever before. Accounting manipulation, stock promotion and rumors are more common than in the past because of the pressure to show performance. The swift moving financial crisis of 1998, which has been forgotten by too many already, came about in large part because of what has been called 'lack of transparency.' Some of the arguments made by the financial industry about computers increasing investor sophistication are as silly as claiming that cell phones increase listening skills. No matter how good the hardware might get, the software will always be flawed when it is contaminated by self-serving sales influence. Handing out solid gold pens to illiterates won't increase the literacy rate and empower anyone. That's what it comes down to with all this talk about technology empowerment. It's still about more marketing and less learning from the professional sales industry. The public fails to discriminate between learning and advertising often because the public relies on reporters in the common press who fail to really question and challenge the information presented. There aren't enough Nancy Shrews in the news business. Eventually though the general press will come out with these great breast-beating tear-jerking 'How could this happen?' 'What can we learn from this?' 'Where do we go next?' articles. I love vulture news analysis. It's the only time you will ever see me smile or hear me laugh.

"Even a teenager can easily become a Dot-Con. With the Internet, one can generate all kinds of phony stock information targeted at millions of readers and pump up the value of worthless stock. Fantastic opportunities for posting fraudulent information have become available through the Internet. Some of the biggest corporate scandals recently are about so-called 'accounting irregularities.' Big name accounting firms that are supposed to provide independent examination of the books of public companies also provide consulting services, which is an incredible conflict of interest. The accounting detectives or auditors, so to speak, sleep in the same bed as those being examined. Even the watchdogs need watching."

"But doesn't that help companies 'be audit they can be' like in the army ad?" asked Bob.

"Are you being smart with me?" screeched Nancy Shrew. "If you don't want a real earful, I'd be a little more cautious about your questions, Bobo. Let me tell you more. Employees from such accounting companies have been found to be investing in the companies they are examining. Accounting failures have cost investors tens of billions of dollars recently in the best of times. Who knows what will happen during tough economic times when it will be more difficult to play around with numbers. It's only lately that the government is finally seriously looking into the subject and is facing an uphill battle against powerful lobbies that don't want things to change much. So what if you get erroneous information faster from the Internet? The Internet greatly expanded the size of the bell curve where only a relatively small amount of information is of significant value. The upside is to realize that becoming knowledgeable is not that difficult. As Cawligula would say 'it's mostly caw caw.'

"The up and downward movement of prices, or market volatility, has become more extreme. The U.S. stock market has been getting more and more volatile. In the technology-heavy Nasdaq stock market—which you will be learning about—from 1995 to 1998, the number of days in which the overall market moved 3% or more upwards or downwards amounted to a single day. In 1999 alone, that market moved up or down by 3% or more on twenty days. Next year will probably be worse. There simply is not enough important information revealed everyday to justify these kinds of market mood swings. The sales guys, though, have the upper hand and the public's attention. Wall Street representatives talk about extreme price swings as a 'sign of the times' and exhort their clients to 'get used to short term volatility.' What do you expect good sales people to say? Investment vehicle salespeople are unlikely to talk about possible signs of financial instability. Brokerage houses profit greatly from volatility: volatility is about buying and selling shares. Why would you expect them to give you anything approaching an intelligent answer? Secondly, their belief is that if technology creates a problem, then create more technology. Wake up and smell the powers, Bobby."

"You seem to be so ill-tempered about all this," Bob observed.

"I'm a shrew," screeched Nancy Shrew. "It's all I know how to do."

Nancy left a long red colored bill for her services under a rock, then slowly moved back into her hole and disappeared.

She then came out again to reexamine the bill and started speaking, "I felt I didn't have the last word, so I came back."

"But you did have the last word," said Bob. "I assure you."

"Don't cross me, Bobo! My perception is my reality. Now be still and listen. I want to say a few more words about computers. A financial chicken will be teaching you about how to spread, or allocate, your assets. Financial firms and advisers often use computers to help create model portfolios, giving a client ideas on how to divide up assets like stocks, bonds and cash for risk reduction and improved return on their 'nest egg.' I have done some detective work on that."

"What did you find?" asked Bob, all agog.

"You could end up with a rotten egg," Nancy Shrew began. "I've seen cracks in it. I'll tell you, but of course it will run up your charges, Bobby. What clients are usually not told is that all the different computer asset allocation programs come up with different answers to the same question. Although these computer programs may be helpful in maintaining some kind of investing discipline, there can also be tremendous overreliance on their importance; and users can get lax about monitoring their portfolio. Computer models can breed complacency and can help create a false perception of certainty."

"A friend showed me a personal chart made for him by a financial company," said Bob. "It was most impressive."

"I'm sure it was, Bobby," said Nancy Shrew. "It's hard not to be impressed with all the fancy colored pie charts, but it's all hypothetical pie in the sky. That's why they have all these legal disclaimers at the end of the hypothetical. It's only a theory of what might happen to your investments after X amount of time has passed. Each financial company you deal with can have a different model of how assets should be allocated—so you end up with different results. Take the same information on your investments, time horizon, risk profile, et cetera, to different companies, and you will see what I mean.

"Aside from different projections, the biggest weakness may be the fact that virtually all these projections of where you are likely to be financially upon retirement are based on averages. Averages include the good, the bad and the ugly. Financial companies like to tell clients about how you can't time the market. Well, they can't either. These projections are based on assumptions that when little Bobby Catz retires, it will be the ideal average time. However, you may retire at some point in the future when markets are acting very ugly maybe for years on end, like they have in Japan the past ten years, forcing you to withdraw a lot more than you anticipated at the worst of times. Your nest egg can end up being fried and your future scrambled. The sales guys make this look like science when it is really about faith—as in great leaps of faith. Text book calculation studies can end up one day being textbook studies in miscalculation. Wall Street has a history of being a study in wishful thinking, and leaps in the dark. So this question becomes for me— for whom the bell curve will toll, you see. And whether it will toll for thee, Mr. Catastrophe. Yikes!" At this, Nancy Shrew curled up in a ball so that only her spines showed. Then she rolled a bit and jumped back on her feet.

"Why did you that?" Bob asked

"Because you always need a fallback position, Bobo," Nancy replied with a shrill voice. With all the medical advances these days, one of your biggest risks is outliving your money. Reliance on computers for judgment can turn the computer, which is supposed to be the technology servant, into the master—and a dangerous one at that."

"Are you finished?" asked Bob impatiently.

"Not on your life! Those asset allocation models also only address what the financial companies are marketing. They aren't even complete. They don't include chief assets like one's home or what is often the biggest asset of them all—the ability to earn income. Nearly half of all mortgage foreclosures in the country are related to disabilities. Now I'm finished. I'm just going to add a few more items to my bill, and I'll be on my way."

Nancy did add more numbers to the bill, claiming that it was "still nothing compared to the bill of goods sold to Internet investors by the capitalist pigs and their buddies, the anxious-to-bring-companies-public financial kangaroos—those deep pocket, short lending arm, hop-a-long cash kitty venture capitalists." She then slid back into her hole. Bob and Sir Real waited and waited, but this time she didn't reappear. They both breathed a sigh of relief.

"A Kinder Gentler Way"

"Do you really think I can learn better from a stubby little dog like you and some wild creatures, Sir Real?" asked Bob.

"Animals are more user friendly and can teach you a healthy suspicion for what is out there. We have senses humans lost long ago or never attained in the first place and can take you on a road not traveled. For the love of dog, Mr. Catz, humans still don't even recognize that *they* are the alien life forms they keep searching for. Why do you think we are having the greatest mass extinction of species since Permian times a quarter of a billion years ago? Duh!"

"I'm still trying to figure out Roman times," sighed Bob.

"The financial system is very connected with animal nature anyway," observed Sir Real. "It is hidden behind a thin veneer of civilization. That's why financial language is filled with references to animals and their behavior. Information from animals has life to it. Even leading business schools are starting to recognize the importance of storytelling to help make information more meaningful. Stories are about who we are and Wall Street. Every day spin doctors shape financial stories. There are stories behind the numbers—stories that you are not likely to learn except from mavericks like us. Education is supposed to be the foundation of investing. Too often in the real world it's a cartoon version with the cornerstone reduced to tombstone size recognition on sales literature. It's not that difficult to become knowledgeable once you realize how much fiction there is in the financial business. That's why brokerage analysts who try to be really truthful often lose their jobs.

"As for me being a stubby little dog, your first lesson is to be careful about first impressions. First impressions don't count for anything in the financial world and conventional wisdom is often wrong. As in the world of Lewis Carroll, things can be different from what they initially seem in our financial wonderland and end up 'topsy turvy.' Sure, I appear cut off at the knees, but teachers are always being shortchanged in this society compared to other professions. A first-class dog is what you need to introduce you to the grubby work of commerce."

"So you don't get much respect, eh?" asked Bob in a compassionate tone.

"We get as much respect these days from the general public," replied Sir Real, "as Rodney Dangerfield or bonds—even though bonds have more fun, especially in rough times. And rich old gentlemen sitting on their big assets prefer bonds as a means to preserve wealth. Furthermore, as I previously mentioned, my views and those of my animal associates are rather unpopular in certain quarters. So I have to keep a low profile."

"You are kidding me, right?" asked Bob.

Sir Real replied, "Do I look like someone who would kid a kidder?"

"Yes," Bob affirmed, "most definitely, with that Corgi smile you do. Will I be learning about bonds?"

"Of course you will," Sir Real announced. "Bonds are about the debt market—the biggest investment market in the world. The bond market is much more of a professional market than the stock market and has a tremendous influence on the price of stocks. The ability of a company to repay its debts may be critical to the value placed on the stock from that company. Credit ratings can be all the way from top-notch to junk as has been mentioned. In many ways, the stock market is in bondage to the bond market. When times get tough credit agencies really get to bare their teeth and can rip a company's prospects to shreds."

"Do you have audiovisual services?" Bob was hankering to know.

Sir Real was quick to respond, "Of course. We have a library of every bond movie ever made. My favorite is when a little old Scottie dog with the voice of Sean Connery jumps out of a spiral in the screen firing off a fusillade of high yield statistics, while saying 'My name is Bond. *Junk Bond.*' Many very low quality *Junk Bond* movies have been made in Russia because of the terrible economic situation there. It's no secret that *Junk Bond* is a hero to many investors, troubled companies, and countries desperate for loans."

"Why is he so famous?" asked Bob.

"*Junk Bond* always offers a sexy, high yield with a license to thrill," explained Sir Real. "He lives in a world of danger: danger of default on payments and/or an investor's principal investment. That's why his rating in Her Majesty's Secret Service is far below zero: double zero plus a number to be exact. Mr. Bond's reputation also has to do with the fact that a junk credit rating means that companies and governments have less flexibility to borrow and have to pay higher borrowing costs. Payback time with Mr. Bond can involve dangerous and even lethal nonpayment. To become a junk bond, you have to be rated below the top four or five credit ratings. It's that easy. He is on our side, though. If you like garage sales, you must know by now that there is good junk and bad junk."

"Yes," piped Bob, "I learned at garage sales that all junk is not created equal."

"Good. It's the same with bonds. Good junk can give you good profits with often less risk over time than many stocks. As I mentioned, first impressions don't mean anything in the financial world. Mr. *Junk Bond* will bring you up-to-date on anything you need to know. Just tell him that you like high-octane returns that can be shaken but not hurt. That's the kind of investor he is looking for. We also have film clips of virtually riskless blue chip bonds like Treasury bonds involving loans to the U.S. government. They are for the most conservative of investors. Thrill seekers need not apply."

"It doesn't sound as exciting as the stock market," observed Bob.

"The bond market is filled with worriers and sourpuss analysts always concerned about payment," explained Sir Real. "The bond market is constantly sniffing for problems and signaling what it thinks. Even *Dr. Green Spin* pays close attention to what it is saying. So risk is much more readily priced into a security when you buy it. The difference in payment or yield between relatively ultra-safe U.S. Treasury bonds and lesser quality bonds is called 'the spread.' Often the wider the spread, the greater the perception of fear of what lies ahead. Investors become pickier and more demanding and it becomes tougher for companies to borrow. This is what is meant by liquidity drying up."

"So bonds are highly rated," observed Bob.

"Yes," replied Sir Real, "at least in a literal sense. With unrated stocks, investors can load up on billions of dollars of what is called junk equity that doesn't even pay interest and is last in line to collect if the company sinks permanently out of sight. Junk bonds can have the last laugh over junk equity."

"Well," said Bob, "I don't know much about stocks. However, I do read in the paper occasionally about expert stock market analysts from leading brokerage houses like *Morrall Stench* rating stocks. They provide lots of free information for small-time would-be investors like me, advertising how they spend fortunes on research— hundreds of millions of dollars, they claim. So I don't quite understand what you mean."

"Funny you should mention that. Ha, Ha, Ha," laughed Sir Real. "That's why you need to talk to our resident laughing hyena stock analyst, Lord Ha Ha. When it comes to brokerage companies and stocks, there is no such thing as a free hunch. These analysts thrive because 'dummy type' investor education is a joke. If small investors were properly educated brokerage hyenas would have been laughed out of business long ago. Hyenas make superb stock market analysts because they help insure that financial companies always have the last laugh. Their expensive 'research' is laughingly unreliable and usually is as informative as a marketing brochure. Analysts are supposed to act as filters between the market and investors but their work is mostly comical—part of Wall Street's fairy tale education system. What they do is indeed expensive—to the consumer. Professionals know that analysts are the biggest jokers in the business."

"But isn't it true," asked Bob, "there was a real Lord Ha Ha too, who was hanged by the Brits after World War II?"

"Quite so. It was for aiding enemy propaganda. Many of these fellows are in a way 'for sale,' engaging in marketing propaganda to promote stocks they can have a monetary interest in. Pimp, pimp, old chump. It's about stock call prostitution. Oh, do forgive me. I shouldn't be talking like this. It's beneath my title. The Queen would be appalled. I don't want to leave you hanging, but Lord Ha Ha can, in exquisite detail, tell you how one can get royally twisted in the wrong direction from their advice. According to haughty Lord Ha Ha, stock analyst ratings are typically suited for what he calls 'the lower clawses' of investors. You seem distracted by the scenery. Why don't you follow me around?"

"Aren't people who take directions from dogs psychotic?" wondered Bob, aloud.

"Not following your dreams is more likely to cost you your mind. Dreams allow you to be right and wrong at the same time," piped Sir Real. "Better an education through fantasy than fantasy education. Don't worry, I say. Dreams help reveal what goes on in a way. For life is only a bigger dream that lasts many a day."

Bob hurried along behind him to a pumping station nearby, which appeared to supply the semi-liquid mass. The station was approximately one-story high and was made of stainless steel. It was in the shape of a gigantic octopus, with tentacles arching upward before burrowing underground as pipes to the liquid mass. A sign read, "Credit is the Lifeblood of the Economy— Federal Reserve Bank." A quotation appeared on a plaque below the sign: "Whether for mortgages or treatment for cankers, little escapes the influence of our central bankers." Enormous flow control valves were connected to the building, with tags for each marked M1, M2 and M3.

Bob was amazed at what he saw. "What do those tags mean?" he asked.

To which Sir Real replied, "M1 includes coins, currency and demand deposits such as checking accounts. M2 includes savings deposits, time deposits and non-institutional money market funds. M3 includes large time deposits and large liquid assets."

Hold the Champagne?

A sudden wave from the liquid mass tossed a champagne bottle labeled *Risky Business* within a yard of Bob's feet. Bob picked it up and the cork popped off. Inside was a small envelope with two items: one was an article that mentioned that a former chairman of the Federal Reserve Bank had remarked at the beginning of 1999 that the world economy was depending on the American consumer who in turn was depending on the health of the American stock market. And that the health of the stock market was dependent on the stocks of just fifty companies—half of which had yet to make a decent profit.

The second item was an invitation to an upcoming meeting of the Federal Open Market Committee to debate the future of interest rates in that strange-looking building. The invitation briefly described, under the heading "The Buck Starts Here," the

Federal Reserve Bank as the nation's central bank to which all national banks in the U.S. must belong.

"What is this Central Bank, Sir Real?"

"The Central Bank is composed of twelve district banks with twenty-five regional branches. It's our national bank, but is not just one bank and it performs many roles, including stabilizing the financial system. Approximately half the banks in the U.S. are members of the Federal Reserve. Central banking first began with the establishment of Sweden's *Riksbank* in 1668. I'm sure you were aware of that."

"Of course," replied Bob, "everyone has heard of the Riksbank."

"Well anyway," Sir Real continued, "there are now over 170 central banks worldwide. However, the Federal Reserve is the most powerful and influential bank of its kind in the world."

Bob examined the formal invitation further. It was signed by the twelve voting members of the Open Market Committee, next to dates, which indicated that these meetings were held about every six weeks. The signatures included one from a *Dr. Green Spin*, M.S.M. (Monetary Spin Meister) listed as the present Chairman of the Federal Reserve, and America's most influential economist. Unlike the others, *Dr. Green Spin* signed his name four times. Each time the name was written in a different handwriting style and referred to the fact that the president appointed him. One signature and comment was slanted to the right, another was slanted to the left and one seemed soft and frail while still another was exaggerated and wild.

"Just hold onto those items for the time being," Sir Real directed Bob. "We'll talk about them later if we have enough dream time."

Bob stuffed the invitation into his pants pocket wondering whether this *Dr. Green Spin* suffered from multiple personality disorder. Bob now refocused his attention on the large body of semi-liquid matter. It was actually a moat. Now that the mist had cleared, he could see that it surrounded a commercial bakery constructed to look like an old-fashioned thick crust pie. The pie-shaped building floated in a stationary position just a foot or so above ground level, but was partially obscured by clouds, as if it were high in the sky. The only way to enter the bakery was via a drawbridge. Steam filled the air from underground vents around the moat.

The bakery name was printed on a green sign with white lettering on the left side of the drawbridge. The sign read: "Welcome to the Let Them Eat Fake Baking Company, a wholly owned subsidiary of Marie Antoinette Delicacies (USA), a publicly traded corporation and leading manufacturer of synthetic dough and artificial treats. If you would like to own a share of our corporate pie, please check our listing on the New York Stock Exchange under the trading symbol M. A. D." A red neon advertising message flashed below: "If you have dough, we want it. If you need dough, we have it. Have your cake and eat it too. We make double messages just for you."

"This corporate landscape is most unusual," observed Bob. "I suppose I will be learning about it and other matters mainly from you."

And Now for Something Completely Different

"No. Not at all," declared Sir Real. "This isn't just about learning mostly from me. I have many friends in low places and love to cross-examine them television style. What are friends for? I can question them on your behalf while introducing you to a wide variety of learning situations and teachers."

"Like who?"

"You will be meeting a professional chicken, a legal weasel, a currency shark, a corporate mole, a financial sloth, a vulture fund manager, and even an accounting cheetah to name a few. Famous characters like *Kenneth Starling*, the ex-government prosecutor who previously stalked the President, will teach. The financial world is about laws and regulations. That's why a legal hound and legal eagle are needed for your education. When it comes to investing you can't run from the law. At the same time, after a century of laws to protect small investors, laws have far more bark than bite. That's why you have characters like Lord Ha Ha. Just because investing is more available and easier to access than ever before doesn't mean it's safer. Kenneth will explain how he now stalks the markets helping you to understand the role of stock exchanges and the bond markets. I like Kenneth. He reminds me of Wall Street: frequently brilliant with occasional signs of intelligence. Since I am a Queen's dog, I even have access to the king of copycats, *Billy Goats*, super billionaire owner of hard-hitting *Microsock Corporation*. However, I should caution you that not everyone likes

Billy or his company. Some even have the nerve to call him *'Bully'* *Goats of 'Macroschlock.'* Can you believe that?"

"No," answered Bob. "Schlock means crummy, isn't that true? I would never talk like that, would you?"

"Sure I do and wuff it too," roared Sir Real. "Actually, it's slang for inferior merchandise. His competitors have, in my opinion, what is called 'Bill envy.' Billy's competitors are in shock 'cause *Goats* is now the richest kid on the block, with a fortune in stock— based mostly on over-complicated schlock."

"How is that possible?" asked Bob totally puzzled.

"The guy with best product doesn't always win," explained Sir Real. "Marketing isn't everything, but creating a captive customer base, that has to buy equipment upgrades, is darn close. Market control is more important than innovation. Any cash cow can tell you that. In fact, you will be meeting one."

"I don't quite follow. Anyway, to change the subject, why does the bakery have a moat around it even if it is doughnut shaped?"

"It's about dough. So is the bakery. That's where all the big dough around here is made. Billy and the bakery moat aren't separate subjects. You need to understand something investors frequently lose sight of. A good company and a great stock are not necessarily the same thing. There are very good companies, for example, with stocks that have done quite poorly over the years despite making steady respectable profits like consumer product companies that had high-flying stocks in the 1980s and the early part of the '90s. Good companies are not necessarily good investment value. It's not just a matter of having a better mousetrap or even building a mousetrap for a mouse that doesn't even exist yet. Factors like investor feeling, the times, as well as company management and adaptability to change, are also critical."

"I still don't quite follow," said Bob.

"Companies that end up with an incredible amount of profit or dough over time like the bakery are often surrounded by some kind of moat," Sir Real explained. "Good companies to invest in have something special to protect them like unique products, exceptional quality and service, hard-to-beat low prices with exceptional management and a well-known brand name, offering the customer more than can be expected elsewhere and/or they have locked up the market somehow so that consumers have little choice but to use their goods or services even if mediocre. The

Sony Betamax video recorder was considered by many to be far superior to what is manufactured by the competition; but you can't buy one anymore because they didn't use the opportunity to create a moat by aligning themselves with distributors through licensing agreements. Sony's superior product ended up as toast while schlock competitors made all the bread, because they understood how to make dough. It's that simple. The creativity usually has to do with making money, not the product. You can be right but still wrong about making money."

"I would like to meet this *Billy Goats*," said Bob. "But isn't it true, Sir Real, that starlings are so detested that even the Audubon Society has nothing good to say about them? Isn't it a fact that they are a British import that aggressively attacks American nest eggs? Are you going to deny that financial education is supposed to help me grow and preserve my nest egg?"

"Yes. Yes. You've broken me. I admit it," cried Sir Real. "You have the makings of a legal hound, Mr. Catz. Starlings are a menace, but that's why they make such great prosecutors. Now, it's my turn. Isn't it true that the phrase 'nest egg,' Mr. Catz, is stale, old and overused? Isn't it true that the financial advertising industry employs terminology like 'nest egg' as an effective, cynical way to trigger knee-jerk emotional reactions from the public—from little investors like you?"

"Yes. Yes. I admit it," cried Bob. "I want a nest egg, too. Stop right there. I should have known better than to challenge a professional television law dog like you in an 'isn't it true' type contest."

"Exactly," spouted Sir Real, "but this whole nest egg analogy is for the birds anyway. I'll tell you what. We'll avoid inviting more birds other than the ones already on our teaching list. I can have the Dogs of the Dow explain dividends and their Dogs of the Dow strategy for investing—which can come in handy if the market rolls over and plays dead."

"What are dividends?" asked Bob with keen interest.

"Dividends are about divvying up a share of the profits or earnings of a corporation to owners of stock," explained Sir Real. "Unlike diamonds, dividends may not last forever. However, in a down market they may be an investor's best friend, providing an underlying support for a stock. I also know a vicious German Rottweiler whom even the IRS and Mike Tyson can't take a bite out of.

He can explain the tax-free Roth account for young investors and what many older investors are missing concerning its value in estate planning. He also knows about something that has been called the 'Super Roth,' which is secret to much of the public."

"Is that some kind of far right idea?" asked Bob. "I am looking for sound investments and the far right is far too right at being wrong."

"Don't worry," said Sir Real, reassuringly. "This is just a farfetched idea hatched by the ultra-powerful insurance industry. It may be a way to deal with some of the restrictions of the Roth IRA. We have a corporate gadfly you will be meeting who likes to pester corporations. Perhaps he can help you with socially responsible investing. So-called green funds have done extremely well to the surprise of many. He knows about companies that wouldn't even harm a fly.

"Another Corgi, Lady Buy, can talk about the mounting astronomical trade deficit. Even small investors like you require knowledge of the big picture. Just remember to address her as 'Your Ladyshop.' Maybe I can invite *Warren Bassett*, the famous value investor, known as the sage of Omaha, the oracle from the Midwest, the greatest investor of all time, the richest investor in history and at least a half-dozen other titles bestowed on him by awestruck financial reporters. Mind you, he hasn't been doing as well as the past."

"How come?" asked Bob.

"Warren claims he can't yet understand the worth of many of these new high technology companies. He wants investors in his investment company *Barkforsure Allday* to be out of harm's way in a market he thinks is not being very rational. To him, the prices placed on many of these unproven companies are just pie in the sky."

"Why?" asked Bob.

"He still believes that value from proven stability and profits always wins out in the long term," explained Sir Real. "He's one of those long time bargain basement value investors who goes around singing 'you can't keep a good stock down.' It's hard to teach an old dog New Era tricks.

"I can also ask our Dr. Root, M.D., a Corgi from Germany, who is a psychoanalyst and author of *Getting to the Root of It: Zah Shtockmarket, Sex Oon Aggression*. Fraud Root, as she likes to jokingly call herself, is currently on a lecture tour to talk about how the basic impulses of sex and aggression are expressed in the financial markets."

"Huh?" gasped Bob. "Even Dr. Ruth on TV doesn't talk like that."

"You seem surprised," noted Sir Real. "Why do you think investors talk about survival of the fittest among Internet companies, predatory bank loans to low-income consumers, poison pill defenses to hostile takeovers, poaching of key employees from competitors, vulture companies, price gouging, forced mergers, sexy technology stocks and so on? According to Dr. Root, sophisticated market activity involves sublimated base aggressive and sexual urges. That's why it's such a vicious jungle out there."

"Will I get to meet her when she returns from her book tour?" Bob asked.

"I doubt it," said Sir Real. "She'll probably be going on another tour for her companion book, *Gelt Oon Guilt. Gelt* is slang for money."

"That's a strange title," Bob observed. "What's it about?"

"Its about the field of inheritance," Sir Real began. "The greatest transfer of wealth in the history of the world is now taking place where the baby boomers in the U.S., the nearly eighty million people born between 1946 and 1964, are starting to inherit the wealth of their parents. Financial advisers and the big brokerage companies are licking their financial lips and salivating like Pavlov's dogs. The big marketing focus of banks and brokerage houses is now on 'wealth management.' It's still a lot of the same old broker approach, but packaged for upscale clients who are far more profitable for financial companies to deal with. Baby boomers are turning fifty at the rate of one every eight seconds, eleven thousand approximately per day. The parents of baby boomers over age fifty number over sixty-four million and currently control more than $20 trillion of wealth."

"That's an astounding amount of money, Sir Real," said Bob.

"A trillion here and a trillion there pretty soon adds up to real money, to paraphrase a U.S. senator of long ago. Studies, though, indicate that approximately 90% of those who inherit money in lump sums spend most or all of it within a two- to five-year period of time. This is what her book deals with."

"Why is it so easy to become an heir today and a goner tomorrow?"

"According to Dr. Root," Sir Real explained, "one can also 'inherit' guilt or self-sabotage feelings about money because it was not earned, and because someone had to die for it to be passed on. Some recipients of wealth who disburse it quickly unconsciously believe that money is bad: hence the ancient expression 'filthy lucre.' I don't know much more about it. You'll just have to wait until her book comes out. Maybe you will even get the chance to meet her. You can also ask her why only 5% of the population, including lawyers, has a will. I'm dead serious."

Mole Skin

"Sir Real, I have a confession to make before I learn anymore," declared Bob. "I'm not really even sure why a company becomes a corporation."

"Did I hear someone make a confession?" inquired a tiny female voice with a Boston accent from a small opening in the ground nearby. The opening was expanded as a gray colored, furry creature with minute eyes and hidden ears tunneled out and introduced herself as Molly the Corporate Mole.

"Excuse me, but I couldn't help hearing that you don't understand what a corporation is. A major reason to incorporate is for a company to get a second skin so they can limit their personal liability. Owners and shareholders are protected from losing their personal possessions like their cars, houses, personal savings, et cetera. Without this kind of protection, it would be too risky to go into many kinds of businesses. There are also tax savings. Let me put it this way:

> *A corporation is established for protection and profit,*
> *The way an army is formed to kill.*
> *It's about life from paper—created by legal will.*
>
> *A corporation is a legal person without a soul,*
> *Able to act in most any role.*
>
> *A corporation has a special suit of armor,*
> *So that taxes and lawsuits can't harm her.*
>
> *Only if the officers of a corporation commit a crime*
> *Can they end up doing time.*

"It's time for me to return to my hidden agenda. I have a job to do in a friendly foreign country working with listening bugs in hotel rooms. It's very big business these days to spy on big business."

Molly returned to her hole followed by a buzzing sound in the air. Someone kept saying, "She bugs me. She bugs me not," but no one else could be seen.

Fly in the Corporate Eye

"What did she mean by officers of the corporation, Sir Real?" Bob inquired.

"I'm here to answer that question. I can give you a fly-on-the-wall perspective. My name is Superfly," said the enormous jet-black housefly the size of someone's fist that now buzzed above Bob and Sir Real.

"Isn't it true that the name Superfly has been linked in the past with the 1970s urban, black movie genre which began with the film *Shaft?*"

"Yes," affirmed Superfly, "but my association these days is only with those who get the corporate shaft. I make it my business to buy shares of stock in publicly held corporations so I can regularly attend meetings and criticize the way the corporation is being run: such as complaining about obscenely overpaid CEOs or Cheap Executive Officers as I call them. The average corporate chieftain makes on average five hundred times the salaries of their average employees and their performance is only average. That's what I call the mean world of statistics. One of my many unpopular recommendations is that if corporations want to effectively slim down they should consider a fat cat-free diet."

"You must be able to bug the hell out of people!" observed Bob.

"Absolutely," declared Superfly, swelling with pride. "Being an annoyance is a serious business. I don't have some fly-by-night operation. Let me answer your question before I have to buzz off. Publicly traded corporations are organized so that holders of the stock can regularly vote for and elect a board of directors with titles like CEO to manage the company's business. This way stockholders can have a say in the management while at the same time having no worries as far as either managing or being personally liable for whatever the corporation does. The maximum one can lose is the money for the investment. Stockholders elect the board of directors. They also vote on the creation of more stock to sell and determine whether any major change in the business will fly."

"Could you give me an example of what directors do?"

"They can declare dividends, the distribution of earnings to stockholders, my dear boy," expounded Superfly. "Unlike me, many stockholders find it difficult to attend annual meetings because they have a real life. So these stockholders tend to vote by means of a proxy, which allows someone else to vote their shares for them. By law, companies that solicit proxies have to provide accurate and detailed information on what is to be voted on. I'm going to another meeting right now to make some more remarks that fly in the face of conventional corporate thinking. Then I'm going to take a well deserved vacation in the fly speck country of Monaco. When the economy cools, mediocre CEOs are going to be dropping like flies, unable to take the heat from disappointed investors."

Sir Real had a question of his own for Superfly. "The financial world is abuzz with talk that you know something about equity without inequity: being shareholders in companies that wouldn't harm a fly. What's the buzz on that?"

"Yes," affirmed Superfly, "you can find socially responsible investment funds by researching sites such as socialinvest.org."

"You've been a great help, Superfly," said Bob. "Now bug off."

Superfly then flew away at great speed.

Step, Step, Stepping Away

"Tomorrow will be the first day of the year 2000," noted Bob. "How long will this information last? Do you think I should bone up on a few basic investment books before beginning my journey?"

"What you learn now will give you a perspective on future possibilities," advised Sir Real. "Moreover, subject matter covered in your learning adventure has to do with basics. I see you have a notepad. So mark down some of the topics we will be covering and have covered already:

> A. Inflation
> B. Taxation
> C. Deflation
> E. Economic expansion and contraction
> F. Risk management
> G. Psychology
> H. Currency appreciation and devaluation
> I. The unreliability of information and predictions
> J. The self-serving recommendations of experts

"The need for this type of information isn't likely to change over time. Learning should be an exciting adventure of discovery on how the different parts of the financial world relate to one another: interest rates, currencies, the stock market, the bond market, the commodities market, et cetera. Learning about a train isn't going to do you much good if you don't understand how it fits on tracks. Do you really want to wade through boring paragraphs of material in some book telling you the same tired old stuff with warning language that sounds like it came from the surgeon general? Bonds are this; stocks are that; cut up your credit cards and make a budget; be spiritual, start starving now, et cetera? It's so high school—with the success rate of diet books."

"Have you read any of them?"

"Oh yes," confided Sir Real. "I must confess that every time I read another one of those self-help 'Step' books, like *Nine-and-a-Half Steps to Becoming a Financial Guinea Pig* or *One Step to Becoming a Wealthy Boar*, I feel like stepping out and buying something nice on credit or joining a twelve-step recovery group for those overdosed on 'easy step' books. If you'd like, I can even speak at child level with sentences no longer than ten words. Once I lived with a successful children's writer who dumbed down business books for the public."

"No," Bob sighed. "The only dumb thing I want is lots and lots of dumb luck. I would also like to learn sophisticated information as painlessly as possible."

"That can be arranged," said Sir Real. "I wouldn't be surprised if you come across information on your journey that even many financial advisers are not aware of."

"How so?" asked Bob.

"Financial training," Sir Real replied, "especially in the big brokerage houses, usually has to do with learning how to make sales calls and market packaged financial products like mutual funds with a 'we rely on what our experts have to say' attitude. Investment vehicle sales information is about selling investment vehicles. It may have little or nothing to do with true understanding. Financial companies don't have to care whether your investment vehicles roll over and kill off your portfolio later on—as long as it's legal. Optimism, enthusiasm and confidence shouldn't be mistaken for knowledge. There are many good brokers, but it seems to have little to do with the training or the brokerage house they come from."

"Could you tell me a little bit about these experts they rely on," Bob requested.

"My favorite use of experts," said Sir Real, "has to do with those financial firms that have several experts with different views. No matter what the results in the marketplace, it allows the financial company to point to one of their experts having made a 'good call.' One guy points to the left, another points to the right and a third points to the middle. You see them on television all the time. These sales conductors have a company wide orchestra playing 'don't worry about short-term volatility because you're in it for the long term' from *The Sound of Financial Music*. It's foolproof, and proof of how easy it is to fool the public."

"Are you saying I don't need a financial adviser?" asked Bob.

"I'm not saying you don't need brokers as a number of financial writers have claimed," clarified Sir Real. "You may or may not. Most everything has an upside and a downside—even comedy. Training aside, there are many knowledgeable advisers who can offer valuable advice. Moreover, surveys have indicated that the great majority of investors with substantial assets like the idea of being able to talk to an adviser—in one survey, the figure was 89% for those consumers who had assets of over $100,000. That's why some discount brokerages like *Charles Schlepp* adjusted their advertising tune to focus on this group and made connections with independent advisers. They didn't want to lose clients who had big bucks to the full service brokerage firms. It's good business to recommend independent advisers who keep their client's funds with the discount brokerage company. Maybe you have seen some of their puzzling ads with celebrities like the ex-Duchess of Pork proudly announcing their decision to become another Schlepp investor 'in it for the long haul?'

"Investors often need emotional support and help with fiscal discipline when it comes to investing. Just tossing money into mutual funds isn't money management. It's wishful thinking about money managers. Funds lose value like any other investment vehicle. Managers are just part of a vehicle that can drive into negative profit territory like a stock or a bond. It's only the marketing that never leaves positive territory. Additionally, there are those who suffer from 'time poverty' where investing simply doesn't interest them and/or it doesn't pay anymore than it would to do one's own work tax preparing, et cetera. However, if you choose to invest with an adviser, the more you know, the better off you will be. Investors don't lose money just because markets go down. Money is also lost buying into sales pitches built on a foundation of blind optimism. Again, training for many advisers is often far more about selling than advice giving.

"As long as you are dealing with a reputable brokerage house, the company itself is rarely of any importance thanks to the great advances in information technology. You can get pretty much anything you want anywhere these days. The only proprietary product any of these brokerage houses have left is access to new companies coming public. If you are a small investor, chances are you will get really slim pickings, even if you have an opportunity. Moreover, these brokerage houses are often linked to the same investment bank making huge profits from bringing the company public. They both can sleep in the same bed to give birth to better profits, which may be hazardous to your wealth. The really big institutional investors like mutual funds often get the significant first crack at the best new offerings. Big brokerage companies seem to be more about bigger advertising budgets, bigger profits, and bigger expectations of making money out of each client to cover their big expenses. For little investors bigger is not likely to be better. There is a saying in the industry 'size can be the enemy of performance.' It can apply to funds, companies, and brokers who have too much to handle. Big brokerage houses don't have any special immunity.

"Professional advisers are running a for-profit business like just about everyone else. However, you need to be aware of how much advice, especially in the big firms, is just canned advice. Also, a certain large segment of the financial business involves advisers who are on a factory-like monthly production sales quota. It's even more difficult to get objective advice from someone who answers to a reward and punishment system set by sales managers. Some of these sales operations resemble puppy mills constantly churning out new brokers, who are put on a computer treadmill that tracks daily sales activity."

"Well I certainly would want to get someone with a title like vice-president," said Bob.

"Titles like vice-president often mean that you are dealing with someone accomplished in sales who has met certain goals—a 'top producer' as they say in the business," advised Sir Real. "Titles in the financial business are often used as marketing tools and to confer benefits on those who sell well. Advice giving plays little or no part. You have to be really cautious about titles. That's why I said you couldn't go by first impressions. Maybe that person is a whiz at marketing unit trusts, which you will learn about, but knows little about financial planning, tax consequences, mutual funds, bonds, stocks, insurance, et cetera. Thanks to marketing techniques, one can be extremely successful with investment vehicle sales and be a total dog when it comes to general financial knowledge. Many wrongly assume the two have to have a strong relationship. But you can be a big broker, consultant, adviser, et cetera with pee wee knowledge. It's not necessary for an adviser to know or even know that he doesn't know to be successful, I'll have you know. These days with the ever rising stock markets even a stock picking monkey can look like an investment wizard. It's called bull market genius.

"In fact, ignorance is actually an advantage when it comes to selling prepackaged non-thinking financial products. I have come across highly successful brokers, 'million dollar producers,' who proudly boast they don't even read a financial newspaper. They rationalize and say newspapers are about yesterday's news and that clients are in good hands with their experts. Analytical thinking gets in the way of their sales production. Great 'producers' may have much more to do with great production than great advice in the great brokerage factories. That's why engineers often make lousy salesmen. They tend to be cautious, spending extra time analyzing instead of selling. Big brokerage houses especially want to gather big assets. You can't just go by appearances like titles and expensive-looking decor. Brokerage titles and decor can have a lot in common with greatly overvalued stocks and nothing in common with sound investing."

"What about investing for myself with no adviser?" asked Bob.

"The most troubling aspect of online trading of securities is that it removes the broker as an emotional buffer or filter for investors who have a tendency to buy and sell on impulse. An important part of the work of many brokers is not only managing investments, but also the emotions and expectations of investors. Selecting suitable investments is just part of the work of investing.

"Trading doesn't even have to come about from impulse and stressful news. This is a culture addicted to activity. Even though doing nothing with the portfolio may produce far better results, there is more of a temptation to trade for many online investors. One recent behavioral science study suggests that women tend to achieve better returns on investments than men simply because of their tendency to trade less."

"But it's so cheap," commented Bob.

"Cheap can be very expensive," noted Sir Real. "Inexpensive trades don't do the investor any good when they lead to expensive losses and unnecessary overtrading. What the glitzy online ads don't tell you is that cheap effective technology can also encourage bad judgment. Self-help psychology books don't work because you can't change billions of neural circuits simply by reading. That's why there are always new books coming out. If the old ones worked, you wouldn't need the new books. The ability to trade online similarly does nothing to deal with the critically important emotional components of investing. Technology advertising may give a one-sided impression that quick response time online is necessary to get financially ahead. Restraint is about power too and the tail side of the same coin. Many investors need emotional distance and objectivity that can be easily lost from online investing. Money is a highly emotional subject. According to studies, nearly half of all arguments in the average marriage are about money. Advanced investing technology has the capacity to propel you backwards financially since there is no filter for emotional issues. A couple of sites have been set up on the Web for online problems: investingcomplaints.com and onlineinvestorshelp.com. Whether or not you use an adviser, at the end of the day it's still about do-it-to-yourself gains and losses. So you need to be knowledgeable."

"I can see you really are a mean dog. Instead of giving me some straightforward black or white one-minute investor advice, you insist on digging up all kinds of factors for me to consider and average out. Anyway, let me ask you this: how can I tell if I'm buying and selling too much?" Bob asked.

"One indication is on Form 1040," explained Sir Real. "This is a federal tax form, which can be a useful tool for examining your finances. On Schedule D, you can examine whether you are paying much higher taxes in the form of income taxes instead of the much lower capital gains rate because you are not holding onto your gains long enough. In a top tax bracket, it can mean a difference of close to 20% if your trading isn't in a retirement account. A cool tax structure may be far more important over time than picking a hot investment. On Form 1040, by the way, you can see how much you spend each year, which is essential to planning how much you will need in the future."

"Where can I get the highest amount of return with the absolute lowest amount of risk?" asked Bob.

"In a location very far from here called Nirvana. This is not a perfect business, except when the answer turns out to be dead wrong. 'Security investing' are words wrapped in contradiction. There is no investment vehicle that truly rides on an absolute guarantee. If you want an absolute guarantee, go buy a muffler or one of those *Fireprone* tires."

"What about government guarantees like FDIC?" asked Bob, hoping to hear something reassuring.

"There is no way the Federal Deposit Insurance Corporation could cover a massive banking failure," said Sir Real. "All it means is that the government guarantees to print money which could end up worthless like in the Weimar Republic in Germany before World War II. The safest investment in the world is supposed to be U.S. Treasury Bonds, which involve loans to the U.S. government for periods of ten to thirty years. During that time, you receive interest and at the end of the period, your initial capital investment is returned. However, the market value of your bond can change on a daily basis. You are not protected from day-to-day changes in price on the open market. In case you have to sell it before the period ends, you could end up losing money if interest rates paid on new bonds are higher than the one you bought. Someone isn't likely to be interested in buying an older bond that pays less interest unless the buyer can get a deal that makes it worthwhile. Even if your bond is paying a high rate of interest, it may be recalled under the contract between the bond provider and bond holder."

"It sounds like a tire recall," observed Bob. "But at least you are guaranteed to receive the money you invested at the end of the period of time, right?"

"Yes," answered Sir Real. "However, the bond guarantees you only that you get your money back, not what your money is worth. The only real guarantee is to print more money even if it ends up being next to worthless by the time you cash it in thirty years later. Technically speaking, there may be a way to never lose money in the markets. If you take any profits from your initial investment and only use the profits in the future, then you might be able to have your cake and eat it too.

"I know of stock traders who have operated that way and so don't have anxiety when they trade securities or make long-term investments. They are only risking profits, while their original principal has been returned. Of course, brokerage firms don't like that concept because it means you are keeping money out of their hands; but it can be a much more comfortable way for many nervous people to invest. The only thing guaranteed is that at some point, interest rates and the stock market will go up or down."

"I suppose I'll have to get used to some of your biting remarks," said Bob. "What do you really have to gain from teaching me if you are not getting paid? What's in it for you? What's your agenda? Even a dog has an agenda."

"My remarks are biting," declared Sir Real, "but it's the dog of inflation, the dog that doesn't bark, which can take the biggest bite out of you and your wallet. This is a major reason why it is important to learn about investing. Your question is a difficult one to answer for someone who has a bookkeeper's mentality. We are working dogs, Mr. Catz—not some canine-to-five fluff ball. As the Queen Mum recently told me before her one-hundredth birthday, 'Work is the rent you pay for life.' Moreover, teaching can be an enjoyable art form like painting for a hobby. Everything doesn't have to be about money, although almost anything in the financial world can be turned into money. Even ignorance can be monetized. Why own just a piece of the corporate pie when you can own a piece of pie in the sky— supported by hype that expands like the square root of pi?"

Smaller Than Life

"Speaking of numbers," asked Bob, "why am I only a fraction of what I am supposed to be? Not only do I look small, I actually feel small."

"Wealth envy can do that," explained Sir Real. "Wealth is the easiest and quickest way to enter the American aristocracy. So wealth envy of late has become an even more popular form of stress. Apparently, you have very small net worth or assets minus liabilities, and simply don't measure up to what is expected of you. Nearly everyone is making oodles of money on the stock market except little you. And it's so easy. Don't you read the newspapers and financial magazines? Sure you do. That's probably why you feel you don't amount to much."

"Wealth envy?" Bob pondered this term. "Is that like the Freudian concept of penis envy?"

"According to our resident psychoanalyst, Dr. Root," Sir Real pointed out, "there are some lengthy similarities."

"Is it really possible that my body state is reflecting unconscious feelings?" Bob wished to know.

"I think so," said Sir Real. "Maybe it's a loss-of-control-type dream. On the other hand, how would I know? Just because I believe the economy will shrink and look shrunk, that doesn't mean I'm a shrink. If it's wealth envy, what I can tell you is that chasing the performance of others can be far riskier than chasing the performance of the latest hot investments. In either case, you are just chasing the ghosts of performance past. You are who you are and you should get a risk profile study to size up your financial personality. As Sigmund Freud said, 'Being entirely honest with oneself is a good exercise.' We do have a psychologist on staff if you need to talk to someone—a black and white Australian Border Collie specializing in borderline personality types. He plans to write for the new *Journal of Psychology and Financial Markets* (www.investmentresearch.org)."

"What does borderline personality mean?" Bob asked.

Sir Real was hasty to point out that:

> *A borderline personality sees everything in terms of black or white,*
> *And gets very upset when you don't agree he's right.*
> *He doesn't understand any boundaries except his own.*
> *Now I think it's time I was paid with a bone.*

"I'd first like to bone up on this subject," said Bob. "What would that have to do with the business you are in?"

"Borderline personalities can wreak havoc in their personal lives and even run afoul of the law. However, they are not uncommon in the financial world and have built enormously successful businesses with the help of their neuroses. Dogs aren't the only ones who can have a great life without ever growing up. Psychology has its upsides and downsides just like the financial business. I suspect you will be meeting some borderline personalities as borderline behavior thrives in some areas of the investment world. I'll let you guess who they are."

"What's the name of your psychologist on staff?" asked Bob.

"The psychologist's name is Dr. No Ph.D., author of the bestseller, *Business News Addiction: Just Say No*. Perhaps you have heard of it. It's virtually all based on the Aussie expression 'No worries mate.' Somehow he managed to turn it into a five hundred-page book. The book jacket prominently displays one of those 'As Seen on *Oprah*' labels. His latest book entitled *Creatures of Habitat* is controversial and also has an *Oprah* label. He maintains that market analysts, strategists, and economists employed by brokerage firms are for the most part just extensions of their company's sales department—what he calls 'creatures of habitat.' No matter what the title, the TV or radio listener is still hearing a sales pitch from investment vehicle sales representatives dressed in chic clothing. Understanding why anyone big would provide little you with free information is the first investment step to know, says Dr. No."

"I can't say I've heard of these books, although I've definitely heard of Oprah," said Bob.

"They are both on the top of the bestseller list at the Internet bookseller *Amazin'StockPrice.Com*," said Sir Real with apparently great pride.

"I can't say I've heard of that company either," said Bob.

"That's simply amazin,'" declared Sir Real. "One of the main pillars of their business plan is brand name recognition. In fact, the company currently is valued at over $35 billion—worth far more than many long-established major corporations in the U.S., even though it has yet to make a profit."

"How is that value determined?" Bob wished to know.

"Well," began Sir Real, "value is determined by multiplying the number of stock shares outstanding in the market place, or floated, times the market value of each share. A hundred thousand shares in the marketplace valued at $10 each on Day X means that the total market capitalization, or market cap, for that company would be $1 million on Day X. If the stock price rises the following week to $100, then the market cap would be $10 million. As for *Amazin'StockPrice.Com* market cap, it currently has a stock price in the range of $113 per share with roughly 356 million shares outstanding—simplah amazin' isn't it, child?"

"It certainly is, Sir Real," Bob answered. "As a television lawyer, you must be aware of lawyer talk about theories holding water. So what's the theory about their amazin' amount of liquidity?"

"One theory," Sir Real replied, "is that what happens in the markets is a reflection of the combined knowledge and intelligence of the investing public. So the public is now saying this is what the company is worth. Those who are critical of sky-high valuations for companies like *Amazin'StockPrice.Com* are told they don't appreciate the fact that the public knows what it is doing. It has to do with a theory about efficient markets."

"Does the public know what it is doing?" asked Bob.

"Probably not, because fantasy is often far more interesting than reality. It kind of reminds me of the story about the finance professor and student who spot a $1,000 bill on the sidewalk. The professor tells the student not to waste time picking it up because if it really was a $1,000 bill it wouldn't be there according to theory. If time is the greatest adviser of all, then the future will tell if the public is better at hit or myth," remarked Sir Real. "What surprises me is how Americans are unfairly accused of only thinking short-term and having little patience. So far, this company has been hemorrhaging enough rivers of money to rival the mighty Amazon. Every time an item is sold such as a book, investor money is being lost, because profits have never existed. In some ways, they operate like a non-profit charity organization. This year the company lost at least fifteen cents for every dollar generated in sales. There still isn't even a whiff of profits. Yet, so far, Americans have patiently and charitably supported it, continuing to buy stock that helps finance their operations. In fact it seems that the only really profitable item they have for sale is their corporate stock and lots of 'goodwill'—that's the difference between what the company is worth in actual assets and what investors think it is worth. They have recently taken out a huge multi-billion dollar loan in the form of a bond as part of their expansion. That could present a problem later on, because the bond world is trained to sense danger and alert others. Maybe a financial ferret will explain when the time is right. All I can say for sure right now is that the company is highly recommended by a leading 'never say sell' stock analyst at *Morrall Stench Brokerage.*"

"How can that be?" asked Bob. "I wear world-famous *Levity Jeans* that can sometimes be sold for hundreds of dollars overseas. Talk about brand name. Yet the company has been doing poorly in recent times and has lost significant value and market share because of competition from other jean manufacturers. Brand name recognition alone doesn't seem to be that important. I must say,

Jack Katz ■ 61

though, that I am impressed that even a dog like you can give such a charitable evaluation of this very poor performance. I would have compared it to valuing a hot dog stand at ten million dollars when it had no past history of ever making a profit."

"First of all," explained Sir Real, "this is an era of cheap capital: a fancy way of saying that there is a lot of money being thrown at businesses involved with the Internet. *Levity Jeans* is an 'old economy' manufacturer going back to the turn of the century. *Amazin'StockPrice.Com* is a 'new economy' retail Internet company that operates on Internet time."

"What is Internet time?" asked Bob.

"It's a high tech definition of time," explained Sir Real, "but I believe it's related to an ancient pseudo-Hispanic word for tomorrow: 'money'ahna.' Internet time means that companies can expand, change and mature at unheard-of speeds. The Internet mantra is 'get big fast.' Time for development has been shortened so much that Internet time has been favorably compared to dog years, something I can well relate too.

"At the same time, we are told by these profitless companies that profits only need to come at glacial speed because of all the effort that is being poured into growth and name recognition. True, they don't have real profits, but they virtually have profits. 'Don't worry,' they say, 'we'll make money to justify the price for your shares in the future'—money'ahna. 'Don't lose this opportunity to invest in a company on the bleeding edge.' Fast talk and talk about 'fast fast' has nothing to do with being swift. As you can see, Mr. Catz, there is a lot of marketing psychology involved, not just trillions of dollars. That's why Wall Street celebrates when such companies announce lower-than-expected losses. Although these companies have none of the trappings of real success Wall Street cheers their trappings of real excess. Big loss can be treated as big gain in never-never land, even with unproven, profitless companies. At the end of the day the fastest results may come in the area of job loss from the fast-is-beautiful preachers. Hooray for Wallywood."

The Mental Is Fundamental

"Why would you hire both a psychologist and a psychoanalyst, let alone even one?" asked Bob.

"It has become increasing recognized in the financial world that understanding the mental is absolutely fundamental," explained Sir

Real. "All you can really know for sure is what happened in the past. Investors are left only with their fears, hopes, perceptions, and beliefs about the future when it comes to the present—which makes them vulnerable. Each has a different perspective. Dr. No is trained in learning theory. He is one of those stimulus response kinds of guys: see the ball, fetch the ball. He likes to explain things in terms of perception and learning theory. For example, just the other day he was talking about the fact that too many investors haven't distinguished between a true high technology company and marketing companies using established technology like *Amazin'StockPrice.Com*. Dr. No also said that when events such as the rapid growth in the U.S. stock market go on for a long period of time, it comes to be seen as the norm. When eventually there is a change in circumstances, the perception can be greatly magnified in the opposite direction. Overconfidence, which can interfere with proper discrimination between safety and danger, is displaced by underconfidence, which can interfere with investors ability to spot opportunity."

"Whew," Bob wiped his brow. "What else does he have to say?"

"Dr. No talks about today's stock market situation as a tale of two stock markets," said Sir Real. "He calls it bipolar: an almost manic valuation of technology, media and telecom-type companies while other parts of the stock market are in a state of depression such as those dealing with commodities like mining and agriculture. Dr. No is concerned that many new investors fail to perceive how much the new economy is really about the old economy and old rules. He likes to say you can't drive a car on the Internet highway.

"He also sees a failure in some to distinguish between the boundaries of traditional investing, which involves the elements of gambling, and pure gambling, as when company shares are bid up or down like commodities at an auction. For example, oranges, hogs, cattle and the like are commodities regardless of underlying worth. Dr. No mentioned that those who go into a gambling establishment or play the lottery don't tend to sue when they lose because the issue of gambling is clear cut. However, today's investing world is getting murkier and more confusing than ever, with financial products that are called investments, but are closer to gambling."

"I guess it's the kind of answer you can expect from someone who comes from the Land Down Under," observed Bob. "And Dr. Root?"

"Dr. Root plays a whole different ball game," explained Sir Real. "She plays that Freudian game about life being the pursuit of pleasure and the avoidance of pain. In fact, her psychoanalytic paper studied how the pain from losing money was a much stronger emotion than the pleasure of gaining it. She has analyzed her dreams and innermost thoughts for years under the training of a psychoanalyst. Her focus is on the hind brain area, the seat of emotions. She deals with concepts like 'denial.' Just like the other day she mentioned to me how a client changed the topic of conversation and never came back after she coyly suggested that tech may turn out to be just another dirty four-letter word. As her patients walk out the door she likes to bark 'emotional eyes can never see.' Dr. Root calls her therapy The Freud Files because 'Zah truth is *nein* out there.'"

"What did she discover after all those years of analysis?" Bob then asked.

"She says that she discovered Barbara Streisand was right all along. Dr. Root keeps singing this butchered version of one of Barbara's songs all day like a broken record. It goes something like this: 'Feelings. Ach, all I goht is mein feelings.' She says our perceptions of the world boil down to simple raw feelings. Feelings determine our perceptions and reactions. Dr. Root sees many investment activities in terms of primitive fight or flight responses. She sniffs her Corgi nose at Dr. No calling him a non-analyzed no nothing. They have been getting into some pretty serious intellectual dog fights lately.

"When I complained to Dr. Root about investors having a rose-tinted view of the market; she answered that I needed to have a greater appreciation for the way feelings color how investors view returns and risks as well as their memories of the past. Unlike Dr. No, she talks, for example, about the herd mentality of investors and how it is rooted in pack behavior. This 'married to the mob' behavior, she says, increased chances of survival long ago when the jungles started disappearing and sparse cover decreased opportunities for ambush. Open plains favored those who hunted and foraged in groups. Even stampedes increased chances of survival. The last time I saw her, she was reading aloud from Dr.

Freud's manuscript on crowds; it was something about crowd sense of invincibility, suggestibility and irresponsibility."

Bob was fascinated. "What else does she have to say?"

"Dr. Root likes to mock online financial ads, which create the illusion of more control through technology," explained Sir Real. She points out that investing is all about loss of control once you buy. All you can do is engage in what is called risk management to balance risk with reward. It's still always up to others what the gains or losses will be. Others include huge institutional investors like pensions, mutual funds and foundations with their combined trillions of dollars."

"This feeling of control must be pretty important if marketing ads focus on it," observed Bob. "Why is this?"

"According to Dr. Root," Sir Real began, "fear of loss of control is related to anxiety about death, the ultimate loss of control. This is one reason she believes financial fortune tellers are so popular, despite their poor records. Dr. Root also makes fun of how financial sales representatives are often trained to sell on fear or sell on greed. As she told me a few weeks ago in her usual loud, hysterical manner: 'Fear is zah key. Greed is always about zah fear, fear of being left behind, fear of not having enough, fear of lost opportunity oon so on. It's about zah basest animal hoarding behavior. Zaht is zah root cause. Don't zeese schveins understand? Zay haven't been analyzed. Zaht's vye. Even behavioral studies confirm zah role of zah fear.' Then she just stomped off and drank a whole liter of Schnapps. She is that ranting and raving type. You would think after seventeen years of analysis, almost half as much as Woody Allen, she would be a little more mellow."

Bob wanted to know more. "What behavioral studies confirm the role of fear?"

"Behavioral studies indicate that investors can be more influenced by losses than they can about gains," Sir Real expounded. "For example, if you were offered a guaranteed $100 versus the chance of winning $200 on the flip of a coin—you would be much more likely to take the $100. However, if you started off with a $100 penalty and the chance to owe nothing or win $200—you are much more likely to take the coin bet on owing nothing. The possibility of restoring your lost money is treated as having greater importance than taking a chance on a possible gain. Yet the chances of winning or losing from the flip of a coin remain at fifty-

fifty. There is a math difference, though, once you lose. If, for example, you have $1,000 and you lose 60% of its value, you would be left with $400. To go from $400 to $800 requires a gain of 100% because you are now dealing with less money. It's not just mental although it may seem that way. "

Of Blubber and Blunder

"Do you really think my problem is mental?" asked Bob.

"Not necessarily. Maybe your body just made a sound business decision," said Sir Real in response. "It could have decided to eliminate excess capacity and redundancies, outsource nonessential activity, streamline operations, engage in a broad restructuring effort, shed low margin output, pare underperforming assets, utilize the least resources to maximize potential, narrow the focus to core essentials, rid itself of core inefficiencies and, of course, let go of unneeded surplus space as well as non-performing functions."

"What kind of silly garbage talk is that?" Bob demanded.

"What do you mean garbage?" returned Sir Real, in a feigned wounded manner. "How dare you talk like that to a Queen's dog. That's how the corporate fat cats, the company bosses with their little suits and fat cigars, talk when they goof up and have to make their bones, so to speak, firing thousands of employees. Thinning the ranks of employees is one of the quickest methods for fat cats to fatten the bottom line and communicate to investors that quarterly earnings will be improving to 'enhance shareholder value'—a euphemism for shoring up a sagging stock price. Earnings, as you will learn from a corporate seal, are vital to the price of stocks."

"I think you are kidding me again," declared Bob.

"I've been teasing you a little to help you appreciate the significant role language plays in the investment world; and shed more light on what is really go on. Corgis are big time shedders, so we understand how corporate shedders can use language to explain away and mask problems. One of my favorite euphemisms is when a company says that a product of theirs has 'a long selling cycle,' which often means that sales are really difficult or totally nonexistent. Another one I like is 'the ingredients are there,' which often means that they haven't yet figured out how to make things work. Fat cats also like to talk about how their company has 'solid fundamentals' and investors are 'buying a company, not a piece of paper.' Translation: it might take a long time for you to make a profit on your stock."

"Isn't it true that corporate restructurings can increase productivity and profits?" asked Bob.

"That's what fat cats say, Mr. Catz," answered Sir Real. "Of course, the fat cats almost always have their nine lives plus gold and silver parachutes in the form of salary and stock compensation packages should things take a turn for the worse. They are well insulated from personal financial hardship with even backup chutes for their parachutes. If the company stock price takes a dive, despite their efforts, the parachutes cushion their fall should they lose their jobs or decide to leave 'to pursue other interests.' Their distaste for fat rarely ever includes themselves."

"Well at least I can safely assume that fat cats still suffer somewhat like us worker bees if the stock price goes down. At least their pay is still linked to performance," Bob pointed out. "Isn't that important?"

"You might be assuming wrongly," Sir Real replied. "You see, there are some really cool cats who wear what are called 'zero-cost collars.' Their compensation packages are arranged so that there is a collar, a ceiling and a floor around the company stock price. It's a hedging-your-bets technique they learned from the master hedgers—the financial hedgehogs. Even if fat cat performance amounts to zero and the company stock plunges in value with lean times for lesser employees, these guys still enjoy fat times."

"So, apparently, they don't have self-image problems like normal humans," Bob commented.

"*Au contraire,*" exclaimed Sir Real. "Fat cats are extremely 'wait conscious.' They know that investors don't like to wait long to see higher profits or earnings. However, company cost cutting cuts more than one way. It can be beneficial when fat is removed, but too often it cuts down to the meat and bones. Problems occur when the cost cutting corporate cats are better at selling the marketplace on the changes to be made rather than creating imaginative solutions to sell more of the company's product.

"Fat cats like to talk to the media and Wall Street about their ability to change the situation and improve the bottom line, meaning earnings. It's easy to do. Companies can quickly cut their way to higher profitability by quickly lowering expenses through lower salary pay outs and by reducing the amounts of money owed that the company is paying interest on. Fatter profits keeps investors, who like quick turnarounds, feeling fat and happy. Fat cats make out well too, exercising stock options which allow them to buy the stock, which is now floating at a higher price at a fixed low price."

"How is that done?" Bob asked.

"Say the stock price went from $5 to $25. A fat cat could exercise the right to buy the stock at a preset lower price such as $10, pocketing the difference: times all the rights they are allowed to use. Even though fat cats might have a razor thin salary to show how they are tightening their own belts, stock options allow them to feed off rising stock prices and fatten their paychecks other ways. According to Dr. No, there's not necessarily a relationship between rising stock prices and the adequacy of a top fat cat in running the operation. The bell curve is alive and well with the fat cats too, with highly paid fat cats who are merely average, below average and even retarded in performance."

"You seem to be tugging at the leash to say something else," observed Bob, noticing Sir Real stretching beyond usual.

"Fat cats aren't the only ones who can wield a hatchet," Sir Real blurted out as he straightened up. "Despite all the preaching in the financial media about long-term investing, never have investors been so short-term in their thinking. If performance of a stock doesn't fulfill bloated expectations, then the stock price can be cut dramatically. Stock prices may rise in response only to fall later when turnaround artists turn out to be nothing but short-term, below-the-bell-curve performers who haven't laid down a proper foundation for future growth and have also cut into company morale and creativity. Often the cuts are mainly to please the market, so cuts eventually won't cut it anymore. Fat cuts by fat cats during lean times, without significant positive changes, usually lead to even leaner times ahead.

"The top line in a financial report, which has to do with sales or revenue, also is the bottom line. Sales are much more difficult to manipulate than profits. Fat cats can be busy for a while showing that they are like tough Mafia hit men going 'bahda bing' and 'bahda bang,' knocking off employees and plants. Eventually, it may dawn on investors that a good percentage of fat cats who come in as 'champions of shareholder value' are no better than dumb thugs who can't create anything new or demonstrate leadership. This leads to a cycle of more layoffs and closings. Fortunately, these are the good times.

"Investors demanding quick results help create this type of result. You have to be careful of long-term investing in companies that have rapid earnings growth that is not matched with growth in sales revenue. There are many other methods companies use to boost stock price. That's why you may need to talk to a cash kitty later about how companies borrow money to buy back stock to make it look more valuable by decreasing the number of shares in circulation.

"To tell you the honest truth, I like seeing you small. I am so tired of reading in the news all the time about the growing importance of the retail investor on Wall Street, the so-called 'little guy' or 'small investor,' but never actually seeing one."

"Why haven't you seen one before?" asked Bob.

"It's probably because the eight-hundred-pound institutional gorillas like pension, mutual funds and foundations are really the ones who move the markets—despite what some reports might lead readers to think. Retail investors only affect about a third of the market. However, here you actually exist; unlike those expressions such as 'they say,' but you never actually see 'they,' if you know what I mean."

"I think I'm getting a headache," moaned Bob. "By the way, why do you have a saddle on your back?"

"The saddle on my back is for you to ride on now that you have been downsized," said Sir Real, giving Bob some welcome news. "According to Welsh folklore, we are enchanted dogs. Fairy warriors would ride on us and use us to pull fairy coaches. They still do, but only at midnight. It's true. You can check the harness-like color markings on my back. Underneath this saddle are also the indentations from the ancient 'fairy saddle.' According to Celtic legend, it is the Fairy Folk who first brought us to the British Isles long before humans did. Now you can accompany me through the investing forest where money really grows on trees without labor—what we call unearned income and capital gains, and perhaps learn more about how fairy tale numbers are created by fund managers and companies wanting to make their earnings reports look fabulous.

"All you have to do is grab one of my velveteen ears and saddle up. The financial forest is just on the opposite side of the bakery moat. It's supposed to be greener on the other side, with trees that will one day touch the sky, according to the belief of many absolutely green investors. That's what they say."

Jist Whit Kind Of A Furriner Is You, Dawg ?

"You seem quite knowledgeable for someone who doesn't have an American accent. Where exactly are you from?" asked Bob.

"Presently I live in America and have a legal residence in a tiny community north of San Francisco called Dogtown. I'm originally from a village on the island of Anglesey, off north Wales called *Llanfairpwllgwyngyllgogerychwyrndrobwllllantysiliogogogoch*. Ah, I see your smile and look of disbelief. That's good. You will need a sense of humor for your journey, but I can assure you such a village so named does in fact exist. In ancient Welsh it means 'St. Mary's church in the hollow of the white hazel near a rapid whirlpool and the Church of St. Tysilio of the red cave.' It is the biggest village name in the U.K. and is filled with dogs like me. The word Corgi means dwarf, which is quite appropriate these days. As you will see, there are happenings in the American financial markets that dwarf whatever has happened before. Keep in mind, too, that it can often be very helpful to surround yourself with dwarfs when you need to feel like a giant."

"Are you Corgis pretty smart or just smart alecks?" asked Bob.

"Oh yes," replied Sir Real, "we are considered to be among the smartest of all dogs, but are extremely bossy, so don't take it personally. As you may have noticed, I haven't given you much of an opportunity to say anything. I just keep talking and talking, trying to move the conversation in the direction I think it should go. It's really a matter of good breeding. Corgis are incorrigible herding dogs who now nip at the heels of financial sheep and cattle."

"Okay. But what kind of credentials do you have?" demanded Bob.

"*Bahdges senhor*? I dohn haff to show you no steenkin bahdges," piped Sir Real. "Ah, please forgive me, Mr. Catz. Perhaps I have seen one too many of those old Hollywood bandito movies on late night television after the lawyer programs. Seriously, I am licensed as a registered representative to market securities and give financial advice at the federal and state level. I don't have a rich book, what brokers call their clients assets, but I do have a very rich imagination and a wealth of knowledge."

"So what does that mean?" asked Bob.

"Licensed registered representatives who arrange trades of securities such as stocks, bonds and mutual funds between buyers and sellers, often go under titles such as broker, financial adviser, planner or consultant. The National Association of Securities Dealers regulates the testing and activities of those who buy and sell securities. NASD is the parent of the Nasdaq Stock Market, our second largest market for buying and selling stocks, after the New York Stock Exchange, which is the largest in the world. The NASD also currently owns the American Exchange."

"How can I be sure you are telling me the truth?" Bob demanded.

"With the creation of a new central location for information," explained Sir Real, "you can now check out my past history as well as that of others on the Web at www.nasdr.com. Just click on 'About Your Broker' for my employment history and list of states where I am licensed. You have to be licensed in every state in which you conduct or solicit business of this kind. If the screen indicates a 'disclosure event,' then it means there is a potential black mark against me. You can ask for a report that will be sent by mail. Although advisers are required to be registered, there are no education or work standards which need to be met."

"I'm still surprised conservative financial institutions would give a little barker like you the chance to be a top dog broker," Bob remarked.

"As long as you have a clean FBI record," explained Sir Real, "and meet minimum educational requirements, the brokerage company often has only one main question: 'Can you sell?' They scream that question in your ear during the interview. Just kidding. Although I was never treated like a dog, I sometimes worked like one. Dogs are not an unfamiliar sight on Wall Street. There are professional traders who work in the trading pits called pit bulls. Traders are those who treat stocks and bonds like rentals rather than ownership."

"Do you have any of those letters after your name that usually start with C indicating you have advanced training?" Bob inquired.

"You mean like CFP (Certified Financial Planner from the College of Financial Planning)," said Sir Real, "CLU (Chartered Life Underwriter for insurance agents), CMFC (Chartered Mutual Fund Counselor), CPA (Certified Professional Accountant), ChFC (Chartered Financial Consultant, insurance and financial planning) and so on. No, I have no advanced training or advanced degrees, but my therapist claims I'm advancing by degrees. And, naturally, I have a long and distinguished pedigree."

"Seriously, Sir Real, are certifications necessary?" asked Bob.

"Certifications can be helpful or misleading. Someone can have credentials longer than a giraffe's neck and still not be any good at helping you. Be careful of so-called marketing degrees like 'wealth management' (translation: I want to deal with lots of money using my nifty software program). You have to look beyond all that to the experience and integrity of whom you are dealing with. Trust is of vital importance in this business. By the way, one can have financial planning training and not be a broker. You need to pass exams like the national Securities 7 exam to become a broker and trade securities. Relatively few planners and insurance agents have a Series 7 license. The majority has a lower level Series 6 license which enables them to sell only a limited number of products such as mutual funds."

"I see," said Bob, beginning to get the picture. "What if the broker you are checking on isn't listed?"

"If the person talking to you about buying and selling securities isn't listed, then you could be dealing with a fraud. Tens of millions of dollars are taken from unsuspecting people every year by total frauds that are not even licensed. You must have noticed all the steam coming up from the ground nearby. It's not just because the economy is running at full steam. Some of the vapors are from underground boiler rooms. Don't worry, it's environmentally friendly. Hot air from snake oil stock salesmen pumps up the value of the stocks they market which then deflate in the marketplace.

"Ironically these fellows, filled with hot air, do what is called 'cold calling'—calling potential clients or marks all day to convince them they have this great stock buy. It's called pump and dump operations and they thrive because there are so many sitting ducks out there. You buy the heavily promoted stock at a pumped up price and then the price takes a dive. 'Buy, lie and sell high' then watch the stock die is the musical way I remember the process. Boiler operators tend to concentrate on stocks priced at less than $5 that don't sell on major markets like the New York Stock Exchange or Nasdaq. They send out newsletters and post messages all over the Internet to excite potential investors. The phone number of the NASD is 800-289-9999 in case that's of interest. It is better to check out in advance any suspicions than to have to call 911 after you realize your investment vehicle was taken for a joy ride to a chop shop. By the time your learning adventure is over you may see similarities between boiler room operators and tactics used by leading blue chip companies. Snake oil is served at some of the finest establishments on Wall Street. It's not exclusive to slippery brokers operating out of underground offices."

"What rights do I have in case I get duped anyway? I thought blue chip was one of those strange looking organic tortilla chips." Bob wanted to know.

"You have the right not to remain silent," Sir Real announced loud and clear. "You can contact the federal government's Office of Investor Education and Assistance at 202-942-7040, www.sec.gov on the Web, and your local state securities regulator. The office of Investor Education has a section called 'News You Can Use' with brochures like one on avoiding certificates of deposit with misleading maturity dates. There is also Web site information that my be helpful for financial legal issues such as bankruptcy and debtor/creditor relations at sites such as www.MyCounsel.com."

"What's a certificate of deposit?" asked Bob.

"A certificate of deposit, or CD, is issued by a bank or financial institution. You are making a loan in return for guaranteed interest over a fixed period of time. The interest is often higher than prevailing rates in other accounts in a bank because you are losing liquidity. The cost of buying CDs is built into the price in the form of an interest cut that you don't see. It is not free of charge as some think. Furthermore, the federal government insures the CD for up to $100,000. If you have more than that amount, get CDs from different banks. It's not a good idea, in my opinion, to get a jumbo CD for hundreds of thousands of dollars from the same bank. A brokerage house can offer choices of CDs from banks all over the country, often with better rates than the local bank. To verify whether a CD from a bank is federally insured, you can call 800-934-3342 or 800-276-6003 or go to www.fdic.gov. The agency has a search engine for determining whether a bank in question has FDIC insurance. If you want to check on the best rates look at www.bankrate.com."

"What kind of category are CDs under?" asked Bob. "They aren't stocks or bonds."

"CDs can come under the description of money market instruments," explained Sir Real. "If you have at least $100,000 to invest for the short term, you may be interested in 'commercial paper,' which is a short-term loan to the biggest, most credit worthy companies in the U.S.—the so called 'blue chip' companies. They are promissory notes—promises to pay back money loaned within 100 to 270 days. It is often cheaper for major companies to borrow from the public than from banks. Commercial loans, in fact, are the biggest source of funding for top U.S. companies. In short, they are company IOU's. These loans may provide a better yield for you than short-term loans to the government like Treasury bills, or T-bills, and they offer a relatively high degree of safety.

"There are also special kinds of CDs called Equity-Indexed CDs, which allow you to link the value of your CD to stock market performance. Like a regular CD, the holder is guaranteed 100% of the original deposit, the principal. The worst that can happen is that you don't receive any interest. You can't lose your original investment because of federal deposit insurance. Unlike a regular CD, you usually can't cash the CD in until maturity, although you may be able to sell it on what is called a secondary market where you might take a loss.

"The good news is that if you hold the CD for the entire time period agreed, until the date of maturity, you might make a lot more money than if you had held an ordinary interest-bearing CD. It all depends on stock market performance the CD is tied to. It may be an attractive way for very conservative investors to participate in stock market performance without the usual risks of loss. Or, in the parlance of the brokerage world, they can be great for 'investment phobes'—those who are terrified of investing. The equity indexed CD holder has growth potential combined with federal guarantees of getting at least your money back—what is called preservation of capital. Can I get back to our subject?"

"Why not?" said Bob. "You Corgis are so one-track-minded."

"There is also the nonprofit National Fraud Information Center at 800-876-7060 or visit at www.fraud.org," resumed Sir Real. "They will fax your complaint to dozens of law enforcement agencies. You'll probably also need an attorney to help retrieve money lost. The con artists are very creative and chameleon-like. When the markets cool down they will switch from stock scams to conservative-sounding ones like money market, insurance, and promissory notes from worthless companies.

"Actually, you should always check things out, including the brokerage firm. Not all verification is easy though. Recently, there was a newspaper exposé of the claims of a popular financial author with a following among women. Women, by the way, are more likely to live longer than men, have lower incomes, and be single later on in life, so their need for financial education is even greater than it is for men in general. Financial seminars directed at women are basically about meeting the special needs of those doing the marketing. Can you imagine the reaction if there were seminars for men only? It's forward-looking marketing and backward-looking learning. Women are a big target these days for the three 'marketeers': brokerage companies, booksellers and insurance companies. That's why I would like to introduce you to a little fellow I know from the Ferret or Foul Detective Agency. The ferret knows some handy ways to use a computer mouse to track a rat and access objective non-sales financial information. Being a successful investor involves learning to like financial detective work."

"Since you watch all those lawyer television programs, what exactly is fraud?" asked Bob.

"Fraud is one type of misrepresentation: intentional misrepresentation of a material fact such as knowingly making a false statement of importance with the objective of deceiving. All the elements need to be present, such as demonstrating reliance on the information to your detriment. It's not sufficient that you have been lied to in order to demonstrate fraud."

"So what if it isn't intentional?" asked Bob.

"If you have misrepresentation, but it isn't intentional, such as a broker making a false material statement without proper grounds to believe it is true (like not verifying a rumor), you may be entering the area of negligent misrepresentation. Negligence is about failing to act prudently according to the standards of the profession. Someone in a profession is judged by what his or her peers would have done. Again, you have to have all the elements. A statement can be false (for example, a broker lying about the food quality at a restaurant in a conversation), but not of material importance to the subject of investing.

"Fraud and negligent misrepresentation are not only concerned with the disclosure of material false information, but also by deliberately or negligently failing to disclose. For example, a broker can recommend a company, deliberately not mentioning that the company has severe financial problems. An intentional or negligent act of omission is no different than the commission of an act." Sir Real sniffed the air and cried out, "I smell smoke."

"The Call Of The Mild"

Even monkeys fall from trees.

—Japanese Proverb

"Don't tell me about the law. I know all about the law. The best kind of law is preventative law. That's why I am warning you to protect your bagels and put lox on them," yelled a four-foot-high smoked chicken that rushed towards Bob with smoke streaming out of the top of her head. It wore tiny red high-heeled shoes.

"I see so much smoke, but I don't see any fire," Bob remarked.

"You probably will see the fire when you eventually feel it in your wallet, but it might take another year or two," the giant chicken responded with a cackle. In a breathless manner, the smoked bird then introduced herself as Noella Coward.

Bob could not believe his eyes. "You are the biggest delicatessen chicken I have ever seen."

"Thank you," clucked Noella with pride. "Organic chickens have their limitations. I'm on steroids just like this economy and the hyperactive financial news media."

"What do you mean?" asked Bob.

"Don't you read the news?" demanded Noella. "Don't you know that the economy is moving at such speed that it's starting to overheat as supplies for goods, services and labor find it more difficult to keep up with demand? It's not just my non-livable minimum wage job at the delicatessen that's got me so burned up."

"I had no idea. So what?" said Bob.

"What kind of an attitude is that?" Noella demanded to know. "Look at me. I need to protect my retirement nest eggs. Hot demand for products will make it easier for companies to start passing along price increases and feed inflation. The economy is simply sizzling. In the last three months of 1999, the economy grew at a seasonally adjusted annual rate of 7.3%, the fastest growth rate in GDP in sixteen years, with the lowest unemployment rate in thirty years."

"Isn't that good news?" Bob asked.

"It's the kind of growth rate you can achieve in a developing country where it doesn't take much to stimulate high growth since you can be starting from such a low point economically," Noella explained. "However, this rate is happening at the tail end of what will probably be the longest economic expansion in the history of the country. Everything is booming including companies coming to market and merging together, which is why investment banks that handle this type of activity are reporting record profits. The banking industry is exploding. Even food banks can't seem to keep up with demand."

"What is GDP?" asked Bob.

"GDP refers to gross domestic product, the nation's total output of goods and services—a general measure of economic health. It is the strongest quarterly performance since the long expansion began in March of 1991. If the present economic expansion lasts until February of 2000, it will surpass the previous record."

"What about all the great advances in technology to prevent things getting out of hand and costs going up?" asked Bob, hopefully. "It's supposed to be a new economic era."

"You are talking about productivity: the amount of output for each hour of work. Sharp rises in productivity because of factors such as technology advances have helped blunt inflation by allowing companies to raise wages financed by increased output rather than raising the prices of their products, which is inflationary. In fact, during the last quarter of this year, productivity rose 5%, the highest in seven years. This year it was 3.6% for the entire year. In the mid 1990s, productivity levels sped up after averaging only around a measly 1.5% per year for the previous twenty years."

"That's what I'm talking about, I guess," said Bob.

Fowl Language

"These much-ballyhooed productivity advances are not permanent, and we may not know for years how accurate they really are. Information technology sellers have been hyping productivity improvements but are probably one of the least reliable sources of accurate information. The public is missing out on a really good joke because the punch line comes so much later," explained

Noella. "Eventually these advances, whatever they are, will slow down or not be able to accelerate at the same pace. Industries mature. There have been enormous investments made for the twenty-first century information age. Nearly one-third of growth in GDP the last few years has been related to technology spending. It is doubtful that it will continue at the same accelerated pace year after year. Demand will slow down and maybe even decline, having effects throughout the economy. Whether trains, planes, or computer gains, major technology changes are usually permanent and extraordinary—but the benefits over time become common and ordinary. Competitive pressures also come into play. Technology can't repeal the business cycle.

"In the meantime, there are complaints of not enough employees to fill key jobs. Employers are starting to run into a productivity wall of new employees who don't have the work experience to keep up the pace. Advances from innovation will reach a point where they simply can no longer cover losses from elsewhere. One day in the future, this extraordinary productivity may prove to be a statistical freak. Over time, things tend to average out. That's what I keep squawking about."

"What else do you have to say? Don't be chicken," urged Bob.

"Productivity advances also can't make up for imbalances such as the record trade deficits, record low savings and record borrowings by corporations and individuals," Noella continued. "Costs for raw materials and labor continue to steadily rise. Food companies for example, are now starting to offer less weight per package so they don't have to increase prices. If companies can't absorb these costs in the future or pass them on to customers because of competition, then profits will drop. Stock prices depend on future profits.

"Moreover, the expectation of continuing boosts in productivity, which may not happen, is believed to be helping bid up stock prices to what some claim are unrealistic levels. Rising stock prices have helped productivity by making it cheaper for companies to access capital. The bigger a company's market cap, or total value in the marketplace, the easier it is to attract lenders offering cheap rates for example. This helps profits, making the company look more productive. What is going to happen if stock prices can't keep going up like before? Investors tend to buy stocks when they are more likely than not to go up. Moreover, some complain that the rise in prices has been too fast and too much, fueling excessive levels of consumer spending because people feel richer from unrealized paper gains and don't feel they have to save. The economy can only produce so much—stock prices are related to how much value is placed on profits from selling goods and services. Investors are placing greater value than ever before on economic production."

"I think I see the picture," said Bob. "What can be done?"

"I talked to *Dr. Green Spin* who has some chicken blood in him after already having experienced the 1987 stock market crash shortly after he took office," Noella began. "He said that the Federal Reserve will have to press on the monetary brakes and cool the economy with interest rate increases before a four alarm blaze breaks out, and the economy skids out of control. The Fed has set a desired speed limit of 3.5% believing that continued growth above that level increases the risk of inflation and the economy driving into a sudden recession pothole. A recession occurs when the economy goes into a downturn for two consecutive quarters or six months and unemployment shoots up."

"You seem exceptionally nervous even for such a big chicken," observed Bob.

"Yes, I know," squawked Noella. "I have even been seeing Dr. Root. I'm not only running on steroids, I'm also running a little scared. I told her that last year household wealth, which is a broad measure that includes stock price gains, grew twice as fast as incomes. This seems to confirm what some are saying about the prices of assets like houses and stocks going up too fast because of speculation as investors place greater and greater values on what has been produced. During therapy, Dr. Root always seems to ask questions—questions I have a hard time answering. Recently she asked me how one determines when boom is really excess. She says I'm suffering from the usual neurotic stuff, plus an actual condition called investment stress. That's where the investor no longer trusts anyone's advice."

"Everything is just smokin,'" observed Bob. "Why would you be stressed out? Not a week seems to go by that I don't hear a reporter on the nightly news talking about 'the hot booming economy' in a booming voice."

"The smoke may be a smokescreen for a credit-driven boom, a borrowing binge. It kind of reminds me of how for many years consumers have been buying water-soaked chickens without knowing the true water content. A mock chicken I work with at the delicatessen named Moxie said that no matter how you slice the economic statistics, many of them still end up looking like New Era baloney," Noella responded.

"Personally," said Bob, "I prefer real old-fashioned pastrami, but I can't find any. No one knows what I mean. They are clueless in Seattle."

"In spite of the U.S. stock market going up and up on average," explained Noella, "more than half of the stocks traded last year went down in price from the previous year. The success of the market rests on a narrow group of mostly high technology companies. The market has very bad breadth. It reminds me of a group of stocks long ago that led the market called the Nifty Fifty. They weren't so nifty when the market turned sour."

"Why are you running around shaking your head?"

"Because I'm not a chicken without a head," explained Noella. "Lending is booming, too. Some economists have suggested that it is because interest rates are too low. Debt in moderation can be a good thing as the driving force behind growth. However, never in recent memory has debt been so popular with individuals and corporations for all kinds of things. Companies and consumers are more indebted than ever with the debt load over $14 trillion and approximately double the nation's annual gross domestic product. Bankruptcy judges are complaining about being overwhelmed. Borrowing from brokerage houses to buy stock, called 'borrowing on margin,' hit a new record this quarter. By the end of this year, investors had a tab of approximately $142 billion. That's a $100 billion more than the $42 billion margin debt just before the 1987 crash. In 1990, the amount was a mere $35 billion. Next year in 2000, borrowing on securities is expected to go much higher.

"These figures don't even include all the money individuals have borrowed through home equity loans to put into the stock market. Unlike home equity loans from banks, loans from brokerage houses have to be covered if the value of the holdings borrowed on margin decrease too much in value. Investors can be forced to sell, driving the market down even further, and triggering more demands to cover and magnifying losses. These kind of economic imbalances may come home to roost during a slowdown of the U.S. economy, particularly if it's an abrupt and deep one. Many believe that *Dr. Green Spin* rules the economic roost. Investors seem to be counting their paper profits before they are hatched. I worry especially that retirement investors will be smoked without ever having inhaled as the 'wealth effect' from the Clinton years turns out to be as ghostly as smoke."

"What does Dr. Root have to say?" Bob wondered.

"She says that easy loans can later become hard debts and that concern about this heavy borrowing is way past due," answered Noella. Bob and Noella's conversation was interrupted by the sound of flapping wings above them.

Fuhgettaboutit

"Margin call. You have a margin call—a demand for immediate payment," shouted a tough scruffy-looking web-footed bird with a hooked beak and long, narrow wings who flew overhead and landed on a large tree stump several feet away. The bird introduced itself in a heavy New York accent as Lowen, a financial albatross from the Bronx. From underneath its left wing, he pulled out a business card with his beak, which was dropped into Bob's open hand. The card read: "Have Margin Call, Will Travel Inc., wire Bird Song, Bronx Zoo, New York."

"I'm rather impressed with your card," said Sir Real. "It's like the one on the old television show with the professional killer for hire, *Have Gun Will Travel*. You should really use an e-mail address in these modern times. Please go on."

"That's right, so shaddup already. I was flyin' over the wahtah and heard you discussin' my business," said Lowen. "So I thought I'd come down and seeze if I could explain a thing or two. Margin borrowing allows investors to borrow up to half the value of their securities just as a straight loan for any purpose or to buy more securities. If you have say 50% buying power, then you have what is called 50% margin. If you have for example $10,000, you may be allowed to borrow an additional $5,000 (50% of $10,000 amount) to buy more securities. Brokerage houses are makin' fortunes off dese kinds of loans. This can work in your favor by giving you power or leverage to buy more securities, which hopefully will be going up in value magnifying your gains. However, if the market gets cold and flies far south like the boids in winter time, then the margin loan can be an albatross around your neck. Margin magnifies gains but it also magnifies losses, soz your brokerage account becomes more like a broke-or-rich account."

"What do you mean?" Bob wished to know.

"Unlike a regular loan," explained Lowen, "the value of securities used as collateral for the loan can't drop below a certain point. The amount has to be worth at least 25% of dah value at dah time of dah purchase, see? Soz your securities can't be allowed to sink so much in price that you wouldn't be able to repay dah loan. The securities are supposed to enable dah brokerage company to feel secure—not you Pal. So you have tah pony up mo' cash and/or securities. If you borrows on your house to play dah stock market and dah house goes down in value, dah bank isn't goin' to call you if you continue to pay your loans on time. Borrowing from a broker is quite different. You must sign a margin agreement that may allow a brokerage house to sell off your securities without even notifyin' you. I'm only here because of courtesy, 'cause I happen to be an upright guy from the Bronx.

"I'm the guy from New York City, like dah old pop song, 'cept I ain't kind of cute and don't wear no mohair suit. We don't have to notify nobody about nuthin.' Hey, look at me when I talk to you, Pal. With or without notification, you have to come up with enough dough and/or securities to raise dah value of your holdings beyond the minimum level set. In a fast downward moving market, margin calls can lead to even greater selling by dah public to come up with money, escalating losses which lead to more selling to cover. The greater the amount of borrowing on margin in general, the greater dah potential for a massive sell-off, like lemmings going over a cliff, if dah market tanks suddenly. Even though you may never use margin the more you knows, the more you will develop a nose for trouble. That's how you become a wise guy. You see what I'm sayin'?"

"I think I follow you," said Bob, scratching his head.

"I don't care wit ya tink or wit you follow," said Lowen. "Do I look like some kind of bird brain to you? Do I look like some computer wimp from Seattle who would order a non-fat double tall mocha from *Lattesbucks* instead of real coffee? Then don't treat me like I'm stupid or somethin', 'cause you'll regret it. If ya don't come up with enough dough to cover your losses quickly, I get to swoop down and sell off or liquidate your securities used as collateral at whatever price I can get. Do you tink you follow that or do I need to talk slower?

"I love dat term 'liquidate.' It puts me in touch with my inner wild, while I still come across as real polite and professional-like. You would never knows I was from da Bronx. Dat's why I'd advise ya to use my services with a clear understandin' of the margin loan agreement. If the money don't come in like it's supposed to, then we can have what companies call 'a revenue recognition problem' or 'unexpected shortfall,' but what I call 'a situation.'"

"That sounds almost illegal," Bob said with a tone of irritation. "Are you sure you aren't from New Joisey?"

"Naw, it ain't illegal. You remember that song about fightin' dah law and dah law winnin'?" Lowen asked.

"Vaguely," Bob responded.

"Well you better get more familiar. Just 'cause I don't talk so nice sometimes don't mean what I do is illegal. I've usually got the law on my side fighting for me. You can play dumb like you don't understand later on; but it won't do ya much good wit da judge when I have your signature indicating your knowledge and acceptance of the margin terms. No one forced you to sign the agreement. I'm covered even though your securities might not be. Online investors really take to margin. It's so easy to apply. Do ya think it's a coincidence that margin investin' has mushroomed at the same time as online investing has become more popular dehn ever? Me, I'm just an ordinary guy, a bird of play, who likes to tink inside the box—usually a pizza box. So I'm off to get some tomato pie, as they call it in da Bronx, at the Let Them Eat Fake Bakery. Do ya have a problem wit' dat? 'Cause I pride myself on being a real problem solver ever since I was little."

"No Sir, Mr. Lowen, although you still look rather little, not that I have any problem with that of course," Bob hastened to say.

"Good. I kind of like you Bob. Go break a leg," added Lowen. "But one more ting before we part company. I don't want you to get the impression I only puts the squeeze on little investors like you Bob. I'm what they call an equal opportunity destroyer. People often got the wrong impression dat my call work is just marginal. Dis distoibs me."

"I don't quite understand. I'm only familiar with the expression 'equal opportunity employer.'"

"It means, Pal, wit all payment due respect," Lowen continued, "that I hit the high-end types too, not just guys like you. During these boom times, company owners and big time insiders in companies have been encouraged by the brokerage houses I represent to borrow on margin against their holdings for all sorts of good-sounding reasons. Stock prices, especially those classified as technology related, have been going up and up. So it seems to make sense to borrow and not have to sell your shares when they will probably go up still more and the seller would be hit with taxes on gains that were made. This way you can also easily have liquidity without having to deal with no complicated bank loans. Don't it make sense? If not, I can give you lots of other reasons put forth by my porcine colleagues at brokerage houses. They are optimistic kinds of guys."

"Yes, I guess your example does make sense."

Collateral Damage

"Well you probably guess wrong, Pal," Lowen said. "The Wall Street suits and their spin doctors like to talk to the media about how the stock market keeps going up and up because with the new digital economy they can break all da rules and make pigs fly. The media paints them as New Era wise guys wit dah assumption their companies are insensitive to the economic cycle. Listen Pal, where I come from dehr are real wise guys who know dat pigs in space only exist in Muppet shows. Right now, this being December 31, 1999, dah Nasdaq is flyin' high at a level of 4,069.31. Dese investors feel rich and getting richers. Real wise guys know dat break-da-rules gain can also mean break-da-rules pain and don't assume nuthin'. Do you hear what I'm saying? It don't take no genius to understand dat if ya can break rules on da upward side of da economic cycle, dehn you can break dehm on da downward phase too. Sooner or later, a lot of dese sky-high valued shares are going to be fallin' out of da sky like dead ducks wit company credit ratin's deterioratin' faster than my English is now. When da barometer of high tech growth, the mascot of da New Economy, called da Nasdaq Stock Market, comes to mean da Nosedive, dose CEOs are gonna see lots of 0s. Dey gonna be rich alright, rich wit problems. Me, I'm gonna be a real early bird placin' lots of mournin' calls about dyin' portfolios witch gonna suffer severe collateral damage if dey don't get a quick money transfusion to cover da collateral. Am I gettin' true to you?

"Da funny ting is that these guys use margin so they can avoid gettin' whacked and havin' even more benefits. Dey want their cake, and dey want to eat it too. Dehn the market goes down and whacks them. Dehn I whack them. It's wit dey call a one-two punch. You'd tink dat these paperweight wise guys wuhd wise up to da sales pitches from da brokerage heavyweights. Huh? I gotta go. I've just been sent for. Just one more ting, dough. If you don't want guys like me dumping on you wit margin calls and sellouts dehn you should check out the free calculators offered by the SEC at www.sec.gov. Dey will give you a boids eye view of the risks of margin borrowing. Margin is mainly useful when you need a quick loan or/and the market is doing extremely well. Otherwise, you can end up looking like a dunceky who listened to some goombah at a brokerage company. You hear what I'm saying? 'Fuhgettaboutit!'"

Lowen then took to the sky. As he flew away, he shouted to all who would hear "You have a margin call. I got a contract out on youse. You have to come up wit more securities or/and cash as collateral or we is gonna have some serious investment issues." Soon he disappeared in the distance.

"Now I can get back to answering your question," said Noella. "Dr. Root with her theories about herd behavior says that too much is being mentioned about herd behavior 'in zah shtockmarket' and not enough about 'zah shtampede into debt.' The debt load for corporations has climbed some 60% in the last five years alone, representing close to 50% of GDP—the highest amount ever recorded. If too much debt goes bad later on, bankers will have a difficult time making new loans as in Asia where greenhorn lenders have now pulled in their horns. What is interesting, too, is that despite all the news reports about booming this and booming that, half of all American households, according to some reports, have less than $1,000 in net financial assets—that's what is left over after you deduct what you owe from your assets."

"How can you deal with all this worry," asked Bob, "especially with your Chicken Biggie personality?"

"Worry is expensive, especially when the worries later prove to be groundless. Dr. No reminded me that chickens can only fly so high, even though I'm better off than many of his online investor patients who are learning to fly when they don't even have wings. Dr. No also pointed out that I'm no spring chicken while time also flies. He taught me some techniques to prepare myself for the time I become an old hen. These techniques provide insurance against my obsessive worry: 'What if I'm wrong?' while helping me grow my money so I don't end up with chicken feed. I will share them with you later. Now it's true I'm nothing more than a big chicken pumped up on synthetic hormones, but please listen to me. What I have to tell you is strictly kosher:

> I just read a bestselling book on Scandinavian humor.
> All the pages were blank—much like your future.
>
> Investment theory assumes the future is a continuation of the past.
> But the future is still the future—even if the past was a blast.
>
> Economic predictions are as reliable as a flip of a coin.
> So if you have an opinion, feel welcome to join.
>
> I'm told times are really different now.
> Kindly remember to remind me how.
>
> The financial markets aren't just about dollars and cents.
> Much of what happens defies common sense.
>
> There is also something from which you can't hide.
> All investments have both an up and down side.
>
> What's on top can be toppled
> Safety can't be canned or bottled.
>
> You want to lower your risk, not just maximize your return.
> You want to light a fire, but you don't want to burn.
>
> You must learn not to put all your eggs in one basket.
> So you don't create a financial casket.
>
> If you want to profit and not take a lickin',
> Learn to become a professional chicken.

"That's pretty good, Noella. Too bad you can't do it in Rap," Bob commented.

Noella twirled her charred chicken wings in response like a gunslinger. Then she advanced towards Bob in a swaggering manner with her wings jabbing the air like pointed fingers, while saying, "Hey college boy, les be cool. Ah won't pestah no 'dummy type' investah. Ya can go to that pohpulah financial school ah call Mostly Fool. But just remember, ahm from the hood and knows what's bad about bein' good. Main Street to Wall Street to Mean Street. Ain't so sweet when ya portfolio look like mah rap sheet. 'Cause fool, ya ain't got no chicken feet. Let me give ya some pearls of wisdom from an oystah shuckah. Unless yoa want to be a financial suckah for some cocksure 'equities beat all other investments' sales cluckah workin' foh some big Wall Street mutha f . . ."

"Okay, okay," Bob interrupted. "Let me ask you another question. Which comes first, a financial chicken or something that happens to a nest egg, which then creates a financial chicken?" Bob asked Noella.

"I can't say eggs . . . actly. All I can tell you is that the answer is hanging somewhere on a huge financial myth tree in the shape of a question mark, which grows in a flat, dry, fragmented landscape that looks somewhat like an uncompleted puzzle," said Noella, enigmatically. "It's quite a mystery, isn't it Mister Real?"

Before he could reply, Noella then raced out of sight without another word. "You'll be seeing more of Ms. Coward later," said Sir Real, "when you learn about spreading your risk. It's not just the heat that bothers her, it's also the humility. Americans have this kind of economic arrogance that she saw in Japan at one time. Ms. Coward is an aspiring playwright, who works at the new Mercury Dinner Theater and Delicatessen. Mercury is the god of commerce. Unfortunately, her first play, *The Importance of Being Chicken*, which dealt with the need for investors to learn to factor in risk as well as reward, was both panned and roasted by the critics."

"That's terrible," said Bob. "How come?"

"The general public with its strong appetite for risk couldn't stomach the play's contents," explained Sir Real. "Instead, many investors beefed up their holdings this year in popular high priced technology stocks. It seems that anything that smells like technology comes up roses these days. One day, though, the bloom will come off technology. A pox on their chicken short attitudes is all I care to say."

"What's her next play?" Bob was eager to know.

"She is working on two actually," said Sir Real. "The first one is to teach you about the need to spread your risks through asset allocation and is called *Misery Loves Company*. The second play is titled *Days of Swine and Roses*. It focuses on how prominent investment banks like the Let Them Eat Fake Bakery, anxious for fat fees, lowered their standards in order to rush new, untested money-losing Internet companies to market. By lowering their standards, the capitalist pigs allowed companies to come to market that would never have been acceptable in the past—companies with unproven business plans and fledgling management. Many little investors who went hog wild over these new stock issues ended up losing significant amounts of money while, ironically, the capitalist pigs took home the bacon. You wouldn't believe the profits being reported by well-known names such as *Morrall Stench*, *Pain Later*, and *MoreGain Strangely Darn Wittier*. These are the same companies that lecture the public about the need to practice sound investing and why they deserve the public trust for retirement planning. It's a wonderful story about New Era and new error financial engineering; and how the moat got pumped up with so much extra liquidity from the contributions of small investors anxious to get their piece of the pie in the sky."

"Could you give me an idea of the figures involved?" Bob requested. "How much garbage was fed to the public by the pigs?"

"This year there were 545 IPOs of which three-quarters were unprofitable," Sir Real began. "These unprofitable companies acted like pigs too, feeding freely on money provided by the public at the equity trough. A whopping 90% of these newly public companies became listed on the Nasdaq, raising some $69 billion in capital. Think of what 7% commission on $69 billion is. The public is, in effect, funding many new operations just like high-risk rich venture capitalists. I'm sorry. Don't you just hate it when someone spoils it by telling you the guts of the story in advance, like a bad movie reviewer, when all you need are some useful comments?"

"Yes I do. Let's change the subject. Why do you animals sometimes speak in rhyme?" asked Bob.

"We believe that humans can value things way beyond rhyme and reason," explained Sir Real. "Rhyme and reason help to remind our students to take the middle path. Noella will be teaching you about an all-seasons strategy for investing. One of the best ways to make money in the markets is to not lose what you have invested in the first place—your principal."

"I would like to learn more about asset allocation now," declared Bob. "Do you think we can chase after her to find out?"

"Just saddle up and let's go find her," announced Sir Real. "I heard she wanted to go try out for some popular singing group called 'The Dixie Chicks.'"

"Before I saddle up," Bob asked, "can you tell me what that smell is in the air? It's so strange, it's like a horse stable."

"It's actually a famous French perfume, *Cheval No. 9*," said Sir Real. "Cheval is the French name for horse. It must be Goldie Beef Tech from Val D'Or, the valley of gold, in northern Quebec next to James

Bay. She has been wearing that perfume lately to cover up her stench and her singing too, I imagine. Do you hear it?"

Bob now heard someone singing in a high-pitched female voice, "Goldstinker, she loves old, only old. She loves o.o.o.o.o.o.ld." A calf the color of gold approached. It had a nose ring, sunken cheeks covered with rouge and the hind legs of a bull.

Goldstinker

> *Ignore the past and you are blind in one eye. Forget the past and you are blind in both.*

—Russian Proverb

"Allo, allo," said the golden calf, in greeting. "Pardohn. Excuse my appearance. I used to be a gleaming full-fledged commodity bull in the 1970s. Times have changed. Let me ask you a question if I may. When does 300 grams of gold weigh 320 grams?"

"I don't know," answered Bob.

"You don't know? *Mon dieu*. My God," said the calf. "When it's fool's gold, *Monsieur* Dot Catz. Pure real gold can only weigh more from added fool's talk. Apparently as a little investor, you aren't familiar yet with gold rush mentality and the worship of false gods. I find this most surprising considering you live in a gold rush city like Seattle. Before this *petit* investor learns anymore about *le* stock market, may I suggest, Sir Real, that he learn about the real stock market first, as in livestock. If he doesn't understand the role of commodities, then he will be missing an important part of his education. I need to introduce him to all I know about leather, lace and heavy metal among other things."

"Ah, so that's why you have a butch name like Beef Tech," commented Bob. "Now, obviously, I don't have to ask 'where's the beef?' However, may I ask 'where's the tech?'"

"*Mais oui*," answered Goldie. "If you promise to avoid more assumptions. "You see, *mon ami*, my name has been Americanized from the French word *bifteck*, which means steak to remind *petit* investors like you about the linkage of commodities with technology. Many in the public don't appreciate yet how much high tech growth is dependent on cheap commodity prices from markets that currently stink. It is largely because of stinking prices for commodities that this New Era Economy has had inflation-free growth. Cheap energy in particular has fuelled this great long economic expansion. Let me tell you a little secret *les* techies haven't told you, *cherie*. Electronic systems don't run on air. They are extremely power hungry. There is a great sucking sound only a few hear.

"Sure there have been great improvements in productivity, but overemphasis, in my opinion, on the role of technology. I'm not just talking about commodities either. There are other factors like magic accounting and the doubling or tripling of work loads with communication devices—creating high tech sweatshops. Such activities can come around and bite back into productivity. Madame Beef Tech believes that there is a lot more sizzle out there than there is real steak. Even though the 'productivity miracle' is all-American and the envy of the world, it can still over time end up with a French name—mirage. Even the sizzle may turn to fizzle. The real miracle will be when it is proven to be a miracle. I have to tell you *mon ami*, I am so *fatigay* from hearing about e- this and e- that from the locusts of electronic salesmen and preachers that I often wake up in the middle of *la nuit* and scream e . . . e . . . enough! *Tahbernac*! There are *mauvais* e-words too, as in exaggerated economic expectations. Those who think the world is mainly about bits and bytes don't understand one bit about the bite of commodities and how much of this may prove to be e-phemeral."

"What about the fact that Clinton won the presidency using 'it's the economy stupid' as part of his campaign?" Bob asked.

"Yes, George was bushwacked by that slogan as easily as he was by Saddam Insane, but it should have been 'it's the commodities stupid'—a spike in oil prices," Goldie replied. "Meanwhile, political 'leaders' talk about the future while the clock continues to be turned back with clockwork shortsightedness, losing opportunity after opportunity to take advantage of dirt cheap energy prices, or *un bon marché*, as we say in French. It's much easier to claim credit for the booming economy and be a dumbull, with bullish forecasts, instead of protecting the future. Cycles, in part, are about remembering the sins of the fathers, and forgetting the sins of the grandfathers. That's what they say."

"In the '70s, many thought I was very attractively high-priced. I commanded much more attention when commodity prices could shoot through the economic roof and the bottom line of many a company's profits. They used to call me 'Commodity Jane.' Those days will be coming back, *mon cherie*. I would keep your umbrella handy, despite the sunny financial forecasts of New Era economists. Virtual reality won't repeal the actual realities involving business cycles of boom and bust.

"In the meantime, commodities and industries connected with them such as farming, mining and energy equipment manufacturers have been having a very tough time. It's like two worlds at the moment. Where you come from, *Monsieur* Catz, in Washington State is a good example. While Dot Com companies are sprouting in Seattle with thousands of high tech jobs; Eastern Washington farmers, miners and apple growers are in a state of economic desperation. However, when commodity prices start heading towards outer space, you will find that commodity prices can be far more important than cyberspace. Farmers nationwide are being driven out of business while huge agri-conglomerates gobble up their land. Enjoy the low food prices while they last. Change is already in the air."

"You really think so?" asked Bob.

"Of course," Goldie said. "Have you ever heard of the invention of the airplane, the radio, television and cars? Have you ever heard of the invention of electricity and the railroads? There are always major changes, but you still have up and down cycles in business and the same old 'New Era head' financial types claiming times have changed so we now have to calculate differently."

"Isn't there some kind of French word or expression for 'seen it before' to describe this kind of situation?"

"*Ah oui*, you must mean *deju voodoo* economics. Your French is not too bad *Monsieur* Catz. Let me add, commodity prices can be the key to the start or finish of a business cycle because they affect inflation and, in turn, interest rates or the cost of borrowing money. In the past there has been a strong relationship between the price of oil, inflation and interest rates, which you can readily see on a chart."

"What about the Internet?" asked Bob.

"The Internet," explained Goldie, "has had a deflationary or dampening effect on inflation by making companies more competitive; but how much we don't really know yet, because you have so many companies selling at a loss like *Amazin' StockPrice.Com*. A national give-away of billions of dollars by Internet companies selling at a loss will certainly make buyers look more productive and profitable. Who knows what the real figures are? Moreover, many of those new highly speculative Internet companies remind me of how investors would drive up the price of newly discovered nickel, silver and gold mines in the past."

"You sound a little like a techno pessimist," observed Bob.

"*Mais oui*," answered Goldie sweetly.

"So how did commodities become so cheap?" Bob wanted to know.

"Prices are all about supply and demand," Goldie began. "In our financial world, we don't use words like cheap because it sounds cheap. We say prices are very 'soft.' It takes energy and raw materials to make products as well as labor. In 1997, commodity prices, which had been weak over the years because of a number of factors including new discoveries, cheaper extraction methods, et cetera, collapsed in large part because of the financial crisis that started in Southeast Asia. This crisis swept across Asia to Russia and Latin America. You will be learning more about it from a currency shark. Major reasons for the crisis included massive corruption and greenhorn bank lenders."

"What's a green horn lender?" asked Bob.

"You'll find out soon enough," Sir Real answered. "I hear and smell one coming. They smell just like one of those crisp scent removers you put in a car; maybe it's the artificial smell of their money from the decline in value."

"Hey, are you talkin' about me pardner?" interrupted a young Texas longhorn with green horns that called himself High Roller. "Consumers sometimes read about loans going bad because the borrowers couldn't pay. It kind of makes it look like it was the borrower's entire fault. Bad loans are not only the result of bad borrowers, but also bad lenders. I believe the crisis in Asia was connected not only with corruption, but also with a credit bubble bursting due to too many bank loans to high risk customers in the so-called Tiger economies like Thailand and Malaysia by greenhorn bankers like me—except I got my experience in Texas."

"How did this happen in Asia?" asked Bob.

"Investors in Asia were encouraged through loans to take huge gambles on real estate and all kinds of industries," explained High Roller. "Easy money tends to encourage risky behavior. These gambles were followed by enormous losses. Now don't think we are immune in the states. It's a known fact that the worst loans are made during the best of times."

"What do you mean?" asked Bob.

"Companies and individuals have recently built up record levels of risky debt, which has drawn the attention of our central bank. *Dr. Green Spin* has been warning banks to tighten their loans. It's been called a ticking debt bomb that could go off in an economic slowdown if debt payments can't be met. You see, commercial banks, which loan to corporations, usually carry loans on their books at par or 100 cents on the dollar, as long as borrowers are still making the interest payments. One often can't tell from surface appearances the true state of the bank's loan portfolio. The public tends to view the word risk as a nasty four-letter word like pain. However, a proper sense of risk is necessary to prevent excesses such as occurred in Asia and what is happening is this country right now."

"Could you give me an example of the kind of risky loans you are referring to?" asked Bob.

"Sure, pardner. U.S. lenders have been making in the past two years way over $200 billion in subprime loans for purchases of mortgages. Subprime is a fancy word for below top grade, like the beef business I was born into. This has helped many highrisk borrowers to get new homes. In 1993, only $20 billion of subprime loans were made. High risk lending brings good returns and banks can demand more interest. Easing lending standards helps banks to grow much faster in the short term, keeping investors happy. Investment banks are also creating bonds based on credit card loans and auto loans helping to fuel the debt party. However, a deep recession with high unemployment could be a disaster.

"Moreover, borrowers are learning that by going through certain brokerage houses, they can use their stock portfolios as collateral in lieu of a down payment on a house. You already talked to that feller Lowen from the Bronx, I gather. Margin loans of such a nature tie you to the brokerage company. The advantage to the borrower is that you don't have to sell your stock and get hit with taxes on profits made when you want to come up with money for a down payment. It can be quite a useful tool for wealthy investors. The downside is what might happen if the stock market takes a sharp dive, especially for non-affluent investors. These borrowers have to come up with the money to cover the loss in value if they don't have enough stock set aside for such a decline.

Then there are all those home equity loans that have been used to buy stock."

Dust filled the air behind High Roller. When it disappeared, Bob could see several artificial-looking tigers. They looked like they were made of paper maché. The eldest one with grayish stripes spoke and said his name was Paper Tiger.

"Economic animals come in many stripes," he began. "We represent the battered economies of Southeast Asia where the worldwide economic crisis of 1998 started in 1997. News magazines referred to our economies for many years as the 'tiger economies.' It made for great reading although highly inaccurate. Greenhorn lenders, anxious for profits, loaned money to high-risk individuals and companies during the good times. Borrowed money was put into risky ventures, overvalued real estate and companies that didn't have enough customers for their goods, leading to oversupply from unneeded growth, which is called overcapacity. 'Lend and spend' was the philosophy until the economic bubble burst, first in Thailand before spreading around the globe. Please excuse our appearance. We look almost as bad as some of the skeletons in American bank closets. Banks are some of the biggest gamblers in the world. It's their image that is conservative."

"What happened next?" asked Bob.

"The financial crisis led to the collapse of many overseas businesses unable to access further bank loans," said Paper. "An excess supply of commodities was created as there were fewer customers to buy raw materials. Sellers of commodities and manufactured goods overseas, desperate for money, had to lower prices. The value of our money dropped too; and your relatively stronger currency in the U.S. could now buy more foreign goods. This surplus of cheap foreign goods from Asia was now available to supply the increased demand from the expanding U.S. economy. American manufacturers alone could not have met the increased U.S. demand for goods; and if this surplus had been missing, then prices in the U.S. would likely have increased in response.

"The crisis also increased the influx of illegal immigrants in the U.S., who number, by some estimates, six million or more. Official statistics leave out the enormous impact of illegal underpaid workers in keeping costs down. Good old-fashioned cheap illegal labor may prove over time to have been a major support for New

Era productivity figures. Even *Dr. Green Spin* has made indirect reference to their importance in a comment about liberalizing immigration policies to help dampen inflation prospects."

"It sounds like your bad luck was our good fortune," Bob commented.

"Yes," affirmed Paper. "The misfortune of others became the good fortune for U.S. consumers because it helped keep inflation low. At one time, a barrel of oil was selling at the lowest price in real terms (factoring in inflation) since the Great Depression. In June of 1998, the price of oil dropped to $10.11 a barrel. In fact, in many parts of the country a gallon of gasoline recently was cheaper than a gallon of bottled water. Just before the beginning of this year, in December of 1998, prices for oil adjusted for inflation were equivalent to prices in the 1950s. That's a major reason why vehicles like SUVs became popular. I have even seen articles claiming that the oil cartel is finished. Consumers in the U.S. willingly believe these articles in national publications. It's one of the reasons Sir Real smiles all the time.

"Oil of course is used in plastics, heating, cars and planes, among other products. The beneficial impact has been enormous, and not truly appreciated by many who worship the gods of technology—and won't be until low tech black gold goes up in price and stays there. Even with all the benefits and cost reductions associated with technology advances, the U.S. is still the biggest consumer of oil in the world and very vulnerable to price increases, which can easily infiltrate over time into goods and services throughout the economy. The government mentions slick statistics to show how consumption per capita has dropped and that the nation is far more fuel efficient than before.

"It's not only about crude petroleum, but crude snake oil talk for the American public from politicians and business people. The U.S. still consumes one-quarter of the world's oil supply. These 'experts' often proudly talk about how the nation has shifted more to natural gas without factoring in how natural gas prices are starting to climb because of tighter supplies. Furthermore, not only do price increases worsen the trade deficit, if the dollar is allowed to get weaker, the cost of more expensive oil imports could skyrocket."

"So what happened next, I mean after the economies overseas hit hard waters and started providing goods and commodities cheaply to the U.S.?" asked Bob.

Goldie jumped back into the discussion to answer Bob's question. "The financial money valves in the U.S. central bank were opened further because of the crisis overseas, making borrowing easier to restore confidence and encourage spending. The Federal Reserve reluctantly became banker to the world. Easier access to borrowed money helped nurture and sustain the U.S. boom, creating greater demand for products while helping the Asian and Latin American economies get back on their feet. Low commodity prices have played a big part in the golden age of stock investing in the 1990s and what has been called the Goldilocks economy: just right, not too hot (fast) and not too cold (slow), like the porridge. I like to think they named it after me, even though they didn't.

"With the recovery of countries overseas, things likely will be changing as the surplus of cheap raw materials and manufactured goods start to vanish. There should be renewed demand for oil and other raw materials. Oil prices are already more than double at the end of 1999 and heading higher. Some think that oil might even go over $30 a barrel in the not-too-distant future. During the last thirty years, every time oil prices have spiked upward the economy has gone into a recession. Even though many of these countries we rely on for imports have been brought to their financial knees, they can later export higher prices—demonstrating a future reach that far exceeds their current gasp."

The greenhorn lender and paper tigers wandered away as Bob continued to talk to Goldie.

"You have such a soothing lovely voice," Bob complimented Goldie. "I have never heard such a voice before."

"*Merci*," replied Goldie. "Thank you. Actually, I have what is called a golden voice. Don't you love those clichés like heart of gold, pot of gold, golden tongue, golden touch, golden opportunity and of course golden years? Too bad the price of gold recently hit a twenty-year low. The expressions don't seem to have the same value they had in the past. However, gold, unlike money, can't be just made out of thin air."

"Tell me what you can about gold," Bob said. "Is it no longer important?"

"At the present time," responded Goldie, "it is not as important as it once was. It has become more of a commodity like livestock than what used to be known as the emperor's metal except perhaps in India, which is the largest importer of gold in the world for cultural reasons. As long as the Federal Reserve clamps down on inflation, it hurts all the precious metals. Gold trades in U.S. dollars. With a strong U.S. dollar, currently it pays many investors and producers of gold to hoard dollars and sell gold.

"Furthermore, the price of gold can be a barometer of future inflation, as investors switch to hard assets when they start to question the value of paper ones. The great contrarian, former French president DeGaulle, believed that in a real economic crunch gold would always be far more trustworthy than the U.S. dollar. He may prove to be right one day. Even *Dr. Green Spin*, who likes to dine on a full plate of economic data such as wholesale and consumer prices, inflation figures, retail sales and industrial production, looks at the price of gold. I remember some twenty years ago when gold bullion peaked in January of 1980 at $850 an ounce. Experts were writing and talking about how gold would continue to rise in price until it was $3,000 or more an ounce by the end of the century because inflation was a given. It has been downhill since then."

"Weren't there experts talking about where the price of oil would be?" asked Bob.

"Yes, there were the black gold or oil experts predicting how the world was running out of oil and how we had to build multi-billion dollar nuclear plants. According to these doomsayers, oil was going to be at least $100 a barrel by the year 2000. What was supposed to be an energy crisis later turned into an energy glut. Soon the politicians and those in the energy business who stand to make big profits will start talking again in the same manner as they did in the 1970s. Only some of the faces will have changed. Energy is just another commodity responding to cycles of supply and demand. Right now it really doesn't pay to conserve because energy is so cheap. The Clinton administration doesn't want to increase taxes on energy because it would hurt the fabled prosperity of the last decade. The government would prefer to do nothing, rest on their laurels, then blame the foreigners in the oil cartel when prices rise again.

"As for gold, it's still below $300—as I'm talking to you at $290.80 per troy ounce. Gold has fallen so much in price that $300, which would have at one time been considered an insanely low price, is now regarded as the benchmark. If gold shoots up to $400, it would be a major news event. All that glittering expert advice was not gold. The joke now is that gold is a hedge against making a profit and paying capital gains taxes. Past performance really is no guarantee of future results."

"Do you have any more nuggets of information?" Bob asked.

"Although gold has not been a great hedge against inflation except for brief periods of time, gold for the foreseeable future will still be an excellent hedge against disaster," Goldie replied. "Investors in Southeast Asia who had holdings of gold besides their own currencies were far better protected. Gold is absolutely liquid, meaning it can be turned into cash virtually anywhere. It can be hidden and in an asset collapse, tends to lose far less value than other assets like stocks, bonds and real estate. No matter how cloudy the gold situation appears, there is still a silver lining. Financial writers tend to be herd-like, recommending what is popular at the moment. It's like their writings were branded with a capital P. There are relatively few mavericks with nonbranded contrarian recommendations. Right now technology is riding a high horse and gold is in the doghouse. Gold is presently an investment pariah. As energy prices rise writers will rush in like a herd to recommend the obvious. It kind of reminds me of closing the barn door after the horse has left."

"How do you determine what the price of gold should be?" asked Bob.

"There is a rough measure of determining the value of gold," Goldie continued. "The gold bugs have noticed that since the time of Shakespeare (born 1564), an ounce of gold has been worth about what it costs to buy a fine man's suit. Over time, of course, a man's suit is influenced by the price of goods and services. The price of the suit rises with inflation. Prices go up for labor, materials, energy and so forth. So if a good suit costs more than $300, then an ounce of gold is by this measure undervalued.

"I think you can figure out the answer for yourself at this point. I have to leave now. Sir Real, as you know, operates in real time in the financial world. However, where I come from, we have *joie de vivre*. We take our time and drink our wine. In late afternoon, I get hungry for Quebec sugar pie and ice covered with maple sugar syrup. Sugar for me has been a great antidepressant for all the bad news in the commodities markets."

"Is sugar a commodity?" wondered Bob.

"*Mais oui*," responded Goldie, "sugar is a commodity. Did you know that in the early 1970s sugar prices went sky high until corn syrup came to market? Customers were raising cane, even stealing it from restaurants and hoarding it—just like animals. I have to go now, *cherie*. I'm returning to Val D'Or and will make a stopover in New York to visit the New York Federal Reserve Bank. There are supposed to be around ten thousand tons of gold stored by the U.S. and foreign governments at that bank—more gold than anywhere else in the world.

"Commodities are among the least-wanted investments at the moment, but the oil bull has been let out of the corral. At the beginning of the year, oil was around $10 a barrel. At the end of 1999, it was more than double and above $25 a barrel. Base metals such as aluminum, nickel and copper have risen in price as well. The commodity bears are starting to retreat as the commodity bulls get hungrier for higher prices and are able to make them stick. It all comes down to cycles."

"Is there any way I can track what's going on with commodity prices in general?" Bob asked.

"There is a general measure of how commodity prices are doing called the Bridge/CRB Index found at www.crbindex.com on the Web. CRB stands for Commodity Research Bureau. This index deals with a basket of seventeen different commodity prices. At the time of the financial crisis in 1998, the Index reached the lowest it had been since the late 1970s, dipping below 200 from a previous high near 265 in 1996. In August of 1998, it closed at a twenty-one year low of 195.35. By the end of the year, a barrel of oil had dipped below $10. Those prices are starting to rise again. In the past when commodity prices started rising, so-called growth stocks started under performing relative to those stocks labeled as value. Remember that when you start learning about growth versus value. It happened in 1987-88 and 1993-94.

"Just this month there was a report from the National Association of Purchasing Management, which represents U.S. manufacturers, that the cost of raw materials is rising. Eighteen out of twenty industries reported that prices for raw materials had increased. For the past eight months, the price index which measures price growth has been over 50%, but in the last four consecutive months, it has climbed to over 60%."

"Any final words of advice?" Bob asked.

"*Mais oui*," answered Goldie. "If paper wealth in the stock market ever goes down significantly, there is the possibility of money flowing into commodities and commodity-related investments once again as a store of wealth. One thing you can count on is that there are always large numbers of investors looking for safe havens for their money. Alchemists were never able to turn lead into gold and financial alchemists will probably never create paper instruments that can replace hard assets. So don't be surprised if the commodity bulls come back for 'revenge of the herds.' If you still need to contact me prior to my departure, I'll be spending the night at The Fools Rush Inn. It's open twenty-four hours a day and popular with the late-to-arrive financial crowd."

"You're such a tease," Bob remarked affectionately.

Goldie departed singing, "Que sera sera, whaddever will be will be, dah future she is hard to see, que sera sera."

Stalking The Markets

As soon as Goldie disappeared in the distance, the sunlight was temporarily blotted out as a huge bird-like form descended from the sky. It had a short tail, pointed wings, and dark, iridescent plumage beneath a vest on which there appeared a proverb written in Latin that translated to: "Tell me whom you live with, and I will tell you who you are." The enormous bird dropped a federal court order in front of Sir Real when it landed. Bob picked it up. The document said that Bob could not continue on his journey until he listened to what the bird had to say using language like mockery, travesty, hypocrisy, complicity and duplicity. Every single word ended in -y, supposedly to indicate that this was a serious legal document. The document further introduced the creature as the great legal eagle, former prosecutor of the president, and best-selling author of *Suing is Believing*. The gigantic bird then began to speak in a flat hypnotic voice:

My name is Kenneth Starling,
My aim was to become a legal darling.

I was a prosecutor by trade,
And thought I really had it made.

I made no concessions,
To my stalking obsessions,

Sometimes I acted like a shrike,
Impaling my victims on a legal pike.

But now I'm reborn and know better,
After being dismissed with a legal letter.

I am less serious and know how to play,
Realizing that stalk market can be spelled another way.

I started improving my manner,
Becoming a financial planner.

A Jaybird who was domestically violent,
Became my very first client.

I met Ornithol in court,
Where he was called O.J. for short.

A jury didn't fall under his spell,
Costing him everything except the millions in his creditor-protected
   retirement shell.

Money can be placed in a legal shell called a trust,
Protecting you from taxes, overspending, and creditors driving you
   bust.

"You must be one of those lawyers who specializes in poetic justice in the financial industry," Bob said.

"Oh, you don't need a high priced lawyer like me for that, although my specialty is an area called the law of diminishing returns, which comes under the law of the average according to past rulings from the Superior Court of What Goes Around Comes Around," answered Kenneth. "Anyone who values investments beyond rhyme and reason will get lots of expensive poetic justice on their own. Contrary to the liberal views of those equity pushers on Wall Street there is no constitutional right to a rising stock market, double digit returns, single digit returns, or any returns at all. I'm here to give you an overview of the markets before you continue on your journey. My former job as a prosecutor was to really teach people a lesson, so I hope to be of help."

"Sounds great to me," Bob announced enthusiastically.

"Let me first ask you a question if I may," said Kenneth. "How much money have you lost on the stock market so far?"

"Objection!" growled Sir Real. "Leading question, argumentative, assuming facts not in evidence. Mr. Catz has never even played the stock market, let alone bought any stock market dogs. I thought you said you changed for the better. You can't pull those stunts on my client. This isn't the *Monica Lewd'nsleaze* case where you wasted obscene amounts of taxpayer dollars. Back off. You're in the Sir Real world now."

"Okay, okay," responded Kenneth, "I just miss being a prosecutor and change isn't as easy as I thought. There are all those neural circuits you talked about. Anyway, the Dow Jones is a small list of stocks used to measure market performance. When people talk about the stock market, they're often referring to the Dow, even though there are much more complete measures. For example, there is the Wilshire 5000, which represents over seven thousand stocks and is followed by *Dr. Green Spin* because it is the broadest measure of performance.

"The Dow measures the performance of thirty key companies that are worth about a quarter of all stocks on the New York Stock Exchange. There is also the Dow Jones Transportation Average, which monitors railroads, airlines and trucking companies—as well as one for utilities like gas and electric; and one that averages all of the others, together. There are other broad measures of market performance. For example, there is the Standard and Poor's 500 Index for large stocks—the five hundred leading companies on the exchange. Investors sometimes think that this is the true stock market. However, it only deals with large company performance. The Russell 2000 represents the smallest two-thirds of the three thousand largest U.S. companies. Of course, there are also foreign stock exchanges all over the world."

Bob, who was straining to take all this information in, interrupted Kenneth with the following question, "What is meant by a stock exchange?"

"Stocks," Kenneth began, "are traded on an exchange, and the New York Stock Exchange or NYSE is the world's largest, worth currently more than $15 thousand billion. To be listed on the NYSE is difficult and expensive, so way back in 1971, Nasdaq was founded—the National Association of Security Dealers Automated Quotations. It is now the world's second-largest marketplace as determined by the market cap or value of all the companies listed. Many famous technology companies like *Macroschlock* are listed on the Nasdaq. The NYSE would like *Macroschlock* to list with them and have reserved the letter M."

"Isn't it true the name of the company is *Microsock* not *Macroschlock*?" asked Bob.

"Yes it's true," admitted Kenneth. "I was just testing and probing to see if you remembered. As I said, it's hard to change who you are, although I occasionally try. Dr. Root told me a tale about a frog that generously gave a scorpion a ride on its back across the moat to the bakery after the scorpion assured the frog that no harm would come to it. The bridge was down at the time. In the middle of the moat, the scorpion bit the frog. The dying frog wailed, 'Why did you that? You will drown also. Now we will both die.' The scorpion answered, 'Because it's my nature, stupid.'"

"Excuse me, Mr. Starling," Sir Real cut in, "but we really don't want to hear about your therapy at this moment. It's way beyond the scope of the subject matter at hand, and I believe a violation of our agreement found in document number 48, page 17, paragraph 8, subparagraph B, line 46, microline 7. At least you have given a good example, though, of the need to stick to an investing discipline to override personality characteristics since even you can't control your behavior. Now please continue with the subject matter agreed to."

"Okay," agreed Kenneth. "I was only trying to teach your client about the law—the law of unintended consequences. You are one heck of a television lawyer, Sir Real. Now, where was I? Oh, yes. The NYSE has a central trading floor that goes back to its origins in 1792. It's an old style auction system where brokers negotiate prices haggling back and forth for buyers and sellers. In order to buy and sell stock on the NYSE, a financial company like a brokerage house has to buy a seat on the exchange. It has been said that a floor broker walks an average twelve miles a day on the exchange floor. There is also the American Stock Exchange, or AMEX, which is a much smaller exchange with a heavy focus on trading of foreign shares.

"The Nasdaq involves electronic trading systems where independent dealers compete in the buying and selling process. It's done through computers rather than on an exchange floor: a virtual exchange with no physical presence. The electronic system makes it easier to check on how well your own buy and sell orders are being handled by your broker. If you go to www.island.com, you can determine the number of buy and sell orders as well as prices offered for any of the Nasdaq stocks. For further information, look at www.nyse.com and www.nasdaq.com on the Web. There are also regional stock exchanges in addition to national ones."

"Are bonds sold the same way too?" asked Bob.

"No," responded Kenneth. "The bond market is made of numerous markets involving millions of daily loan agreements. Unlike typical loans from a consumer bank, these loans can be sold to others through the bond marketplace. There is no central location like a stock exchange even though the bond market is far larger than the stock market. It is also a more professional market than the stock market and influences the health of the stock market by way of the level of the interest rates set on the loans made to corporations. If the pros in the bond market are worried about the economy, it translates into higher borrowing costs, which has a negative influence on the stock market.

"Bond prices go up and down or fluctuate just like stocks. However, bond prices are affected mainly by interest rates, when the bond matures (so you can get your loan money back), and how good the credit quality of the company is. Before buying from a broker, it may be a good idea to check with the Bond Market Association's free Web site at www.investinginbonds.com. It can give you a baseline price in bargaining for the best deal on the retail market."

"So if there is no central market for bonds," Bob interrupted, "how are they bought and sold?"

Kenneth was happy to respond. "They are sold OTC or 'over-the-counter' by financial institutions to the public. Like stocks, there are new offerings floated. Buyers can later resell them and get more or less than the price paid if they don't wait until maturity to get their initial investment back. In the meantime, the bond pays income on set dates. This is why they are known as fixed income investments."

"I'm not sure I understand how that works," said Bob.

"Well," explained Kenneth, "stocks, as you probably know, are about shares of ownership, while bonds are about loans to governments of all kinds, and corporations. With bonds, you don't acquire ownership. You generally buy them at par, or face value, usually in units of $1,000. They're called fixed income securities because bonds pay money at a fixed rate on a regular basis. Unlike stocks, promises are made to repay the entire amount involved at maturity, which can be as long as thirty years after purchase."

"What if I have to sell sooner?" asked Bob.

"If you have to sell sooner," Kenneth explained, "then you can be paid more or less for your bond. If the new bonds are paying higher yields because interest rates have gone up, your bond is worth less and you have to sell the bond at a price reduction or discount. If the interest rates and new bond yields are lower at the time you want to sell your bond, then your bond is worth more and you get paid extra—what is called a premium. High quality bonds can also command a premium when money is looking for safety during times of financial turmoil.

"A bond only guarantees you receive all your principal, what you put in, if you wait the whole time stated on the bond—ten, twenty or thirty years, for example. It doesn't guarantee day-to-day market value if you have to sell to someone else before the end of the time period. If you don't sell your bonds, your statement every month will show what the bonds are currently worth. On paper you can have major losses even though you may continue to receive the money as promised and the principal in the end. Even those who purchase ultra-safe Treasury bonds can get upset seeing the losses on paper because they have difficulty understanding day-to-day market risk in case they choose to sell their bonds earlier than the length of time indicated on the bond. In fact how the market for U.S. Treasury bonds behave can be a good proxy for how the 'smart money' investors believe the economy will behave in the near future."

"How have bonds performed in general in 1999?" asked Bob. "I know the stock market has done well. Even the Nasdaq has become a household word."

"This year has been one of the worst years for bond performance since 1994 because new bonds coming out have higher yields due to interest rate increases, making older purchased bonds worth less. That's why it is good to create what is called a bond ladder where bonds mature at different periods of time. You don't want to just lock all the money into one time period. This way some portion of your overall fixed income investment is coming due every year or two for greater liquidity.

"The ladder approach is not just for bonds, but all kinds of fixed investments like CDs. It also helps in dealing with reinvestment risk—not knowing what the interest rate environment will be in the future. The ladder creates an average. If interest rates nudge upward, the average also goes upward when you purchase a new bond or CD and so forth, with the money you receive from a maturing fixed investment. If rates are on their way down, most of your fixed-income money is still depending on probably higher past rates. It's a hedgehog strategy of hedging your bets."

"This is all very interesting," Bob commented. "What about mutual funds that have bonds?"

"Bond mutual funds like to advertise about their professionalism and ease of diversification. It is an advantage, but may not outweigh the disadvantages of not having the guarantees and maturity dates of owning your own bonds. This isn't rocket science and buying high-grade corporate and government bonds with triple A ratings doesn't require great knowledge. The Internet is making it much easier to buy bonds on your own.

"Bond funds might be best for junk bonds if you are looking for the possibilities of high yields and don't want to spend time evaluating risks. Such high yield funds are still high risk. Bond funds in general are not the safe havens many seem to think they are, even though most small investors use mutual funds to invest in bonds."

"How do the interest payments work?" asked Bob.

"Well," began Kenneth, "a bond's interest rate is called the coupon rate, because at one time before electronic book entry, holders of bonds received certificates with coupons attached. They would receive their money when they clipped their coupons and exchanged them for money. Sometimes you hear people talking about wishing they could quit their jobs and just clip coupons. That's how the expression came about.

"The interest paid according to the coupon is not necessarily the same as the yield. The yield is about the real rate of return— what you are really earning by taking into account the market price of the bond. You can't just go by the nominal interest rate mentioned by the coupon because the bond might be costing more or less than $1,000."

"So how do you figure out what the real rate of return is?"

The coupon interest rate is divided by what the market price for the bond is times the nominal price of the bond," Kenneth began. "If you bought the bond at a discount, the yield would be higher than what is stated in the coupon. A 6% coupon interest rate on a $1,000 bond has a 6% yield. However, when the bond's value drops to $800, the coupon rate is still 6%, but the yield is now 7.5% because you are now dividing by $800 instead of $1,000. An older bond that pays a lower interest rate than new bond issues has to go down in value to boost the yield making it worthwhile to buy.

"The opposite happens when you pay extra for a bond. If it's a bond that is in demand, the price will go up, dropping its yield. If a high-quality $1,000 bond paying 6% interest is in such demand that it can be sold for $1,200, then the yield will be 6% divided by $1,200 times the nominal $1,000 price or 5%. That gives you a true picture of what kind of interest you are making."

"Most interesting," Bob commented. "You're not such a bad guy, Kenneth."

"Thank you," Kenneth responded. "I have to be on my way. Perhaps I can depose you some day? I've just received wonderful news that I've been hired by the enemies of *Billy Goats* to file a 'friend of the court' brief in support of the government's efforts to break up *Macroschlock*. Dr. Root was right: it's hard to change basic nature. I'm so excited I feel I can fly, which comes naturally when you're a legal eagle."

The great legal eagle, *Kenneth Starling*, rose vertically in the air like a majestic bird and flew away over the bakery.

"Neither Black Nor White"

Bob grabbed one of Sir Real's velveteen ears, lifted himself onto the saddle and grasped the reins. They then galloped around the moat as Sir Real talked about how what goes around can come around. Soon they approached a large tropical looking tree with $1,000 bills as leaves. It was the only tree in sight and it was filled with exotic looking animals. What caught Bob's attention was something small moving around that looked like a living, breathing American flag.

It was a parrot with a long, saber-shaped tail and brilliant red, white and blue plumage and stars all over it. The parrot flew out of the tree and landed on the left-hand side of an old log near the base of the tree. It had a miniature legal briefcase in its beak. After releasing the briefcase onto the ground, it then pulled legal-looking papers out of the case and returned to the log. It examined page after page while muttering to itself. Its beak looked strangely familiar, almost like a human nose. The odd bird finished with the papers and approached Bob.

"I've been wondering who you could be," Bob greeted this strange bird.

The multicolored bird responded, "I could be anyone, becoming someone or no one. I could be from anywhere going somewhere or nowhere. I could be making anything yet still end up making absolutely nothing. I'm an entrepreneur. I'm the self-made billionaire, *H. Ross Parrot.*"

"I think I've heard of you," said Bob. "You have lifelike animal figures on the grounds of your company, *Parrot Systems*, to remind employees what a jungle the business world is."

"That's right, pardner. I remember the day I did my IPO with *Parrot Systems* like it was yesterday. The stock shot upward like a rocket the first couple days because it was wrongly assumed by the investor herd that it was an Internet company. Yep, IPO definitely meant in this case It's Probably Overpriced. The stock price later hurtled downward like it was pumped chock full of lead from a Colt 45. My interests in education are well known. I thought I would stop by and give you a few lessons on investing so you don't get branded with ignorance. Do you have your notepad ready? I hope so. I don't like to be kept waiting or deal with those who are less than 120% alert."

"Yes, Sir, *Mr. H. Ross Parrot*," declared Bob, at the ready to take notes.

"You can call me *H. Ross* now that we're friends for life," said *H. Ross*. "Just don't ever forget the *H.*, although I'm not sure anymore what it even stands for. Everything is about marketing these days. If I was just *Ross*, I might not get treated the same. Now here is your first lesson, Boy: Buy securities like stocks for the long term—buy and hold. Experts will advise you during rough times to 'stay the course,' 'invest in patience,' and to 'stick to your guns.' They know best. If it works don't mess with it. Got that, Son?"

"Yes, *H. Ross*," Bob affirmed.

"Now here is your second lesson: Buy with the trend, because the trend is your friend. Buy when the market dips and sell on the highs. A fast nickel is better than a slow quarter. Just holding on to investments reminds me of that New Ager 'trust in the universe' child-like approach to life. There just ain't no higher power in a brokerage firm. And it takes no time or skill to advise someone to just hold and buy, Boy. Am I going too fast for you, Little Feller? I just don't want you to invest like an ostrich with your head in the sand. Simple long term faith can be simply foolish. Always keep in mind the Ayrahb proverb: a wise man sometimes changes his mind, but a fool never."

"Okay, *H. Ross*," said Bob.

"Lesson number three: Buy low and sell high because trees don't grow all the way to the sky. Take your profits before they are taken from you. Today's great looking investment vehicle can be tommorow's funny looking Edsel. Those who treat their investments like fire-and-forget missiles can expect one day to have their high flyin' portfolio shot down to earth. Got that?"

"Yes, *H. Ross*," Bob once again affirmed.

"Lesson number four: Buy high and sell higher. Got that?"

"Yes, *H. Ross*," said Bob once again.

"Lesson five: Financial advisers teach that you can't time the market. It's great advice, Son. Only a fool times the market. Expahrts like to say 'it's about time in the market, not timing the market.' 'The darkest hour is just before dawn.' Wait and you will see the light."

"Got that, Sir," Bob declared.

"Lesson six: Watch for brokerage recommendations that mention stocks with a target price expected to be reached within a certain time period. This can help you time when to buy. When the stock market goes way down, expahrts will keep telling you that it has hit bottom and it's time to buy in. Even when it keeps going down more they know best when the time is right. If you forget they'll keep reminding you. Expahrts call it 'timing the market bottom.'"

"Y . . . Yes, *H. Ross*," Bob once again affirmed.

"Don't ever hesitate or doubt me. I thought I heard a pause. If I were you, I would be a lot more careful with my tongue, Boy. Now here is your seventh lesson: Historical evidence suggests that markets rise over time and that bonds beat cash, stocks beat bonds, small stocks beat large stocks. Got that, Little Puppy?"

"Yes, *H. Ross*," said Bob.

"Good. That sounds more positive. I demand loyalty. Here is your eighth and final lesson: Historical evidence suggests that past performance is no guarantee at all of future results. And always remember Son, the same expahrts who will be advising you when to buy at a market bottom are the same jokers who failed to warn you that your portfolio was going to go off a cliff. If you can't see a cliff, you can't see a bottom pardner."

"Excuse me, Sir," Bob interrupted. "I can't help noticing that every time you give a new lesson, you walk to the opposite side of the log and then contradict what you previously said, kind of like lawyers are taught to argue cases. I seem to be led one way, and then led another. I don't mean any disrespect, *Mr. H. Ross*, but I was kind of hoping for specific answers, not a lesson to be contradicted by the next lesson."

H. Ross Parrot jumped into the air excitedly pushing his briefcase to the ground and cackled, "Now you are starting to understand, Tenderfoot. I was just funnin' with you Boy, like the financial comedians. The biggest jokes on Wall Street usually begin with the phrase 'the experts say.' It's not enough to know about junk bonds and junk equity. You have to be wary of junk phrases and stock advice about the stock market from the financial parrots of Wall Street. Those Wall Street boys have sayings with more holes in them than a target range. What may look like teaching is just a byproduct of selling—unfit for little investor consumption. As they say on mah ranch back home, 'These fellers are all hat and no cattle'—just all kinds of bullish advice. Even in Texas, mah friend, there is no such thing as a bulletproof investment—only bulletproof confidence and bulletproof marketing. Ahm gonna share something ah was taught in military jungle survival school because the investment advice world is the jungle: 'Don't believe what you are told, and trust only half of what you see.' About all them time-honored cliches is good for is remindin' me of mah favorite song 'All My Ex's Live in Texas.' Now I thank you for your time, Son. I'm anxious to check on mah mountain of money on my ranch. It's going to help get deals later on from the greenhorn buyers who are betting the farm on what ah call 'New Error Economics.' The biggest tragedy in mah opinion might not be how much is lost, but how little is learned about them financial firms that encouraged so many to become members of the New Era-stock-crazy. It just ain't right. Y'all come back and forth now." *H. Ross* then flew back into the tree and out of view.

Dust rose into the air from a short distance away. Although the sun was in his eyes, Bob could make out a large light colored animal moving at a slow speed towards them. It was an old, worn-out looking, pale riderless horse. As it came closer and closer, Bob could see that it had a saddle blanket made of gold lamé, the tattoo of a guitar on its neck, blue velveteen sunglasses and hoofs covered with matching blue suede. It stood by the tree gasping for breath. After shaking its head and rear end a few times, the horse started singing in a clear, but hoarse voice: "You . . . you . . . you ain't nuthin but a data hound, cryin' all the time. Nuthin' but a data hound, cryin' all the time. You scare like a rabbit and you're always on my mind."

"What's with the Elvis routine?" Bob asked.

"You are entering *Grayland* where the only thing that's really clear cut are the trees," answered the horse that called himself Elvis. "Did you know that a computer can distinguish 256 shades of gray?"

"But you're alive," noted Bob. "Elvis is dead. And you look a little different, if I may say so. Elvis was bigger. I sometimes vacation in *Grayland* but it's on the gray coast of Washington with lots of trees. This is confusing. Didn't Elvis also live in Graceland?"

"I know. I'm just horsing around. However, I'm actually one of the better looking Elvis impersonators. Although Elvis made a lot of money, his financial knowledge was nothing to sing about. Elvis was known for keeping large sums of money in mere bank accounts, which contributed to his financial difficulties. His financial tastes were worse than his gastronomical ones. I mean, who eats fried peanut butter even if it's cooked by the lovely Priscilla?"

"Cut to the chase," Sir Real demanded.

"I represent Elvis' kind of money, what brokers call 'dead money.' It's about money that is not being invested. Brokers like to get what's called 'fresh' or 'new money' to put in funds. That's where the best fees are for commissions. Investors only think I have horse sense in bad times when I'm the King again—the King of liquidity. Right now I'm just perceived as an old nag. I've been hired to greet and coax investors into 'putting their money to work' as they say in the business. Even though I'm a 'neigh sayer' when it comes to investing, everyone agrees that it doesn't make sense to beat a dead money horse. Confidentially, there was talk some time ago about putting me out to pasture the way top executives are treated when they can't produce good enough results. However, money managers in *Grayland* realized I could be put to good use trotting out stories about can't-miss investing since I was raised in a foal's paradise. I've been rounding up lots of investment money from those who don't understand yet how unbridled optimism can be reined in by tough times."

"Who are you singing about?" asked Bob. "It's not a real hound dog sound like the Elvis one I remember."

"My song is about *Green Spin*, the consummate yarn spinner and financial spin doctor."

"It doesn't sound too complimentary," Bob remarked.

"It isn't supposed to be," said Elvis. "He isn't well liked in these parts. His expressions of worry about the economy sometimes scare investors and prospective clients away from my employers at *Grayland's* profit-making funds. Such is *Green Spin's* influence that the slightest alteration in his opinions or the mildest change in his remarks can make worldwide markets gyrate the way I do onstage. *Dr. Green Spin's* obsession with data is well known in the financial world. I read he even likes to soak in a tub every morning and read reports.

"Some financial sales types like to make it look like lots of cash on hand is a sign of pessimism. You are supposed to put your money to work—so *they* can work. Since the money I represent never has to get a real job, I pass the time making up Elvis-type songs which mock *Green Spin* and alleviate the anxieties of investors. You'll come across other singers like me because capitalism is rooted in classic rock'n'roll over economics, boom and bust. Here's how it often works. First, smooth talking highly overoptimistic vendors oversell the public on the need to invest in some new service or product that's supposed to rock and roil the world. Next, massive overinvestment leads in the direction of an economic rock bottom and roll-back slump. Meanwhile, the Pied Pipers of mania continue to sing the praises of progress while downplaying their missteps. Huge expensive failures are blamed on 'the new unfavorable business climate.' Boom and bust is basically about the same old song and dance. After the dust settles Elvis money becomes popular again. This is a rock'n'roll industry, and *Dr. Green Spin* controls the music.

"There is also a lot of theater in this business with star fund managers, star salesmen, star rating systems, star analysts, celebrity experts who act like they know more than they do, colorful meaningless press releases to excite would-be investors, double crossing fat cats, sneaky accounting cheetahs and the like. The entire financial world's a stage. Now, let me formally welcome you to this one horse town. Please bring us anything—just don't bring us down. And do whatever you want. Just don't step on my blue suede hoofs. I'm off to an Elvis impersonation show. I'll be back when more and more investors start realizing that cold hard cash can have a lot more sex appeal than a shrunken portfolio which may never rise again. Success in *Grayland* is all about how you play your horses. If you just bet on making money from high technology stocks you might be betting on the wrong horse. Remember, in the real hound dog song what was thought to be high class turned out to be a lie. Elvis took the word of a hound that it was high class. Then he whined to everyone who would listen how the hound couldn't even bring home a rabbit. There are those who hear what they want to hear. When unrealistic expectations aren't met they go around like Elvis complaining about being tricked by some lying dog. Passing the investment buck responsibility is as American as financial pie in the sky. Fortunately Elvis made a killing on the song. However, little guys like you, Bob, usually end up just singing the blues."

"Hay hay, Mr. Horse Sense, I'm all shook up," Bob shot back in Elvis-style song.

Neither Fish Nor Fowl

Elvis then moved to the side to allow Sir Real to pass. Sir Real started to move when a large, leopard-like cat with brownish-orange, spotted fur jumped to the ground shouting, "Whoa, hold your Corgi."

Bob pulled back on the reins and Sir Real stopped. The jungle cat, which had a strange, familiar-looking mouth then said, with a cockney accent, "Stocks and bonds—don't you want to hear something different for a change and take shelter from the same old financial music? There are other ways to rock and roll."

"You seem familiar," said Bob. "Somehow I recognize that unusual mouth and grin of yours. I'm sure I know you from somewhere. Yes. Yes. Oh my God. I can't believe it. You're the lead singer from the greatest rock and roll group of all time . . . *Mick Jaguar* of the *Rolling Stones*. You must be here in my dream to sing one of my favorite rock songs, 'Gimme Shelter.' Let me guess; since the song is about drug abuse, I bet you have altered the words, for strictly financial reasons, so you can sing about tax shelters. Instead of morphine, you'll be singing about mo' green. I bet it's going to be about all those abusive tax shelters used by corporations to illegally evade billions in taxes every year while their executives whine at cocktail parties about food stamp recipients living in cheesy housing."

"Are you finished?" asked the cat impatiently. "I am indeed *Mick Jaguar*. However, I'm too rich and old for any more of this rebellious stuff—aside from still chasing after jungle kittens. I'm into preserving assets and taking shelter from stormy markets. That's what older types usually do. You have to be careful about playing with your assumptions, Bob, especially if it turns out later that you have been fiddling on the roof of a financial house of cards. No, it's about investment location, location, location. I now abstain from drugs after taking a vow of property. I'm here to talk about REITs, pronounced as reets. I've taken a vow of property because I can't keep rocking forever."

"What are REITs?" asked Bob.

"REITs stand for Real Estate Investment Trusts," *Mick* replied. "They allow for indirect property ownership through a corporation that must invest at least three quarters of its assets in real estate like offices, shopping malls, industrial storage areas and so forth, or real estate securities and must pay out 95% of its income as dividends. Soon the figure is expected to change to 90%. Their performance can be out of tune with other securities, like stocks and bonds, for more diversification and music to my fears. It's part of building up a better performing band for your portfolio. That's why I needed to see you before you caught up with Noella."

"Why would a real estate company convert to a REIT?" Bob was curious to know.

"REIT shares can be more appealing to public investors because they are easier to sell, or more liquid, than an interest in a non-public operation like a partnership. There are also tax advantages for large institutions that, we want to encourage buying REITs. REIT conversions bring in much more outside money to fund acquisitions of property. The public capital markets are where the big money is, not private sources like banks. Commercial real estate is going to have to go more and more in the direction of public ownership."

"So," Bob deduced, "it's like a mutual fund involving purchase and management of real estate instead of shares of corporations and/or bonds."

"Not really, because you have a fixed number of shares being created, unlike the commonly owned open-ended mutual fund. It would be closer to a close-ended fund, which you will be learning about. Both REITs and close-ended funds have only a fixed number of shares and trade like a stock with value determined by the opinion of the marketplace rather than the daily worth of the holdings or net asset value. Mutual fund prices, on the other hand, are determined by the worth of the entire holdings divided by the number of outstanding shares. That's how you arrive at the NAV, or net asset value.

"Tell me Mr. Jaguar," Sir Real demanded, "isn't it true that it's a long way to the top before REITs can rock and roll?"

"Yes. Yes. It's true," replied *Mick*. "REITs are currently out of favor too. After spectacular performance in the early '90s, the sector has been beaten into the real estate ground. The new darlings of the moment are in the high tech section of the market. Many investors, for example, are enamored with anything to do with the Internet, but that will probably change too. It's been kind of rough watching stocks of companies with no profits, but plenty of technology luster, skyrocket in price; while REITs, which have huge interests in real—not virtual—properties, and with real—not virtual—profits lose market value.

"REITs are not considered sexy investments; and they don't necessarily behave like direct ownership of real estate as some had hoped. When REITs were widely popular, many of them used money from overpriced shares to overpay for buildings, malls and warehouses—you name it. It was a case of big-time, bad management. Eventually the REIT bubble burst and investors came down to earth bringing share prices with them.

"The collapse in share prices took our piggy banks away along with over-lending and overbuilding practices throughout the commercial real estate industry. Now many REITs are selling at a substantial discount to the underlying worth of the assets or net asset value. If you factor in the money you can possibly make by a REIT rising in value or capital appreciation plus payment of dividends, REITs offer the potential for a good rate of return. At this time, value investors are looking at its potential."

"Yes," said Sir Real, "but isn't it true that the rates of return are unlike some of those high flying tech stocks?"

"Yes," *Mick* answered, "it's true. Investors these days get off on sexy technology stocks, complaining that REITs give them no 'science faction' and no double digit return action."

"But isn't it true," Sir Real continued, "as a matter of public record too—you keep trying until you're blue."

"Yes," *Mick* responded, "apparently you have reviewed some of my sexy recorded 'no satisfaction' lyrics. However, things are looking up. Under the REIT Modernization Act of 1999, REITs will, for the first time, be able to offer non-real estate management services like parcel delivery and telecommunications to their tenants and others. It opens up whole new revenue sources such as working with e-commerce companies using their facilities. Income from such ancillary services can grow substantially in coming years. Of course, good management will still be needed. Also, the fact that REITs are out of synch with sexy tech stocks may be a plus if tech promises more than it can deliver and rapidly loses its sex appeal one day. The same song and dance appears to be going on with technology as has happened to REITs in the past. Sooner or later the music stops. As an entertainer, that's the kind of thinking I entertain."

"Have you seen Noella?" asked Bob.

"No," Mick said. "However, they say she's headed for Stonehedge where all the secretive hedgehogs meet to discuss ways of hedging bets in the markets. They've erected these giant stones in the moat to pacify the gods of inflexibility while they share their secrets."

Mick Jaguar wheezed and said, "It's time for this old geezer to go back into the trees. I think it's my nap time." Then he silently leapt back into the money tree and disappeared. He could be heard singing, though: a financial version of one of his old songs, "Ti-i-i-ime is on our side. Ah ah guess it is."

No Petting Please, We're Wealth Corgis

"I'm quite fascinated by the fact that you seem to have a perpetual smile, Sir Real," said Bob now that he was alone with Sir Real. "How do you maintain a smile like that living in this stressful financial world?"

"It's easy," Sir Real said. "This is a very funny business. For example, you can legally sell something that doesn't even belong to you and make a nice profit. Investments are called securities, but there is nothing secure about securities, which is why you need to learn about all the risk factors. Those who market securities are trained to sell clients on the importance of building long-term financial security. Yet they themselves are in an industry with a high degree of financial and employment insecurity.

"Mutual fund companies like to preach about buying and holding for the long term, openly frowning on those who think short-term and buy and sell frequently. Yet the fund companies themselves trade in and out of investments at a frantic pace to boost short-term performance on their funds in the competition to attract and keep customers. Furthermore, the standard measure of inflation, called 'the core rate of inflation,' doesn't even include energy costs.

"Yes, I do have so much to smile about. Smiling, though, is a Corgi characteristic. Unlike humans, we love being made a laughing stock.

What you call my perpetual smile has been a real benefit in the major financial center of Wall Street in New York where I occasionally live and work. Corgis like me look and talk positive or what they call bullish. Even during the stock market crash in October of 1987, when the market dropped in value by some 22% in one day, we just walked around smiling all the time and picking up bargains. When Japan was ridiculed in the 1950s for manufacturing cheap imitations, we bought lots of Japanese stocks of companies, which later became household names. We like to dive into the moat and find stocks that are underwater in price because of psychology not fundamentals. We seek 'bad company'—bad things that happen to a good company. Wall Street loves our bullish look and sound.

"We like to look bullish, but only when it comes to bargains. We make much of our money focusing on negative outcomes as part of our overall contrarian, going against the popular view, investing style. Corgis are often bearish or pessimistic about various financial markets and investments we believe are overvalued. At the same time, our investment philosophy is also to search for undervalued securities and find the proverbial bone. Our basic strategy is to capitalize on what we think are exaggerated or underestimated prices. Either way, we profit from what others see too late. This all comes quite naturally to us."

"What is natural about dogs being bearish?" Bob asked.

"Bears and dogs share a common ancestor," Sir Real explained. "You, no doubt, have heard about dogs being descended from wolves. However, go back millions of years as early as the Oligocene period, some thirty million years ago, and this common ancestor of bears and dogs existed. Humans think history is about hundreds or thousands of years. Ha!"

"Of course, the Oligocene period. What must I have been thinking when I asked that foolish question?" Bob asked.

Sir Real continued, "A million years ago, there even existed a bear-dog, a species about the size of a black bear, but looked like an enormous barrel-chested dog. Intelligent investing is not just about competence and understanding how things work. It's about knowing where you are coming from."

"This is pretty heavy," Bob sighed. "I thought just understanding financials was all I needed to know."

"The crux of all investing is to know yourself. Financial advisors have to follow the 'Know Your Customer' rule. They are required to ask you questions about your personal finances, education, taxes and investment history; how you react to fluctuations in the value of securities, or risk tolerance; family obligations and investment objectives. Without this information, they can't take step two: finding suitable investments. Whether or not you use a financial adviser, you have to somehow determine how well your personality, goals and financial state meshes with your prospective investments. It can be to your advantage."

"How?" asked Bob.

"According to a survey conducted by the Consumer Federation of America and NationsBank in 1997," Sir Real replied, "those with an annual income in the range of twenty to $100,000, had twice the savings of those in the same income bracket if they had a financial plan. Those with $100,000 or more of annual income who had a financial plan saved approximately 60% more than those in the same income bracket without a plan. You can get a good plan for a few hundred dollars. The most expensive way to find out who you are is probably in the financial markets. So get a plan."

"Not so fast," said a weak voice coming from underground. Dirt flew in the air as a small, dark, furry creature with tiny eyes and what looked like no ears emerged. It was Molly the Corporate Mole.

"I have some down to earth news. You have to be careful how you get your plan," said Molly. "I have been listening in on conversations at big brokerage companies such as *Morrall Stench* and *American Excess*. They have their own financial plan—a secret agenda from what I can tell. Financial plans are not just about helping clients sort out their affairs and make better decisions. Listening in the walls, I heard them use phrases like 'uncover client assets' and 'get clients to move assets from other firms.'"

"It sounds like they are trying to gather mountains of assets from molehills of personal information," Bob remarked.

"Exactly," agreed Molly. "Get a financial plan, but is it really wise to let some multi-headed financial monster know all your business? Spreading your assets for safety among different asset classes like stocks and bonds isn't enough. You should lower your risk by spreading assets among different financial institutions.

"There has been a recent repeal of Depression era laws which separated investment banks from other financial areas. Financial companies campaigned for a very long time with lots of political contributions to have the Gramm-Leach-Bliley Act signed into law in 1999. They spent time and money for two decades because it is in their best interests. You don't have the firewall protection anymore in case of a worldwide catastrophe, like the one narrowly averted in 1998. In addition bankers can act more like venture capitalist kangaroos taking on much more risk than before with investments. Investment brokers are selling the public on the 'Too Big to Fail Theory,' like the one that failed in Russia, and convenient 'One Stop Financial Shopping.' It's also convenient for them to know everything about you. I have to go now. Shhh. Do you hear those unusual noises? They have been setting mole poison traps for me. Who knows if you will see me again? It's time for me to get back to my dirty little secrets." Molly ducked into her hole and the earth seemed to swallow her up.

"That was most interesting, Sir Real," remarked Bob. "I have been meaning to ask how Corgis like you came about to be called *Wealth Corgis?*"

Sir Real was happy to respond. "It's because Pembroke Welsh Corgis have been so successful in penetrating the blue blood Wall Street financial system and making money. Money is the great equalizer in this business. I'm not surprised you read about us, even though we almost never grant interviews."

"Why is that?" Bob asked. "Don't you want to show off like everyone else?"

"Of course," responded Sir Real. "Haven't you seen the way Corgis like to lie on their backs and thrust their little legs in the air to the delight of onlookers? We would like to show off more, but we don't want to invite what is called the 'traders' curse.' Superstitious traders believe that anyone who can attract a lot of media attention loses their edge soon afterwards. I've seen it happen. You're somebody until nobodies love you. It's kind of the reverse of that poster song for codependency. However, the media frequently shows our smiling faces anyway on the cover of magazines to help perpetuate the myth that increasing wealth and consumption leads to greater happiness."

"What does the wealth part of *Wealth Corgis* really mean?" Bob asked.

"Wealth," replied Sir Real, "has to do with anything one actually owns, but you have to include what is owed in calculating wealth. It's net worth, or assets minus liabilities, that counts. Brokers talk about 'high net worth' clients, which often means a net worth of $250,000 or more. Those with a net worth of $5,000,000 or more are called 'ultra-affluent.'"

"You do have a wealthy look about you," Bob remarked.

"It's not that difficult to look rich," responded Sir Real. "Thankfully, our government treats you like you're rich even with relatively small sums of money. If you die with an excess of $650,000 in assets currently, this excess is subject to estate taxes with rates as high as 60% if it is not protected. That's one of the reasons Shelley will talk a little bit about trusts."

"Cool," exclaimed Bob, "I feel mega rich already."

The Year of the Buck

"Why are you wearing an army dog tag that says 'Capitalist Dogs' if you are a *Wealth Corgi?*"

"We are not only known as *Wealth Corgis* on Wall Street, but as Capitalist Dogs in many parts of the world. I believe it was actually Chairman Mao's notorious communist Red Brigade swine in China in the early 1970s, who first called us Capitalist Dogs. Those goons who spread terror throughout China, and carried these silly little red books filled with Maoist quotations, meant the expression to be insulting; but we capitalized on the name and turned it into a separate business. That's what entrepreneurs do. They recognize and take advantage of opportunity. Meanwhile, Mao's wife, who started this whole red brigade fiasco, ended up dying in prison by her own hand. What goes around can come around. Don't you just love that expression? A dog must have invented it.

"In those days, it was illegal to import anything from China into the U.S. Who would have thought that by 1999 Wall Street company earnings and stock prices would have benefited so greatly from all the cheap labor and products provided by totalitarian communist China? The new great wall is the one made of great Wall Street profits from China. That's why American industry chiefs are so supportive of trade with China. Who would have thought that blue-collar workers threatened with more job loss would align themselves with environmentalists opposed to environmental destruction from globalization in a 'blue-green alliance?' Money can make such strange bedfellows, can't it?"

"Now you are really smiling," Bob noted, "beyond the usual Corgi smile."

"Yes," agreed Sir Real, "the irony makes me smile even more than I do usually. The new communist leadership still calls us Capitalist Dogs, but it's with superficial politeness. Perhaps they are hoping we will close down our factories here in the states and have our Capitalist Dog clothing line made there. I understand they have some of the best sweat shirt shops in the world supplying leading U.S. corporations. A high communist official from Beijing, some little Shih Tzu, recently told me that they can supply us with employees for less than $1,000 a year without the fuss of the environmental and safety laws we have to deal with in the U.S. She pointed out, quite convincingly, that dogmatic communism has a lot in common with unfettered dog-eat-dog capitalism; while wondering aloud whether I should be classified as a friend or a xenophobic, non-progressive, reactionary, isolationist enemy of free trade."

"Gee, that little Shih Tzu would have scared me, you know, witless," Bob exclaimed. "On the other hand, what's wrong anyway with being free to trade for the lowest wages and minimum restrictions possible?"

"First of all, I'm no scaredy cat, Mr. Catz," Sir Real answered with a calm voice. "Secondly, Ms. Shih Tzu assumed that since we are capitalist working dogs, we would enjoy profiting by working over the American worker. Paw . . . leeze. We're the Queen's dogs, not some corporate fat cats, Mr. Catz. That kind of activity is just too common for us. Besides, there is no connection without disconnection, I explained to her with mock affection."

"May I ask you a personal question? How did you manage to become so successful in the corporate world being so short in stature with such a big disrespectful mouth?" asked Bob.

"*Wealth Corgis* are those Corgis that have used their short size to further monetary gains. According to Dr. Root, we have overcompensated for our inferiority complexes. We have become expert at betting against the market by selling securities like stocks and bonds short; and hunting down low to the ground, beaten down value in stocks, bonds, currencies and commodities.

"Our approach is to sniff for value asking, 'Can we get it wholesale?' We take advantage of the fact that investors eventually go overboard in valuing things too highly or not high enough. You might say we know how to profit more or less, from other investors' market excess. When it comes to buying under-priced stocks and shorting overpriced stocks, we are unequaled and make no bones about it."

Shift Happens

> *Every Dogma Has Its Day.*
>
> —Israel Zangwill

"Value investing style sounds interesting, Sir Real," Bob remarked. "I guess the value approach is quite popular. Everyone likes bargains."

"Value investing involves buying good companies at what are considered cheap prices compared to their earnings potential; and the belief that much of the risk has been wrung out of the price by buying it at a bargain. It's what Corgis call a 'road kill' portfolio," explained Sir Real. "But it is not just about getting a good deal. True contrarian value investing is discovering unreasonably low expectations. For example, in the recent past when the price of a barrel of oil was around $10, *Wealth Corgis* discovered oil and bought shares of oil companies. There was no way in our minds that this was going to last as oil companies couldn't afford to continue selling a gallon of gasoline cheaper than a gallon of bottled water. However, value investing is not as popular these days with the general public in comparison to so-called growth stocks, which are from rapidly growing companies with earnings and revenues that rise faster than average."

"How do the two compare?" Bob wanted to know.

"The value style of investing," Sir Real explained, "looks at stocks that are weak, but have the potential to become strong; whereas, the growth style looks at stocks that are growing strongly, but can get even stronger. Growth stock companies place a greater value on earnings and rather than pay dividends to shareholders, usually channel earnings back into growing. Growth advocates believe that value is where you find it. If a company can consistently increase its earnings by twenty to 40% or more, then it's worth paying a lot extra for those earnings. Companies with high earnings potential are often found in the areas of technology, media and telecommunications. Actually, it's the perception of high earnings potential that's exciting investors. It may turn out to be real or surreal.

"The downside to all this is that expectations are very high. There is a hot assumption fueled by many Wall Street 'experts' that supercharged growth in tech, media, and telecom companies is here to stay. This is after all the New Era Economy. When expectations aren't met, then the investors can brutally drive down the value of the stock. Expectations are so high that more and more companies are cooking their books with all kinds of accounting manipulation. For the time being, growth stocks have become the hot area of investment—even companies that have not yet earned any profits. However, smart growth investors don't ignore value in their selections of growth stocks. Some contrarian investors bought growth stocks before they became popular. However, every dog has its day. Today's best stocks won't necessarily be tomorrow's best stocks. When growth stocks are popular, value tends to fall out of favor. However, when times get tough as company profits come down, investors become more discriminating and value often becomes attractive again, especially value stocks that pay good dividends.

"Growth investing, on the other hand, tends to fall out of favor during prolonged periods of market decline, especially for the stock of those companies that have had high values placed on them simply because they were growing fast without close examination of whether these companies could have long-term profit growth. Their values have been pushed up mainly by enthusiasm. These have been called the growth-at-any-price stocks. Eventually their karma will probably overtake their dogma. As for growth versus value in general, there are charts comparing their performance cycles. Looking at those charts, which span two decades, you can see that when growth is on top, value tends to be at the bottom. When the cycle changes value investments tend to be on top, with growth investments at the bottom."

"Can you find value with growth stocks?" asked Bob.

"Yes," Sir Real replied, "you can find value with growth stocks when something happens to a growth company that drives down the stock value temporarily, like a production problem. However, generally, growth-oriented investors look at the potential for rapid increase in profits and are willing to pay high prices that a value investor wouldn't. The debate is about how much extra or premium one should pay for a stock with superior earnings growth. At the moment, a large segment of the public feels that it is more worthwhile to pay a high price for the stocks of tech companies that are growing at a rate of 30% or more, than a lower price for cheaper 'value' stocks of companies with profits growing less than 10%. To value investors like me, the economic devastation in Asia is filled with opportunities.

"A lot rides on sentiment or feeling. There tends to be high expectations for growth stocks, which at some point can't be met. Ice-cold stocks can turn into red-hot ones, and vice versa. When stock prices, in general, go on a downward trend, expectations also start to come down to earth and fundamentals like long-term sustainable profits become more and more important. Then the cycle can turn to value where investors become choosier, and look more closely at not only profits, but also assets, cash flow and other fundamentals that may have been ignored before.

"Value stocks at this point tend to be far cheaper than the overall market. In a weak or tough market, they are more likely to give superior performance.

"However, just because something is cheap doesn't mean it has value. A bargain stock is only good if its price will rise in the not-too-distant future. A good many of the stocks that have had their prices battered deserve it. The key is to pick those with new products coming out, management changes and so on, which make them stand out as future winners. There are a number of different investing styles which come in and out of vogue over time such as: value, growth, small company focus, large company focus, contrarian and income. Some of these styles overlap. Value can also be contrarian oriented, for example. What all these styles share in common is the ability to recognize opportunity."

The Long and the Short of It

"I have no bone to pick with you," said Bob, "but I do have a question. I can understand buying something of value cheaply then selling it for a higher price later. However, I don't understand what you mean by 'shorting overpriced stocks or bonds.'"

"Holding onto a stock or bond or even money to sell it later at a higher price is called buying long—because it is for the long term," explained Sir Real. "It can be a long shot, but the most you can lose is your principal—100% of the money you invested. Shorting securities is a whole different ball game that *Wealth Corgis* like to play. It is about speculation, not investing. There are three ways to make money: growth in value or capital appreciation, income and speculating. Shorting is about speculating. You don't care about owning a piece of the corporate pie. You sell something in the belief that it is overvalued for quick profits. Some confuse the word overvalued with expensive. It's not necessarily the same. Contrarian short selling is about the belief that the investing pack has way too high of expectations about one or more securities which may or may not be expensive."

"Like some profitless companies that go public?" asked Bob.

"Exactly," agreed Sir Real. "What you are selling, though, are securities you borrowed from someone else, like a stockbroker representing his firm, with the agreement to return the stock or bonds to them. For the privilege of selling something you don't even own, you have to pay interest on whatever that transaction was worth for the period of time that you don't return it. On your account form, from a brokerage company, short selling is listed under liabilities, which is what you owe.

"Here is the strategy. After you have sold stocks or bonds that you believe to be overpriced, you are hoping that in the meantime the security will go down in price, and you can buy it in the open market place and return it to the true owner. The difference in price between what you sold and then bought back minus your transaction costs and interest payments are your profit. However, if you miscalculated and the security starts going up in price and stays there, you lose. If the security keeps increasing in price, eventually you have to make a decision to buy, because the security can keep going up and up in price theoretically to infinity. It's about knowing when to bite the hand that feeds you, Mr. Catz. So, if you think a stock is going to crash, rather than worrying about it turning into trash, you can sell it short and make some cash. You see, when we bet against the market and believe it should go down, we're being 'bearish.' There is big profit to be made in highflying stocks that are turkeys in disguise. The 'bear' truth is that when a stock drops 50%, you can make as much profit as if it went up 100%. For example, if a stock valued at $1 drops in price to 50¢, it is the same as if the stock went from 50¢ to $1 dollar in price. The amount of money involved is the same—50¢ in this example."

"How did a procedure like that come into existence?" Bob asked.

"The story is that a long time ago, shady bearskin sellers sometimes sold skins without informing the customer they didn't own them yet," Sir Real replied. "With the customer's money, they had to cover their sale of the skin they didn't own by finding another similar bear skin, hoping that in the meantime the price had gone down. There is a section in the financial newspapers called 'short interest' where you can see names of companies and the number of short sales made recently; and whether the number of such sales has gone up or down for each of those listed stocks. I call it a "bearometer" of negative feeling. It helps you get an idea of whether investors are getting more or less pessimistic about certain stocks and the market in general."

"Did you learn about short selling when you were trained as a broker?" Bob asked.

"No, not at all," replied Sir Real. "Aside from learning the definition of short selling to pass the brokerage exam to obtain a Securities 7 brokerage license, I don't recall ever hearing of the subject before, during or after training. An investment bank owns the brokerage firm. They don't want you or your clients to think about betting against the market. It's almost like a sin. None of the mutual funds they sell bet against the market and they don't carry any 'external funds' from other companies that bet against the market. You have to find this kind of information out on your own or from stock market animals like us. We are contrarians as you know, believing that profits lie in the opposite direction of whatever is popular with the public in terms of investing style, industry or part of an industry."

Bull, Bear and Beyond

"Could you tell me a little more about this bull versus bear thing?" Bob requested.

"When you hope an investment goes up in value, you are being 'bullish.' Bulls have that 'glass-is-half-full' perception of the financial world. Bulls at one time fought bears in a ring for sport. This may be the reason that bulls are seen as the opposite of bears. Bulls are also associated with heat as in hot stocks, while bears are associated with cold, as in a cooling economy. You can be both bull and bear at the same time. You can be bullish on stocks and bearish on bonds. You can be a macroeconomic bear (or big picture bear on the economy as a whole) and a microeconomic bull (or small economic picture bull when it comes to certain securities that you believe are going to go up in value). You can be bullish on certain stocks and bearish on others. There are numerous ways to hold optimistic and pessimistic views at the same time. Just remember the old Wall Street adage: 'bulls make money; bears make money; pigs get slaughtered.' Now I think it is time we continued on our journey."

Baby, You Can Drive My Car

Sir Real continued his run around the moat by jumping over a huge sinkhole filled with money. Bob pulled firmly on the reins forcing Sir Real to stop and turn around to face the hole.

"How come that hole is filled with money?" Bob asked. "It's even expanding as we speak with more money being added to it."

"Those are sunk costs," Sir Real explained. It's money invested that is probably never recoverable and where investors toss good money after bad. This financial hole is named after a famous New Era myth called 'buy on the dip—it's bound to go up.' Do you remember that Indian leader who complained that white people 'eat land?' He was speaking figuratively no doubt. However pet investments, including land, can turn around and bite back both figuratively and literally. That's basically what sunk costs are about."

"Why does that happen?" Bob questioned.

"Well," Sir Real began, "it has to do with the fact that investors often don't like to admit they made a mistake. They would rather lose more money than face up to the fact that the decision may have been an unwise one. Sunk costs can be like emotional vampires draining you of the ability to move on. Dr. Root explains it in terms of denial while Dr. No talks about something called cognitive dissonance theory."

"What's that?" Bob wanted to know.

"It has to do with finding extra attractions in a situation to justify why you are in the hole, like a lemon car or spouse you can't afford to get rid of," Sir Real continued. "I call it Buy and In The Hole for the long term when it comes to lemon investment vehicles. With respect to investment, the theory is that the cognition or thought that you paid such and such for a security is dissonant or in conflict with the thought of its present value. So you try and bridge the gap by convincing yourself that you made a wise decision. For example you tell yourself comforting thoughts like patience is a virtue, ignoring the fact that there is abundant evidence that patience can be very costly. A twenty-dollar stock that declined in value to $2 is just another $2 stock. However, you search for extra attractions to make you feel better. You tell yourself how in the long run this security will be worth more, and that it is a temporary setback. Or that other like-securities owned by other investors went down in value as well.

"What appears to be faith, persistence, and determination can be a cover for a mistake in judgment. You tell yourself whatever it takes to make the dissonance disappear. Cognitive dissonance may be seen as being addicted to comforting thoughts in order to avoid painful withdrawal and change. So it seems ironic that one of the biggest money pits in the world involves the losing war on illegal drugs. The biggest money pit in the non-military world is probably the one constructed for the Japanese banking system. They are working to get it smaller, but it just keeps getting bigger, better, faster. Oh look, there is someone who is literally climbing out of a financial hole."

A pale yellow-colored lizard with granular skin and independently movable eyeballs rode out of the hole in a miniature convertible version of one of those new German "Bug" cars. The lizard was singing along to a Beatles song blasting away on the radio about becoming a star. The toy-like car had a Montana license plate and a bumper sticker that read: "My Broker Yes, My Banker Maybe, My Gun Never."

"Hold your Corgi. Before you catch up with Noella, there is more for you to know. My name is Lizzzz, Liz Die Hard," the lizard hissed. "Let me tell you something. I am a chameleon and can change into any color I want. But I know deep down that I have only one life to live. So let me live it as a bond. Hee Hee Hee."

"You look and sound like someone who doesn't like to show her true colors," Bob commented. "Hey dude, what do you think of that new 'Bug' convertible you are driving? It's a cool looking car."

"The car is awesome," hissed Liz. "It's built with that famous whatever European engineering. The engineering is so damn good that it must have been built with the assumption that nothing can go wrong."

"*Does* anything ever go wrong?" Bob asked.

"Absolutely dude," Liz hissed. "I had a power steering pump replaced and the whole front of the car had to be removed to get at that sucker because it just isn't supposed to happen. It's those darn inflexible assumptions. Naturally, I'm not like that. I'm quite adaptable. I know how to ride out of a financial slump with flying colors. I represent an investment vehicle that assumes things can and do go wrong. It may help your portfolio ride out of negative returns when a market sinks in value. I represent a hybrid investment vehicle, which can offer yields like bonds but can be swapped for stock: a convertible bond. It's particularly important these days when so many households are connected to the stockmarket that no one is really certain whether the economy is driving the stock market or the stock market is driving the economy. You might not like what you see underneath the hood when things slow down."

"Why do companies have a hybrid like you?" Bob asked.

"Companies that need cash can take out loans from banks or float stocks and bonds in the marketplace to exchange for public money. However, it's not that easy when company credit may not be good enough to get a decent or any rating by a credit agency—especially for a relatively new company like *Amazin' StockPrice.Com*. Banks can refuse to lend or lend at very high interest rates.

"Even if a company can borrow from the public, a low credit rating can mean that the company can only get low junk bond status while paying a high rate of interest, which will act as a drag on growth and profits. Issuing more stock can dilute the value of existing shares as more pieces of the corporate pie get cut up. Then the value of the shares may decline, which can hurt chances of more funding and using the shares to fund acquisitions of other companies and grow. Also, weak shares can make a company more vulnerable to a takeover from bigger fish in the moat."

"What's in it for investors?" Bob asked.

"Investors look to convertibles as an attractive option in volatile markets, in particular, if they have faith that the company stock might do well in the future," hissed Liz. "It's a compromise between stocks and bonds. They look to the downside protection of a bond, which has a better claim than stock on corporate assets if the company gets into financial trouble, plus guaranteed income. At the same time, investors have upside opportunities if the company performs as hoped and the ugly duckling turns into a swan. It's about investors wanting to have their cake and eat it too. Everyone wants to have cake and eat it too. However, not too many are successful at it.

"Convertible bonds from corporations pay an annual rate of interest providing an immediate return on your money. They also have maturity or expiration dates like regular bonds. So an investor can get regular income and return of the money invested or principal at the end of the time period, often five to thirty years. Convertibles have the option to convert to regular stock shares known as common stock in a company for even bigger returns. You can still be a conservative kind of investor with the option of participating in stock market growth. You can exchange a convertible bond for shares depending on the terms."

"When does conversion become worthwhile?" Bob asked.

"Conversion only becomes worthwhile if the shares go up in price beyond what is called the conversion premium," Liz explained. "For example, say you buy a $1,000 bond with the option of converting it into twenty shares of stock. The stock at the time you buy it is selling at $40 per share. You multiply the stock price of $40 times the number twenty, called the conversion ratio, to arrive at $800. Obviously, it doesn't pay to convert at that point. You calculate the difference between the $1,000 bond price and this conversion figure (one thousand minus eight hundred). That $200 difference divided by the bond price (two hundred divided by one thousand) gives you 20% as the conversion premium in this example. Different bonds and bond issues have different conversion premiums.

"These kinds of calculations help an investor determine how much a stock has to rise in price to make conversion worthwhile. If the stock rises enough for conversion to become worthwhile, the company benefits too, since bondholders become shareholders and the company no longer owes the former bondholder money. This removes debt from the balance sheets. In the meantime, the company borrowed at lower rates than if a regular bond had been issued. More likely than not, the issuing company gets to have its cake and eat it too whether the stock rises or falls in value."

"What if the stock falls in price?" Bob asked.

"Even if both the stock and bond markets fall, affecting the market value of the bond and market value of the stock, interest payments are still owed to investors who hold these bonds. This is why they have been called 'equities with shock absorbers.' More and more investors are starting to look at convertibles as a separate asset class like REITs, stocks, bonds, cash equivalents and precious metals. It can help you choose your c- c- c-carma."

"Before you convert my client to your way of thinking," Sir Real cut in, "I have a question. Isn't it true that a convertible investor can't always have his cake—and then eat it too?"

"Yes. Yes. It's true. Even a convertible ride can be bumpy for you, leaving numbers in the black, but battered and blue. I have been known to change only into a long-term lounge lizard at times rather than a profitable stock."

"How is that?" asked Bob.

"Hot potential company stock that a convertible has an option on can turn cold-blooded, shedding all hopes of doing well in the near or far future. If the stock doesn't go up in value for a long time and you can't convert for profits, then you can end up receiving low payments from a bond classified as junk. Rising interest rates threaten the stock and bond markets as a whole and therefore the worth of convertibles. The company stock can get hit while the convertible bonds interest rate becomes less interesting. The model you pick for your convertible investment vehicle can turn into a lemon and is then called a 'busted convertible.' During these boom times an amazin' river of convertible debt has been floated in the marketplace by hot tech and tech-sounding companies like *Amazin'StockPrice.com*. Investors are assuming these high flying companies will continue to have soaring stock prices in the future.

"Junk bonds normally pay a much higher rate of return than other 'safer' types of bonds because of the added risk. Before a loan is made, markets determine the likelihood of repayment. The higher the prospective risk of default, or nonpayment, the higher the interest rate is demanded by the market.

"Convertible bond owners tend to get a lower rate of interest than junk bonds because of the option feature. However, the option can end up being worthless or 'underwater' if the stock doesn't rise in value as planned. It can be bad for the company, too. Some Japanese companies, including those with famous household names, have been going through a redemption crisis for convertibles. Bonds pay interest until the date of maturity when the loan has to be paid back. These companies, already suffering during a prolonged economic slowdown, are forced to pay off convertible bondholders that haven't converted because share prices have plunged. This is making the economic situation of these companies even more desperate. When these convertibles were issued many years ago, the Japanese economy was booming. The Japanese had the same type of booming-voiced news reporters talking about the economy that we have now. It was assumed during these times that both companies and investors could have their cake and eat it too. It was assumed that the bonds would be converted at some point in time when the stock performed well enough for investors to profit from making a change. It was assumed that these Japanese companies would have cheap low interest loans that never had to be paid back while investors collected interest on bonds that would later become profitable stock. Instead of having their cake and eating it too, everyone concerned ended up eating humble pie. Most convertibles are not listed on exchanges, so it may not be easy to get quick prices; and being a smaller market than regular bonds, convertibles aren't as mobile or liquid when it comes to buying and selling."

"Do you care to add anymore to your defense while we judge the worth of your claims?" asked Sir Real.

"Yes, Sir Real," replied Liz. "On the plus side, convertible bonds have been issued from some very well-known companies that are household names. You want to look for blue-chip companies with investment grade ratings if interested in convertibles, which can offer a relatively safer ride. Even leading hedgehogs use convertibles as part of their hedging strategies. Over long periods of time, convertibles may be able to give your portfolio a less bumpy ride. Their payouts can still cushion a market fall with a drop in value often far less than a stock. There are also money managers specializing in choosing and managing convertible bonds for investors. Like any other kind of purchase, it pays to shop around if you want to increase the chances of having your cake and eating it too. Check out sites like www.convertbond.com."

"You know I've come across a number of cross and cross-bred dogs in my life," remarked Bob, "but never a cross-examining dog, Sir Real. You do more than just sniff around."

Liz and her "Bug" car then drove off.

"How Sweet It Isn' t"

"Speaking of having your cake," Bob wondered, "why does the bakery ad say in part: 'Have your cake and eat it too. We make double messages just for you?'"

Suddenly a deep, watery sounding, operatic voice could be heard coming from the moat singing, "Let me double your damage and double my sum: with a double hint, a double hint—of savvy marketing scum. I would be pleased to answer your question at no cost whatsoever. However, don't make any sudden movements or flash any lights; otherwise I'll have to charge you, eh," joked a dark-brown colored, cud chewing moose, who suddenly emerged from the dark liquid mass. "I cross over from Canada, see, to work in this here bakery. American money is in great demand right now, although there were times in the past when it wasn't. My employers call me Chocolate Eh-Claire."

"I thought someone like you would have been given one of those attractive jock names like 'Moose,'" said Bob. "You must be a natural at underwater diving. Until a moment ago, I saw only your antlers when the rest of your body was totally submerged."

"Yes," said Chocolate, "it does look that way; and that's why people commonly and mistakenly believe a moose is a natural underwater diver. We can wander deep into lakes until totally covered, searching for aquatic plants. However, because of our four stomach chambers, which operate like life jackets, we can't dive worth a damn.

"You have to be careful about assumptions. Assumptions are the mother of all financial screw-ups. One of the biggest recently was in Russia when it was wrongly assumed by leading financiers in Europe and America that a major country wouldn't dare default on its obligations."

"You mean Mother Russia?" asked Bob.

"That's right," replied Chocolate. "They call it Mother Russia because there was no way for bond holders to get their money back from those mothers. Anxious investors ran in droves back to the mother of all safe havens—U.S. Treasury bonds, driving the price up and the yield down."

"I don't understand," said Bob.

"Bond prices have this seesaw, inverse relationship to the interest paid," explained Chocolate. "The more you want them, the more pricey they become and the less interest they have in paying you any interest."

"I have come across some members of the opposite sex like that over the years," Bob commented. "Is the bakery sign message difficult for a little investor like me to understand?"

"It won't be a cake walk I can tell you," answered Chocolate. "Even with my four stomachs, it's hard sometimes for me to stomach all these double messages. Here goes: when family-type magazines run stories about weight loss to attract readers, while at the same time filling the pages with ads promoting foods and tasty recipes like chocolate mousse, you have double messages. The publisher makes money from both the readers and advertisers, thereby having his cake and eating it too.

"The financial world is filled with these kinds of messages. Recently, for example, Marie Antoinette Delicacies added an Internet delivery service. This company, like the bakery, is separate, but owned entirely by Marie Antoinette. This new service helped boost stock value because of all the new publicity these days about Internet this and Internet that. About the only real moneymakers from the state of the art Internet so far have been old-fashioned porn sights. However, Marie Antoinette's site has been a steady money loser. So Marie Antoinette Delicacies, Inc. excludes the losses at the beginning of its financial statement."

"How can they legally do that?" asked Bob.

"The company does this by mentioning its net profits or profits after expenses as 'before other items.' Sneaky huh? You have to search in the statement to find out what 'before other items' means. This way the company hopes to enjoy the exposure provided by the Internet subsidiary while hiding its losses in the paperwork—having its cake and eating it too. It's an example of fairy tale accounting but is officially called pro forma accounting and used by famous companies like *Amazin'StockPrice.Com*. You'll learn more when you talk to an accounting cheetah and financial ferret."

"Do companies really try to sweeten their numbers?" Bob asked.

"Definitely. It's often called creative or aggressive accounting and 'aggressive earnings management' in the newspapers. It's really about fiscal deception or what we call sweet nothings in the bakery. They have this attitude: if at first you don't succeed, lie, lie, again. These accounting guys don't see the situation the way you or I might. In their opinion, they are just being good *sum-aritans*. As Dr. Root told me, 'the best liars are those who lie to themselves first.' They are convinced that what they are doing is right. Companies are very sensitive to how their earnings look, so they literally figure up ways to paper over fiscal health problems. With more and more pressure for performance, so-called creative accounting is becoming more and more common. That's why it has been said that cash is a fact, whereas accounting is merely opinion."

"Can you give me another example?" asked Bob with keen interest.

"Happy to oblige. Stocks in the long run average a return of approximately 11% a year," began Chocolate. "I have seen studies reporting lower or higher numbers depending on how the calculations were done, such as length of time measured and whether reinvestment of profits was considered, et cetera. This is a fair round number for our purposes. In recent years, U.S. stocks have been yielding extraordinary high returns—more than double this average. If averages are supposed to be at all relevant, then it should mean stocks in general are likely to have below average returns in coming years.

"The stock market won't necessarily just go down to the average of 11% after being in the high twenties for so long. The numbers could go down to low single digit numbers like 2% or 3% for years, and even go into very negative territory as has happened in Japan recently. Averages are about extremes: highs as well as lows. Those marketing equities tend to publicize the 11% average without discussing in depth what it can mean for the downside. This allows them to use past information for sales while protecting them legally when investor reality sets in sometime in the future. This backward-looking forward-appearing sales approach allows them to have their cake and eat it too. Even sales literature that talks about the need to understand and manage risk is by its nature a double message—since sales literature is slanted education."

"How sweet it is," said Bob. "Anything else come to mind?"

"Of course," replied Chocolate. "Dark brown food is my specialty. The financial industry has warning language on literature that past performance is not a guarantee of future results. Law requires it and studies confirm the irrelevance of past performance. However, sales literature advertises past performance with ratings such as stars, because that's what sells the best. The company is protected from lawsuits by its disclaimer while the ads at the same time suggest that past performance is really relevant. This type of advertising also serves the purpose of distracting attention from the costs of using the financial products and tax implications. I call it the 'We Get You on the Fries' approach."

"I don't get it," said Bob.

"I noticed in my visits to the states that the hamburgers are really cheap," Chocolate explained. "Where these hamburger companies make the big bucks is not on the hamburgers, it's on the fries. It's like a license to print money. They charge you up to a dollar for these stringy little frozen fries that cost a micro fraction of a cent to make. That's why the person who serves you is often trained to mechanically ask 'Would you like fries with your burger?' It's not about being thoughtful for the customer. You're getting a deal on the burger while they make the really big profits on the fries and/or the drink."

"That's also sort of like when you buy a low priced air cleaner, but they get you over the long term on the cost of the replacement filters," Bob pointed out.

"That's right. Financial companies act in a similar manner, but are often so sophisticated with this technique it can be difficult to filter out your true costs You'll learn more about this when you talk to characters like Lord Ha Ha." Chocolate replied.

"Let me ask you one more question," Bob requested. "Does the government act this way too?"

"The government is a master of the double message," Chocolate answered. "Investors are told that the stock market is risky and they should build up firm savings. Yet savings are fully taxed if not in a retirement account, which involves penalties for early withdrawals. The government demonstrates its concern about the possibility that those investing in the stock market might suffer in tough economic times while at the same time collecting more taxes to add to its current budget surplus.

"All this talk about burgers and fries has made me hungry for dessert. Would you like to join me for some of our international award winning, double layered caramel peanut mousse? For four straight years, the bakery has won this award for past performance. The mousse was still delicious when I last ate it just a few weeks ago—before the big management shake up and caramel doubling in price."

"No thank you, Chocolate. I understand now that unless I pay close attention to double messages, I'm going to end up with my just desserts," Bob answered in an appreciative manner.

"It was nothing—a piece of cake," Chocolate the moose assured Bob sweetly. He then jumped back into the moat and swam away singing the macho bakery song, "Matzoh matzoh man, I just wannah be a matzoh man."

Jumpin' Jack Cash

Sir Real pressed on, only occasionally stopping for a refreshing drink of liquid assets from the moat. On and on they went until they smelled a foul gaseous odor and were met by a gray, obese, adult donkey. It was singing in a braying sort of way, "I'm so special. I'm so special. I'm so special, and witty, and gray." When the donkey spotted Bob and Sir Real, it began to bray, "The masses are asses. The masses are asses."

"That's Black Jack," Sir Real informed Bob, "a powerful financial jackass."

"Excuse me, but you don't look at all like a political lobbyist. So what makes you think you're some kind of crackerjack, Jack?" Bob inquired.

"Because this Jack can be nimble and this Jack can be quick; and even an open fund can't hold a candle to my kind of schtick," responded Jack in a sassy tone.

"Just the facts, Jack. Just the facts," Bob insisted.

"I'm what Dr. Root calls anal retentive. I'm extremely withholding. She believes it started in childhood when I found I could drive my parents crazy during toilet training by getting constipated. It gave me a sense of control. In adulthood, I turned it into a career advantage by acting that way emotionally and intellectually. I became a close-ended fund. Typical open-end mutual funds are open to anyone who wants shares. My fund is closed to new investors after a period of time once we do our IPO. I'm very tight with my money."

"What's the advantage of being a 'constipated conservative' and a bum investment?" Bob wished to know.

"Open-end funds have to be concerned about keeping cash on hand in case the market takes a downturn, and investors want to redeem their shares, which they are guaranteed the right to do. I don't have that concern. Bottom line is that with my fund, you have better control over assets because only a fixed number of shares are created.

"Closed-end funds generally do not buy back shares from investors. Our fund shares trade on a stock exchange like any stock. We are fully invested because if someone sells shares, it is to another buyer. We're very withholding so nothing passes through from us to investors who want their money back. Open-end fund assets, on the other hand, expand and contract depending on how many investors are buying and how many are selling."

"Anything else?" asked Bob.

"Yes, there is one thing," brayed Jack. "As I mentioned, our fixed number of shares trade like stock. They can go up or down in value. The value depends on the market. The more investors want to buy, the more the value can go up because there are only so many shares trading on the exchange. It's supply and demand. A profit may be made if you buy my fund at a discount, when demand is low, and sell in the future at a premium just as you would with a stock. An open-end fund's value is strictly NAV or Net Asset Value, determined by all the assets divided by the number of shares in the marketplace.

"With closed-end funds, you not only have NAV, but also a price that can be lower than NAV—discounted shares, or higher than NAV—premium. Since closed-end funds can trade at a discount to the value of the securities they hold, you may be able to close in on deals with discounted funds that are out of favor currently, but have lots of potential later on. Sometimes a closed end fund can become an open end fund. When that happens all shares are priced at net asset value of NAV. If you bought discounted shares in the old closed end fund you can now make a tidy profit just from the change in fund structure. So you see it can be better for everyone involved when a cheap jackass becomes more open minded—even if it's just someone like me.

"Mutual funds are set up, for the most part, so that the only way you can make money is if it goes up in value. Since my fund doubles as a stock and a fund, you can make money even if it goes down in value by betting against it as you learned from Sir Real. Even though it trades like a stock, you still have professional management and diversification often with the same managers who run regular funds. I told you I'm special. I'm a Jack-of-all-trades, stock trades that is. Closed-end funds can help you pin the tail on the market."

"If there are more ways you may be able to hit the jackpot than open funds, how come the average investor knows jack about you, Jack?" Bob asked.

"Because, Bob, open-end mutual funds spend fortunes on advertising to the masses. We're getting a bum rap. Closed-end funds don't collect extra fees like regular mutual funds, which try to attract more and more investors all the time. We're closed to new investors once the fund goes public and we make our money from operating charges, the expense ratio. The bottom line is that we don't have to go around kissing that audience's behind like those other guys because the only way to get our shares is from other investors selling on the stock exchange."

"There are probably not too many of you jackasses around," Bob commented.

"That's right," affirmed Jack. "We account for less than 5% of the overall market for mutual funds of which more than half is invested in fixed income assets like bonds. I'm an old donkey because this kind of investment vehicle goes back to its formation in the late eighteen hundreds in the U.S. Although not very visible, we have been around for quite awhile. Investors in our funds tend to be far less influenced by advertising. They tend to be more sophisticated and know a lot more than jack about investing."

"Isn't it true that your operating expenses can be a real bummer?" asked Sir Real, as though he had Jack on the witness stand.

"Yes," responded Jack. "It is true. One of our advantages is that we are able to zero in on very select markets like Turkey, India and Malaysia, which add to our expenses when dealing with international funds. Since closed-end funds can trade at a premium, meaning you are paying more per share than the underlying worth of the assets, you have to be careful about overpaying on top of what might be high expenses."

"Looks like I have to watch my back, Jack," Bob noted.

"That's right," Jack agreed. "However, we don't have the reporting, trading, accounting, and other charges of open funds with money constantly flowing in and out as new investors are added and subtracted. So many of our funds have lower, not higher, expense charges than mutual funds of the same nature. Moreover, a pool of money that isn't constantly expanding and contracting from investor contributions and withdrawal can be easier for money managers to manage for better performance. That's how we are able to deal with exotic and specialty markets. Closed-end funds have the ability to buy and hold onto anything—even shares that may appear crappy but prove to be a real deal later on."

"I know you are closed-ended," said Bob. "However, are you at least willing to pass on some information on what kind of fund you represent?"

"I represent what are called loan participation funds, bank loan funds, prime rate or senior collateralized floating-rate loans. My fund generally offers about 2% more yield than a money market fund with increased risk and less liquidity. Just like money market funds, my fund benefits from rising interest rates unlike stock and bond funds. In a low interest rate environment, it can help achieve extra yield. My fund can be a fairly conservative way to get more yield without too much added risk."

"So, how does that work?" Jack wondered.

"When you first met Sir Real, he explained that commercial banks might syndicate or sell off pieces of their loans to the market place. Money from our closed fund is used to buy parts of loans extended to corporations backed by the assets of the corporation. The lending agreements with these corporations allow for the interest rate to be reset for short periods of time, like ninety days. As senior loans, they have priority of claims even over bond holders."

"But isn't it true," Sir Real grilled Jack, "that these corporations have ratings below investment grade, too."

"Yes, it's true," affirmed Jack. "That's why we can make all these demands, too. These are not top grade corporations. However, a good fund manager makes sure the loans are highly diversified across industries and heavily collateralized. Translation: we make sure we can grab them by the assets if we have to.

"Again, senior loans tend to be syndicated, which means that the loan is sliced up into different packages that are divided up among the lenders for lower exposure. Syndicated loans are about loans made by a group, like a group of banks. We also tend to select the best loans from the banks. Although banks are able to make more loans this way, they are also accumulating more high-risk loans we won't touch. *Dr. Green Spin* and others in the Federal Reserve are getting quite concerned about what might happen to banks saddled with so many high-risk loans in tough economic times. There is always a new crop of greenhorn lenders."

Sir Real continued to probe, "But isn't it true that these syndicated loans are also spreading risk around the system in a process called 'atomization?' Isn't it possible that this 'atomization' process might have a downside globally if there was a severe economic downturn worldwide? Isn't it a fact you jackass, that increasing global interdependence also has the big downside of increasing our chances for a big down slide or global slump? Can you stand there and dare to deny that this will be the biggest bummer of all?"

"Listen to me you Yankee law dog in Queen Elizabeth's court," Jack brayed sarcastically. "Why would a corporate ass like me care? It's not only the law that can be an ass. Besides, I can always have the benefits of hindsight. Hee haw. Let's talk about something more pleasant for your pygmy investor guest, shall we? My type of fund hasn't been around that long. However, during the past ten years, our share value has been relatively stable, although not as stable, of course, as a money market fund. Investors usually have to wait monthly or quarterly to exit the fund. This is why they don't tend to have the liquidity of money market funds, although this could change. For that, you have to trade off approximately 2% difference for extra yield potential with added risk and restrictions on liquidity Now it's time for this Jack to hit the road and 'come back no more.'"

Jack left singing a song he said was especially composed for closed-end funds by *Mick Jaguar* and inspired by one of his sexy rock and roll songs with Bette Midler: "I don't mind being your financial beast of burden. I don't care if mah share price is hurtin.' Can't you see I'm as cheap and liquid as can be? All I need from you is lots of checks for me."

Full Metal Jacket

> *I read the ads. I see nothing but performance, performance, performance. Why not outline clearly the impact of expenses or the nature of risks?*
>
> —SEC Chairman Arthur Levitt
> Criticizing mutual fund company information
> May 1999

Something off-white appeared to be bouncing around in the grass as Sir Real continued around the moat. The bobbing white form came closer and closer. It was a very energetic, dirty, white male rabbit, with a bloody nose and three little silver bullets apparently glued to its forehead. The rabbit ran up to Bob and Sir Real and yelled, "Get out of my way," even though it had plenty of space to get around them. When Bob didn't move, the rabbit bared its yellow stained teeth menacingly while asking in a quiet, determined, Clint Eastwood tone of voice, "Do you feel lucky? Well . . . well . . . well do yah punks?"

"I recognize your voice from the movies," Bob told the rabbit. "You must be *Dirty Haree*. Are you having a really bad *hare* day or is it because you're just born to be wild?"

"Every day for me is a bad *hare* day you little two-bit investor," *Dirty Haree* replied. "I'm tired of hearing those 'tortoise beats the hare' stories, especially since they often have some truth to them. It looks like you brought your lawyer Sir Real with you Bob. You must have seen that TV interview with Clint awhile back where he said that you need a lawyer with you these days just to go on a date. You'll need one with me. That's for sure."

"You seem as nasty as Jack," Bob observed.

"You might as well get used to it," *Dirty Haree* said. "All of us funds, even the conservative low risk taking ones, are baskets of stocks, bonds and other securities—real basket cases. The biggest basket cases, though, in a figurative sense, are our fund managers who are under so much performance pressure they run back and forth from Dr. No to Dr. Root. Something like two hundred funds closed down this year, during the best of times, because of performance demands."

"Why is that?" Bob asked.

"We're actively managed open-end funds," explained *Dirty Haree*. "We have to try and perform better than the stock market as whole, and it's tough on average. One big problem is that expenses of operation drag down our performance in a market that wants quick results. Now I'm particularly hard to get along with because I'm an aggressive growth mutual fund. I take more risks than average. My fund manager has a reputation of being extremely 'buy and sell' trigger happy—which helps shoot up returns and blow away the competition. One day he might get blown away with my fund because the risks are so high. However, I'm still not as aggressive as some of those gun-slinging hedge funds run by cowboy hedgehogs. When time is on your side and you can afford to be a lot more aggressive or risk oriented in your investing, I may be a good fund to consider."

"Why are mutual funds so popular?" asked Bob. "And I'm not really sure that I understand what open-end stands for."

"With a minimum investment, mutual funds allow an investor to become part of a giant pool of funds used to purchase stocks, bonds and other securities purchased by an investment corporation, which issues its own shares. The company makes the decisions about what to buy and sell in a fund and these kinds of investments are called 'managed money.' As you will discover later when you talk to Black in the Box, this is the lowest level of managed money. In a market run-up or bull market, you may get better performance from stocks if you have enough money to get a decent selection. In a tough market, though, you may be better off with mutual funds if you lack basic investing skills. That's what they say.

"Open-end means not only are they open to new investors—until closed if the fund becomes too big to be manageable, but also offers guaranteed liquidity. Fund companies are required by law to repurchase or redeem your shares at their current net asset value—whatever your share of the entire portfolio is worth at the end of the day. This is calculated by taking the worth of all the securities owned by each fund plus any cash on hand minus any liabilities divided by all the shares in the marketplace.

"With most open funds, you only know the value or NAV after the close of business each day unlike a closed-end fund that trades on a stock exchange where you can find the value at any time during business hours. So although you can buy and sell open-end funds all day long, unlike a stock and with a closed-end fund, you don't know what you paid for it or sold it for until the next business day."

"Isn't it true that the prominent investment bank of Goldfish Stocks issued a report not long ago mentioning that the primary focus in this money-management business of yours is not about managing money?" Sir Real asked rhetorically. "It's really about marketing to attract and keep assets. Whether open- or closed-ended, you are all big asset gatherers, are you not? Isn't it true that this is the phraseology used?"

"Yes. Yes. It's true," responded *Dirty Haree*. "However, it is known by only a few. So what's the point of making me blue?"

"Isn't it true that some brokers may like funds for their own particular reasons?" continued Sir Real, badgering *Dirty Haree*.

"Yes," *Dirty Haree* admitted. "Brokers often like funds because the day-to-day management is in someone else's hands and funds provide what are called 'trailing commissions' a year after a client is in the fund. It can be a lot less work with better pay than dealing with stocks and bonds on a one-time commission basis. You can spend more time selling and gathering assets."

"Isn't it true," Sir Real continued, "that there is a fund sometimes called the fund of fools?"

"I've seen Corgis dig up the ground now and then," said *Dirty Haree*, commenting on Sir Real's persistence. "You *Wealth Corgis* are real dirt diggers, aren't you? There are funds made up of other funds. That's what you must be referring to. This type of fund may provide even less work for the broker with better pay since a fund made of other funds can have extra charges and a computer program that shifts assets around according to how it is set up. Brokers, by the way, may make extra commissions for recommending 'house' funds where they work. Funds made up of other funds can be filled with these 'house' funds."

"What's the name of your fund, and what does it represent?" asked Bob.

"It's called Twenty-Four Carrot Aggressive Growth. At one time my fund was called the Fistful of Dollars Value Growth Fund name after Clint's first decent movie. Names are just another marketing tool. It's a product of the Breedlove Mutual Fund Investment Company. My fund represents a variety of communications technology stocks from small companies with lots of potential for growth. That's what makes me sexy. Investors find me quite appealing. I hum that Rod Stewart 'Do You Think I'm Sexy?' song all day long. There is so much demand for my fund shares these days that prices are reaching nosebleed territory. Do you know that the stock values of just fifteen technology companies at this moment are worth more than the entire U.S. stock market was worth ten years ago? That's no bull although it might have a lot to do with bull. It's actually kind of crazy but I told you that I'm a basket case in a basket case business. My fund offers investors the chance of high rewards with high risks. Everything, my little investor friend, is a tradeoff."

"How is a fund set up?" asked Bob.

"Once you have the money to establish a fund," explained *Dirty Haree*, "a manager is selected to decide which securities to buy and sell while fulfilling the objectives of the fund. Buying shares of a fund means that you are buying a particular investment philosophy and a certain kind of manager with a particular history. The shareholders own the fund, which is held in trust by an entity like a bank."

"What kind of fund managers should I look for?" asked Bob.

"Some of the best kinds of fund managers are ones who stick to what they are supposed to do and don't have what is called 'style drift,' *Dirty Haree* explained. "That's why you always want tigers or zebras—they don't change their stripes. Just because growth is the hot style of the day, a value manager who, say, looks for bargains, should stick with a value approach if that's what he is chosen for; and not pick growth stocks to boost ratings or please shareholders. In addition to style drift, there is also the danger of 'fund overlap.'"

"What's that?" Bob asked.

"It means that on the surface it looks like you have different funds," explained *Dirty Haree*. "However, the funds contain many of the same securities. It's also called fund redundancy. Fund managers are often under pressure for quick results so they can overweight their holdings with what is most popular at the moment, such as stocks like *Microsock*. You can have a half dozen funds with different names and different aims et cetera, but holding many of the same or similar securities. If the market shoots downward, they all go together because you really aren't diversified. As Sir Real has stated, you can't go just by appearances in the financial world."

"There seems to be so many funds in existence," Bob noted.

"There are more mutual funds than there are stocks," *Dirty Haree* responded, "which is one reason investors are getting more and more confused. They breed them like rabbits. Look at me. In 1990, there were around three thousand mutual funds in America. Now there are more than three times that amount—more than the number of stocks being traded."

"Isn't it true," Sir Real broke in, "that so many of these packaged investment vehicles are created as marketing vehicles which add no more value to investors than old fashioned fins did on cars decades ago?"

"Yes. Yes. It is true. It's all true! Dr. No told me that the boundary lines between marketing and investing are getting increasingly blurry. A surprisingly high percentage of funds over the past decade are no longer in business. They can be folded into other funds under new names or the money may be returned to investors. The industry likes to boast about the broad choices investors now have compared to before. However, it can be more and more difficult to find the right and better choices. Like aging humans, funds often just get only older and wider."

"How can you decide which fund to select from so many funds to choose from?" Bob asked.

"What I learned from Dr. Root is that funds are like shoes."

"Huh?" Bob responded.

"At one time, Dr. Root was a guard dog in a shoe store. Her accent scared everyone. She came to the conclusion that people and funds were basically like shoes. Personalities come in about ten different sizes. Despite all the thousands of funds, there are only a small number of true variations. The rest is about LASER marketing: Latest Attempt to Secure Extra Revenue. Dr. Root said the marketing in the fund industry reminds her of shoe marketing and the use of 'spiffs.' Unneeded shoes are spiffed up to make them look attractive. The fund business is a spiffing business. Also keep in mind that you can't just tell what these funds do from the names. Some sound conservative, but invest in very aggressive investments or borrow to boost performance, which can backfire if things take a turn for the worse. You learned about margin borrowing from Lowen. Funds that borrow are an indirect form of margin. If your fund is borrowing to make purchases that indirectly makes the fund investor a borrower. That's why you have to read the prospectus or disclosure statements, which lay out the specific investment objectives and policies of each and every fund you might want to invest in. Focus on the investment strategies and risk. Just because a fund has a name that says U.S. Treasuries, don't assume that's what they deal with exclusively. They can also have securities of other federal agencies, which have none of the guarantees of U.S. Treasuries. *Dr. Green Spin* has warned that agencies don't have the same guarantees and is concerned that investors think they do."

"Isn't it true that the amount of research you have to do with funds often can be as much or more than picking stocks which don't have yearly fees?" asked Sir Real.

"Yes," *Dirty Haree* agreed. "It can be true; and even with research, you might still not have a good enough idea of what is going on as Black in the Box will explain. However, little investors like Bob can get carried away with stocks, turning them into pet stocks that can blunt their decision-making. Funds are more likely to force many investors to remain more diversified than they otherwise would. They can also help investors deal with difficult markets that hold a lot of opportunity, such as those overseas."

"I couldn't help noticing your little silver bullets," said Bob, out of curiosity.

"Yes," responded *Dirty Haree*, "it's my claim to fame. I'm a big shot. To get investors to chase after us rabbits and shoot off their wad on investment funds, we try to get awarded silver bullets for our sterling performance. Competitive rating systems use other methods like stars. As you can see, I have several bullets—the most you can achieve. I'm top gun according to the Morning After rating system."

"It sounds almost like a pill," Bob commented. "I think I've heard of another rating system that has something to do with the morning. Anyway, those bullets do look quite impressive."

"I have the highest rating in my category," said *Dirty Haree*, with pride.

"But isn't it true," said Sir Real, "that your silver bullet rating is about shooting the breeze too?"

"Yes. Yes. I'm actually a long shot rather than any sure-fire bet," *Dirty Haree* admitted. "That's why our ads have a disclaimer about future performance. We like to hold out the promise of the stars while guaranteeing nothing. My attorney, *Kenneth Starling*, told me it's all legal and very compatible with the laws of marketing. It's to dazzle novice investors. I have a rabid interest in new investors. Our fund needs new money all the time.

"All my rating really means is that what I did worked in the past; and you may end up having to bite the bullet and take losses on your investment. You may be buying into nothing more than past performance and the particular rating system used, which might not really reflect relevant information. Silver bullet ratings may leave out unpopular funds that can have great potential later on. Last year's laggard can be tomorrow's superstar. Basically, a rating system is about a shot in the dark.

"A rating system, though, can be big business creating little paper bullets, removing, analyzing and commenting on them. This part of the system always makes money. They can have their cake and eat it too, no matter how shot up my award-winning fund may be later. Dr. No mentioned to me that Napoleon was great at marketing psychology, ridiculing how his men were fascinated with medals like two year olds and would risk life and limb for them. Investors may be taking those kinds of risks with their portfolios. They may be much better off looking at neglected or undiscovered companies and funds with high potential."

"Excuse me," Sir Real broke in again, "but I get riled up whenever I hear of an attack on those who grew up short. In defense of Napoleon, I thought I should mention that it's thanks to him we have canned dog food. Canned foods were invented in France, the birthplace of pasteurization, during Napoleon's reign to help his armies expand the empire. Let me tell you a story, if I may, before you go on. Two of Napoleon's starving troops were trading the same can of sardines during their retreat from Russia. Every time the can of sardines was traded from one soldier to another, the price went up until it was astronomical. Finally, one of the soldiers ran out of money and opened the can of sardines. The sardines were rotten and inedible. The final purchaser complained about the rotten sardines. To which the seller answered, 'What did you expect, this was about trading not investing.'"

"You are interfering with my lesson, you sawed off little punk," *Dirty Haree* exclaimed.

"Please accept my utmost apologies," returned Sir Real.

"So what do I look at?" asked Bob.

"When buying mutual funds," *Dirty Haree* began, "don't confuse short-term results with the ability to perform over the long term. Moderate long-term performance is far more important than unreliable rating systems. There are funds without superstar managers who are the top leaders over the long term in consistent good performance. Medal winning performers can be shooting stars that burn out. Many medal winners take big risks, including leverage, the use of borrowed money. As I said before, that makes a fund investor a borrower too in an indirect way. Some fund investors who would never think of borrowing on margin buy into leverage funds without realizing what is involved. Also, check out how the funds perform in bad or bear markets, all the way back to the early 1980s. It can help you judge risk. My rating is only good for as long as things don't change. And change is one of the few things you can count on."

"But isn't it true," asked Sir Real, "that your rating system is independent?"

"Yes, it is true," answered *Dirty Haree*. "I know that is a trick question, so I'm going to confess now. If a rating system is really irrelevant when it comes to future performance, then being independent is just as irrelevant. What you need to look at is a fund manager's record, the level of risk and the expenses of being in the fund. Rating systems, including my silver bullet one, are not a silver bullet for investment success. Your portfolio can still get riddled with losses because only the marketing is teflon coated. My fund has been in existence only a couple of years, and has a really high level of risk and phenomenal expenses because I have a 'buy-and-sell' trigger-happy fund manager anxious to shoot up returns. He can easily get blown away if the market moves away from currently popular high tech investing. Frequently you see magazine articles touting the best funds, and the only funds to buy. Try to find these funds in the magazine in the following years or even months. It's about selling magazines, which often include many ads from financial companies. Sometimes the older a successful fund gets, the better it used to be."

"Isn't it true," asked Sir Real, "that despite your aggressive personality, you're still no match for the aggressive tactics of advertisers? Tell us about what sometimes comes out in the government washes, *Dirty Haree*."

"Yes. It's true," replied *Dirty Haree*. "No one is as tough as some of the guys in our marketing department. That's why the federal watchdogs of the Securities and Exchange Commission, which oversee the financial markets, have stepped up their attacks on mutual fund companies providing misleading information to the public, especially on fund performance. Companies have been known to post out-of-date ads about award winning performance, which is no longer going on. Advertising is so powerful that it can create misperceptions about fund performance even when done legally. And one has to be careful about fund studies, which say this and that. Always look to see who funded the fund study. Remember all those cigarette studies paid for directly or indirectly by tobacco companies? It certainly isn't any different in the financial business. Now get out of my way, Sir Real, or do you still feel lucky?"

Make My Day

"One more little question, Mr. *Dirty Haree*," said Bob bravely. "You have silver bullets attached to your forehead, which have been explained. However, why do you have cartridge belts loaded with lead bullets crisscrossed on your body like a bandido?"

"It's because I'm a loaded fund," *Dirty Haree* confessed. "It means if you load up on my shares, you can be loaded with sales charges. They can be in the form of entry charges called front loads or exit charges called back loads. It is not only designed to make money for the fund, but help insure that you are encouraged to stay with the fund for a period of time.

"Back load funds can have exit fees that decline every year you stay in the fund. Unlike front load funds that charge you up front for getting into the fund and reduce the amount invested in the fund, back load funds have no charges for entry—only for unloading your shares of the fund. Each year the cost of leaving the fund should go down until there are no charges at all and it becomes the equivalent of a no load fund. No load funds have no entry or exit charges."

"Well," Bob commented, "naturally I would want to buy a no load fund."

"It's not that simple, you twit," said *Dirty Haree*, beginning to thump his foot. "Mutual funds can play a weighting game, where your load is apparently lightened one place and then increased somewhere else. They can fry you on the fries. The true determination of whether a fund is expensive relative to other funds is not whether it is load or no load, but its 'net performance' after you deduct all expenses. On the other hand, you have to be cautious about that too: mutual funds can ask you to focus on total return to distract an investor from unreasonable expenses. The mutual fund industry is loaded with marketing gimmicks."

"How do you mean?" asked Bob.

"All funds have fees called 12b-1 every year whether no load or not," explained *Dirty Haree*. "12b-1 comes from rule 12b-1 of the Investment Act of 1940. Funds have to make money somehow and pay for advertising and distribution, for example. They appear in what is called the expense ratio. 12b-1s have become a supplement to or replacement for sales costs. Fees of no load funds can be high or start low and drift higher from year to year. Fees are important because expenses compound just like a mortgage interest does. The cost of all fees and expenses related to management and administration divided by the net assets of the fund gives you what is called the expense ratio. This is what the financial shrimp, Barbi Q, was complaining about. It's a numbers game."

"Is there any way to do cost comparisons between funds?" asked Bob.

"Yes," Sir Real spoke up. "If, for example, you want to determine whether a no-load fund with a 1.2% expense ratio annually or a load fund with a 4% sales charge and a .60% annual fee is a better deal, you can check on the securities and exchange commission calculator at www.sec.gov.

"Again, you probably shouldn't just go strictly by load or no load. Overall performance is also what you are looking for; and I'm not just talking about fund performance. No load funds also give no advice that you might want in a tough market. When investors get scared, they often want to talk to someone other than dial an 800 number where advice can't be given. If the advice is good for load funds, you may be much further ahead. Basically, you have to look at the whole picture concerning the possible need for good advice, not just low management expenses and no loads. A good adviser can act as buffer during emotional times and counsel patience. Investors with load funds can end up with higher overall returns simply because they are less likely to be moving in and out of different funds. It's about overall costs versus overall benefits. Cheap alone can end up being expensive. I have the feeling that talking to you two characters isn't cheap either. You both look like gun-shy investor types who think high risk is moving cash into a money market fund. You make me sick. Get out of my way!"

"Good-bye you dirty son of a gun," Bob said affectionately.

Dirty Haree began singing as he stood up: "I'm just wild about Haree, but Haree's wilder than me. Even Clint sang in movies," Haree said defensively as he hopped away.

"Mirror Mirror On The Wall Street"

Bob pulled the reins and Sir Real stepped aside. *Dirty Haree* hopped past him only to be replaced by a huge multicolored ape that had been standing nearby with his right ear pressed to a vine. The vine, though, wasn't connected to anything. The ape, named Mimic, was shackled like a prisoner to two large iron balls and had to drag himself in Bob's direction. He came so close to Bob that he now towered over him.

"Could you please give us a little breathing room? I need to have some personal space."

"Of course," said Mimic. "I would be happy to do that. I just heard about you on the grapevine. No problem at all. I'm so sorry if I've troubled you in any way. Please accept my sincerest apologies."

"I keep hearing you, but somehow I get the feeling you aren't sincere," said Bob.

"Very perceptive," Mimic commented. "I really am insincere beneath my surface appearance. I'm into double messages: a massive passive."

"What's that mean?" Bob inquired.

"I like to drag my feet," said Mimic. "Many times I ask for advice, then ignore it; or pretend I don't understand so it has to be repeated over and over again. I'm rarely on time and enjoy driving forty-five miles an hour in a fifty-five mile an hour zone. By being withholding, I'm able to exert power and control. My personality is quite passive-aggressive. Although I can be extremely aggravating to deal with, my neurosis helps me excel in my work."

"Oh," exclaimed Bob, "you must be a claims adjuster or an attorney for a home and auto insurance company."

"No," said Mimic, "although I dreamed of being one or the other when I was very young. Instead, I became an index mutual fund. With just a small selection of stocks, I passively ape general stock market performance. I try to capture the general performance of a market like the leading five hundred companies or sectors of the market. It's based on the theory that even a dart throwing monkey, chimpanzee, or ape can select a stock portfolio that will perform as well as professional money managers who try to beat the market like the kind who manage Twenty-Four Carrot Aggressive Growth Fund represented by Mr. *Dirty Haree.*

"There are all kinds of funds like me, constructed different ways depending, for example, on which measure of general stock market performance you are looking at. Some index funds will measure the entire market of over 7,000 publicly registered U.S. stocks like the Wilshire 5000. Others deal with international markets. Still others focus on segments of the U.S. market, like the performance of the leading 500 companies which represent about 80% of stock market value."

"It's like that movie *Planet of the Apes,*" Bob then said with excitement.

"There are a few funds that even ape the performance of raw material commodity prices, which you learned about from Goldie," Mimic responded proudly. "Little investors like you, Bob, don't commonly know about them. With oil prices and other commodity prices going up, they did very well this year. Commodities can deliver strong stock-like performances when stock returns are weak. They are also different from natural resources type funds that focus mainly on energy."

"So you mirror the markets, I guess?" Bob asked.

"That's what they say, day after day," said Mimic. "But to do a good job you can't just passively follow the various markets. You have to be aggressive in choosing the right securities to match the overall performance of hundreds or thousands of stocks. An index tries to mimic part or all of the stock market activity like the Dow Jones 30, which is made up of many leading industrial companies and used as a measure to determine general market performance.

"An index fund really is aping a mimic. Our value is derived from the value of another, which in turn is derived from the value of another. Even an ordinary mutual fund is indirect ownership. You don't directly own the securities in the portfolio held by the investment company. It can go on and on and on. That's how you get into a subject called complex derivatives, which are bets on bets on bets. It can get so complex with trillions of dollars involved that no one is really sure where it can end and what it all means.

We nearly found out the hard way during the financial crisis of 1998 as the system started to unwind."

"What else can you tell me?" Bob asked

"I can tell you how to build a nest in the jungle to sleep in," said Mimic, "or which leaves are most succulent . . ."

"No, no, I mean about index mutual funds," Bob broke in.

"Oh, that," replied Mimic. "Index funds don't have active management like other funds. With active management, you don't just want to say match the performance of the leading 500 major companies, but beat their performance. My job is to just passively follow the general markets, not try to outperform them. A kind of monkey see, monkey do approach, I like to say. Active managers of funds have to charge more for doing what they do; and lately haven't been beating the market, by and large.

"Some of these active managers have become what's known as 'closet indexers,' slyly trying to mimic the index like I openly do and engaging in style drift. Although my expenses are very low in comparison, my fund still requires some aggressive action in making proper selections. My passive-aggressive personality makes others go ape sometimes, but is ideal for this line of work. Since less is required from me, my expenses tend to be much lower and I'm commonly thought of as quite tax efficient."

"How so?" asked Bob.

"We have relatively very low portfolio turnover," explained Mimic. "We don't frequently buy and sell securities like the active fund managers. Funds are required by law to distribute 90% of income in the form of profits and dividends to shareholders. Otherwise, they will lose their tax-exempt status. So when these trades make profits, then the profits as well as taxes are distributed accordingly. Index funds just buy and hold the securities of whatever index is being followed. Only when dropping or adding companies changes the underlying index do we have to change our very passive state to reflect the new reality. That happens very infrequently. Aside from those changes and payment of dividends from companies that produce them, we tend to hold onto our gains, going up in value without the tax problems of active funds."

Sir Real could no longer stand being still, "But isn't it true that your taxes aren't necessarily few?"

"Yes. Yes. It's true," returned Mimic. "I left that out especially for you. This year while my value shrank, distributions grew with lots and lots of new taxes, too."

"What does that mean?" Bob asked.

"It is commonly thought that since we are so mirror-like that there is a lot less trading going on, which means less immediate profit to report," Mimic explained. "Due to the high volatility of the market recently with investors wanting to redeem shares, apes like me have had to sell off profitable holdings much more frequently to raise cash creating tax consequences. We aren't mirrors. We are mimics.

"Many index funds have been downright tax unfriendly to investors who have held them outside tax shelters. Investors can go ape when they get the tax bill. Investors looked at our upside, but didn't really examine the downside. Neither did financial commentators who just parroted the mantra about index funds being automatically more tax efficient. We aren't really set up to go down because unlike actively managed funds with stock pickers, we don't keep a lot of extra cash on hand for bargains. When investors want to redeem shares, we have to sell off what we own if there are not enough inflows of new investing money to cover what we owe. This can trigger profits and tax consequences these days while the fund may be going down in value. Again, first impressions don't necessarily mean anything in the financial world."

"Why do you walk around with huge balls," asked Bob, "if your fund merely tries to match a market and doesn't take any risks as funds with active managers do?"

"The downside of index funds is that they are in one way or another a prisoner of the market or segment of the market's performance being tracked. I am chained to these balls. If the general performance of stocks you are aping goes up, then the investor benefits. The reverse can also occur when stock performance goes down. Index funds can become a real drag. Many little investors wrongly assume that profits from index funds come as easily as picking fruit off my low-level vine. Market funds can wither and die on the vine. Index funds can make a monkey out of investors who may be going bananas over something they don't fully understand.

"Highly priced tech stocks now make up almost a third of the S&P 500, up from a little over 10% three years ago. And the biggest stocks on the S&P 500, the top ten, make up nearly a quarter of the value of the index. If they get hit big, so will those who invested in that index fund. I call it toxic weight syndrome. The benchmark indexes that we follow are weighted differently. It's a weighting game. You can't just toss money into an index fund and think that it's going to work for you. What works now may not work later. The investor has to be aggressive too, not just passive."

"Is there anything else I have to actively look out for in passive funds?" asked Bob.

"Some index funds borrow money and are therefore 'leveraged.' Leverage is like buying a house with a small down payment. They can also place bets on where stocks might be. These kinds of index funds are called 'enhanced' index funds. They are more aggressive than your ordinary passive-aggressive fund because they are designed to beat the performance of the general market. The leverage of borrowed money allows the fund to do even better in good times than the market being followed. Different index funds following the exact same market like the Dow can have very different personalities depending on how they were constructed. They can be much more aggressive than is passively assumed.

"Some funds can do 150% of market performance. It's based on the belief that good isn't good enough. In bad times, the reverse can occur with some index funds performing far worse than the actual market being followed. If the market being followed drops say 20%, your index fund can drop maybe 30% if it's leveraged. There are all kinds of index funds and they do have the ability to help you diversify better than many other kinds of funds. I have to go now. It's time for me to check my electronic grapevine and see how the market is doing."

"Hold on a minute," Sir Real shouted. "Isn't it true, that an ape like you, can be more than a mutual fund too?"

"Yes, its true," replied Mimic, "but you are talking about my competition, aren't you? There are index funds now that are closed-ended, sharing similarities to Jack. They are called exchange traded index funds or ETFs. Unlike mutual fund index funds, they can be bought and sold throughout the day at market price rather than once a day after the market has closed at 4 P.M. Eastern Standard Time and the net asset value for the day has been recalculated.

"It is a convenient way to bet on overall trends in an entire market in different countries, sectors like utilities, technology, et cetera, going up or down the way you can with an individual stock. It also is appealing because like regular index funds, you can buy into an entire market of leading companies with just one purchase. Without having to hold cash positions like mutual funds to pay off those who want to redeem shares, you have even more exposure to the market or a subset of the market like the energy sector. Not only that, the way ETFs are constructed as well as real time pricing, means that information can be readily available on their holdings.

"As Black in the Box will confirm, mutual funds only report once in a while such as quarterly, so you never really know what your mutual fund owns. Actively managed stock funds typically replace at least three quarters of their holdings during the year. The information printed for you is often out-of-date and meaningless. It's like putting your money in a black box. I'm not the only one who drags my feet. My parent mutual fund investment company is reluctantly being forced to look at ETFs being promoted by their competitors. They will eventually change their attitude, but only because they have to and as little as possible. Where do you think I get my passive-aggressive personality?"

"What else can you tell me about them?" asked Bob.

"Mutual funds like me have to sell off stock to redeem shares, often selling off expensive stock and keeping lower priced stock. This can create taxable gains if not offset by losses elsewhere. Shareholders are taxed on any gains since mutual funds are required by law to distribute their gains. The taxes can act as a drag on your profits or even eliminate them altogether. ETFs as a closed type index fund don't have to redeem shares. Shares are not sold back to the company, but to other shareholders.

"The securities representing the ETFs are held in a secure place like a bank. ETFs are like warehouse receipts for goods in a warehouse. They are traded all day, but the stock or other type of security it represents stays in the vault untraded except for changes to match the index. Less trading activity overall makes not only for lower expenses, but also makes them less likely to create distributions for greater tax efficiency.

On the other hand, little investors like you, Bob, are more likely to trade these kinds of hybrid index fund investments that trade like stocks, trying to speculate on which direction markets all over the world will go. You cannot only bet on the U.S. markets, but also those of many other countries. There are country specific funds of this type. If you are buying them for tax efficiency and low costs, the purpose will be defeated and you may be better off with your standard passive aggressive like me."

"Aside from the fact that a closed fund ETF passively follows a general market, while Jack's actively managed closed fund invests in many different ways," asked Bob, "what else is there different between the two?"

"With a close-end fund like Jack's," replied Mimic, "the value depends on what investors think it's worth, not just the value of the underlying securities. Even if the securities drop in value, it might not affect share price very much or at all. Similarly, securities represented by the fund can climb in value while the close-end shares don't respond.

"The value is not determined by the worth of the underlying portfolio, but the whim of other investors. Sophisticated investors can thrive on that kind of behavior. However, investors in general may have a difficult time with that kind of reaction. With ETFs, you don't have discounts or premiums. The price you pay represents daily changes in the value of the shares represented by the ETF. It is priced just like a regular mutual fund. There is a website called indexfunds.com where you can find further information. Now if you don't mind, I'm fashionably late for a reception."

Looking for Mr. Good Dog

Mimic then dragged himself out of sight and Sir Real continued on always staying close to the cement-like walls of the moat. After what seemed like a long time, a group of foul smelling, unwashed, purebred show dogs with ribbons of gold and silver stopped them. They were all large old dachshunds with brown and black coloring. One dachshund, approximately two feet long with a wrinkled brown coat and bright brown eyes approached, introducing himself as Frank.

"We represent a unit trust," said Frank. "Right now we have had some problems getting our stock price up. However, we expect to become hot dogs again in the not too distant future."

"Is this some kind of prank, Frank?" asked Bob. "Maybe you little, old and down on your luck wiener dogs should be calling yourselves a eunuch trust."

"Talk like that sounds especially funny coming from you, little weenie investor man. You know how dogs can get excited day after day seeing the same thing, like their owner. That's what a unit trust is about. Nothing changes once the basket of securities is selected. Mutual funds, open or closed, are about baskets of securities, which can be bought and sold on a daily basis. Once our portfolio is selected, it remains set for a period of time determined by the trust with no changes for say one to five years until the trust matures. Since our securities are fixed for the remainder of the trust life, maybe it should be called a eunuch trust. However, it's called a unit trust because we are sold in units and the securities are held in trust."

"What's the purpose?" questioned Bob.

"Unit trusts, or UITs, as they are called," explained Frank, "are designed for the buy and hold type of investing. You know right from the beginning what stocks are selected and held right to the end of the time period, which can be as long as five years. As Black in the Box will explain later, you often can't be sure what you own in a mutual fund. Only a limited number of units are created, so the UIT is considered as close-ended. With none of the day-to-day trading and administration common among mutual funds, yearly expenses can be lower. At the end of the designated time period, the proceeds are distributed to shareholders."

"But isn't it true," said Sir Real, contentiously, "despite what you do and your claims too, there have been allegations leveled against you?"

"Yes, it is true," Frank answered. "It's just that I had no idea you knew. I guess I should have thought this through. Our unmanaged fund has some stiff up front sales charges with more charges that come later if you want to roll the money back into a new trust when the fixed term trust expires. It's a popular investment vehicle for brokerage firms that's been called an expensive marketing vehicle, which locks in consumers. If investors want to bail out of the fund before the expiration date, then the company that sold them the trust makes a commission again.

"Unit trusts are useful to take the pressure off brokers who get frequent calls from small investors monitoring performance. Once an investment is made, the investor often has little choice except to sit back and wait the term. It helps deal with expectation management. The shares don't have the liquidity or ease of sale relative to other types of funds or ease of tracking performance in daily papers. Usually, you receive a monthly statement with out-of-date information. Since the fund is unmanaged, nothing is done until the end of the term to change the portfolio in adverse times. You have to stick it out to the end, which might not necessarily be a good one in terms of performance. Sure, you know what you are purchasing and selling, which can be a great improvement over mutual funds. However, it's about timing.

"The maturity dates are about timing the market despite lectures from brokerage houses that you can't time the market: one of those double messages you learned from Chocolate the moose. It can end up being a dog of an investment if the holdings haven't appreciated in value or, worse still, is in negative territory. The only option you have is to roll over into another trust and wonder what's going to happen over the next period of time. The brokerage companies that make up these special lists of stocks in each portfolio publicize what stocks are selected. You can buy them yourself on the open market and have more control."

"Do you care to add anything to your defense?" demanded Sir Real.

"Yes," replied Frank. "So far, the performance of these trusts in general has been quite good, although so have general market conditions. They are a convenient way for small accounts to participate in the market and do one stop shopping. For as little as $100 in a retirement account or $1,000 in a non-retirement account, you can get a piece of the action in select markets with professional handling that you couldn't afford otherwise. UITs follow a disciplined strategy for better or worse; and the consumer is tempted away from frequent monitoring of the portfolio, which is professionally selected. I now rest my case—just like UITs rest their case on their one time selection of securities."

"What are your securities?" asked Bob.

"I'm surprised you haven't guessed by now," responded Frank. "We are a select group of stocks representing a portion of some of the leading companies on the stock exchange. We are the dogs of the Dow. The Dow, as you may already know, is a selection of thirty top companies that gives a snapshot of how the market as a whole is doing. We represent companies on the Dow index that pay dividends from earnings. Because our stock is currently out of favor and fallen in value, the yield has gone up. A high yield indicates an out of favor stock or a 'dog,' as we call it."

"So how does that work?" Bob asked.

"This strategy is about low price to dividend," explained Frank. "It's about buying stocks of leading companies at bargain prices while they pay you a relatively high yield as you patiently wait for them to rise again in price. To arrive at dividend yield, you take the stock price and divide it by dividend per share. Say you have a $1 stock that pays a yearly dividend of 3¢ on the dollar. This gives you a yield of 3%. If you buy the stock when it drops in value to 50¢ while still providing a return of 3¢, your yield has now doubled. Companies on the Dow, for example, can get into the usual problems of oil spills, chemical disasters, et cetera, bringing on lawsuits, which pummel the stock value. It doesn't have to be that dramatic. They can also be ignored by investors in general because other sectors look more attractive."

"So they are treated like dogs for one reason or another," Bob commented.

"Frankly, yes," Frank assented. "Eventually, their underlying value may be recognized and the stock value once again climbs while you are still collecting dividends. The dogs of the Dow strategy often uses a selection of five to ten of the highest yielding stocks buying equal stakes in each one of them. They are held for a period of time, and then a new selection is made. You can purchase such stocks individually or buy shares in a unit trust like ours. The objective of this strategy is to outperform the Dow average, 'the market' as a whole. The fewer dogs you use, the more risk taking or aggressive your strategy is likely to be.

"You have already learned about bonds I guess. Bonds have a fixed rate of return. Dividends can decrease, but in high quality companies, they tend to increase over time. If reinvested, they can substantially add to the worth of a portfolio and provide a cushion during tough market times. Yes, dividends do smell badly to some. However, a foul odor can sometimes smell like opportunity to a smart investor. Dividends are a way for an investor to share in a company's earnings."

"Could you give me a good example?" asked Bob.

"Certainly," replied Frank. "If you bought one share of Looking for Mr. Good Dog Corporation at $50 and the company pays 50¢ quarterly, then you receive $2 a year: a yield of 4% (two divided by fifty). Now say over the next twenty years that $50 stock is worth hundreds of dollars more and you are getting paid $10 a year in dividends. On that original purchase of a share at $50, you are presently making a 20% return or $10 divided by $50 plus all the capital appreciation from the growth of your stock. Ugly duckling dividends can turn out to be beautiful swans later on in life by becoming a significant part of total return."

"Dividends these days have been considered especially meager in comparison to decades ago when they often paid more than bonds. They are also taxed at full income tax rates rather than lower capital gains rates, outside of retirement accounts, which postpone or defer taxes to a time of distribution. Dividends are taxed when declared while stock gains aren't taxed until sold and, if held at least a year, the capital gains tax rate is much lower. Most importantly, when you have stocks these days growing on average in the double digits, it's difficult to get thrilled with single digit payouts. In fact, the mood of many investors is 'why bother with dividends when the money should probably be used by the corporation to boost earnings and the share price.'"

"I see," said Bob.

"See can become saw," Frank continued, "if the investment environment changes, dividends may become quite fashionable again. What if stocks started going steadily down in value for years on end like in Japan? You may not have even single digit appreciation. They might have negative worth—less than what you paid for. Income provided by dividend yield is now being neglected because of the focus on share value increasing or capital appreciation in a low inflation environment. If inflation starts hurting stock prices then reliable, dividend-paying stocks may become a lot more attractive. If you want to figure out what percentage of company profits is being paid out by a company that pays dividends, then divide the dividend by the earnings. It gives you a figure called the payout ratio."

"Isn't it true that this strategy is an against the crowd contrarian type of approach?" posed Sir Real.

"Yes, it's true," Frank responded. "However, it is also a conservative type approach since we represent blue chip high end companies."

"Thank you for your long, frank explanations, you filthy rich dog," Sir Real blurted out.

As the Dachshunds dispersed in different directions, Bob glanced again at the enormous pie-shaped bakery protected by the moat.

"Mama Said There'd Be Years Like This"

Markets can remain irrational longer than you can remain solvent.

—John Maynard Keynes

"Why is that pie-shaped bakery floating in the air?" asked Bob. "I have also just noticed that a piece of it is missing. I guess that is for realism."

"The missing part," explained Sir Real, "is actually a reminder of the Paretto principle: that 80% of the pie comes from 20% of the work. It can apply to portfolios too because it's all about putting your money to work. As for your first question, I'll leave it to others to answer."

A bird dropped out of the sky spinning round and round apparently out of control before suddenly swooping low over Bob and then hovering like a Harrier jet fighter. It appeared to be a hawk and said its name was Limbo as a number of pages from *Fortune Magazine* dropped from its mouth and landed beside Bob. They were mostly from an article dated 25 December 1995 and entitled "The Last Great Bargains" with a subtitle "Japan: Up is the Only Way to Go." The article mentioned how leading experts thought the Japanese stock market might be recovering soon.

"That was one heck of a tail spin you went into. I thought you would never recover," said Bob.

"That tail spin is nothing compared to the tale spins of stock promoters from which others sometimes never recover," declared Limbo. "That's why I came to explain. The bakery is an engineering marvel designed by some of the best fortune tellers on Wall Street. You see, no one really knows the future. So when financial types talk about the future, all they are really doing is guesswork— constructing castles made of imaginary dough in the air.

"Five years after that article was written, the Japanese stock market is still going nowhere. In fact, the opposite occurred. Three years later, the Japanese stock market lost thousands of more points. Up was not the only way to go. Sooner or later, the market may rise and then the experts who urged investment in Japan will become 'I Yah Toll Yahs.'

"It is commonly thought that financial markets just either go up or down. It's time we talked turkey, Mr. Catz. Sometimes the investment philosophy of 'buy and hold' for the long term ends up being a classic tale of 'time and punishment.' Markets have no morality. What goes up or down can also just keep hanging around. Sure, a market can eventually go back up, even higher than before— but not necessarily in your investment lifetime. A financial market can stall, then hover and zigzag in a narrow trading range like a Harrier hawk for years. It can just stagnate like commodity markets that deal with raw materials have recently. Everyone has heard about Wall Street. Few have heard of Stall Street."

"That's hot news for me," said Bob.

"Good," exclaimed Sir Real. "It may be useful to think of financial markets in a temperature sense as they run from hot to cold. Cold is merely the absence of heat, but your investments can get burned from the cold. Lack of heat from strong investor enthusiasm and participation can keep a market cool for years and years. You hear much about future expectations based on an investment policy of long term buy and hold. Stock promoters and futurists often like to talk about the upward bias of the markets; and that one can take warm comfort in the belief that Wall Street makes good in the end. You need to know about the cold hard facts: sometimes rules are made to be frozen. There's also buy and cold."

"Can I still consider this a hot investment tip?" asked Bob eagerly.

"The U.S. stock market, as you know by now, is often represented by an average or index like the Dow," explained Limbo. "The purpose of such an index is to give a snapshot of the 'mood' of the overall market where thousands of stocks are traded everyday. So an index, for investing purposes, is a collection of stocks or other securities to help you get a picture of what is going on in the market as a whole or in certain segments of the market without having to know everything that is going on."

"Yes," said Bob. "I'm aware of all that from the former star prosecutor *Kenneth Starling*."

"Yes, but you are not aware of patience," retorted Limbo. "Investors these days have seen the Dow climb a thousand points in a matter of months and think that's the natural order of things. This year the Dow topped 10,000 on the 29th of March 1999 then hit 11,100 six weeks later. The technology-laden Nasdaq Stock Market has gone up even faster than the Dow has. Let's go back in time for a moment. In 1961, the Dow hit a record of 734.91 and was approximately at that level nineteen years later. It was not until January of 1987 that the Dow broke the two thousand mark.

"In the 1972-73 period, the market declined some 40% in part because of a sudden spike in oil prices. Eventually, something happens that can be magnified for those who are unprepared. It was a slow grinding process—death by a thousand cuts. Meanwhile, gold, which had been languishing for years, as it has been recently, rose 1,462% in the '70s from $35. Stock promoters like to talk about how historic evidence indicates that over the long haul, the U.S. stock market moves upward. This is historic evidence, too, that by strictly following their advice, your portfolio can end up out on a limb. Markets can go from 'irrational exuberance,' to quote *Dr. Green Spin*, to 'irrational melancholy.'

"Can you give me a more recent example?" Bob requested.

"Ten years ago to this day of December 31st 1999," Limbo began, "the Japanese stock market was the biggest stock market in the world in the world's second largest economy. The stock market briefly touched 38,916 on the last day of 1989 on their version of the Dow Jones Average called the Nikkei 225. On December 31st 1989, the Nikkei had gone up 492% during the previous decade. In 1985, it was approximately 13,000. From 1985 until 1989, the market in general posted year after year of double-digit gains. Investors were brimming with confidence. The longer a market goes up, the more likely investors are to be optimistic of continued upward momentum. Those were the days my friend; they thought the trend would never end."

"So what happened?" Bob asked.

"During the past ten years, the Nikkei trading range has been less than half of what it was ten years ago," Limbo explained. "Financial advisers in the media often parrot that one should ignore short-term fluctuations in share prices. However, how many really define what short-term is? The question may turn from 'Can you afford not to be in the market?' to 'Can you afford to wait year after year with no idea of when the market will resurface and climb upward?' As *Dirty Haree* would say, 'Well, can you punk?'

"Sure, a market can go back up and you can have sellers remorse, but what if the waiting time were ten to twenty years? This is what short-term can mean in the long term. Short-term may be better defined as the time it takes an investor to realize that simply putting money in mutual funds doesn't mean you're going to come out ahead in the long term. The message: you can't just rely on general upward movement of the market, which may or may not occur in the time frame you expect. Remember this when you think about index funds, which are used by many investors as an inexpensive way to capture the general movements of markets or sectors. It's also a reason to learn about the importance of dividends when the market just drifts along for protracted periods of time. Remember it also if you do one of those fancy computer retirement hypotheticals, which can't take this kind of future possibility into account. You can retire close in time to when a long bad market takes effect. Your retirement account can become a long-term prisoner starving for decent returns with virtually no chance of a profitable escape—The Account of Monte Cristo. That's why computer hypotheticals are 'hypothetical' with legal disclaimers so you can't claim in court one day you relied on this information to your detriment."

"Gee," exclaimed Bob, "it gives a whole new meaning to the word 'downtime.' What a difference a decade can make. I think I understand the gravity of a market being suspended for a long time in a narrow price range. Please tell me more."

"The Nikkei's 'Excellent Adventure' reached an apparent bottom of 12,880 on 9 October 1998 in the wake of the Asian economic meltdown. It now goes up and down like a yo-yo in the lukewarm 20,000-point range, just as it did five years ago when that *Fortune* article was unfortunately written. Some have said that the Japanese market is a mirror image of our own, and one day the tables might be turned again in their favor.

"In the meantime, the value of many Japanese companies has now hit a twenty-five year low. Pretty cool huh? The floating world is no longer just about geishas in ancient Japan. It's about their stock market in modern times treading water month after month, year after year. President de Gaulle of France, a man of incredible gall, once described Japan as a nation living in rabbit hutches, in reference to their cramped housing. Now their once seemingly invincible economy has gone down a rabbit hole with Malice loose in Wonderland. What happened in Japan can happen in the U.S. for very different reasons. There are no guarantees."

"I remember reading all those popular business books in the 1980s about how Japan was going to replace the U.S. as number one," Bob commented. "Tokyo was going to be the financial center of the world, not Wall Street. Where are those authors who encouraged us to follow the Japanese example?"

"Probably busy writing best-selling books for the Japanese market on why the Japanese should be copying the *American Miracle*," replied Limbo.

"Oh, oh, it's coming back to me," said Bob excitedly. "Experts in the past said that Japanese investors would continue to pour money into the stock market no matter what happened because of their rapidly aging population not being able to rely on the government. Japanese investors were also said to be naturally more patient than poorly disciplined Americans with their quick buck attitude. Logic dictated that these 'samurai investors' just had to keep investing in that market and were the best savers in the world. Meanwhile, America was supposed to be a declining manufacturing power soon to be eclipsed by the Far East. It was hard to go wrong. That's what they said."

"Did those experts tell you that the Japanese had the equivalent in their language to our version of 'it's a new era?' Financial contortionists devised all kinds of ways to explain to a receptive public amazing values placed on securities like stocks and real estate—just as had been done in the U.S. with many Internet companies. With the phenomenal success of Japan in the world marketplace and enormous trade surpluses, an educated and dedicated work force, and so on, boom and bust business cycles were now considered a thing of the past. Japanese bankers figured out how to loan money faster, cheaper and dumber than anyone had ever accomplished before. It was said that you could drop a woman's scarf in the Ginza district of Tokyo and wherever it landed the section covered would be worth a small fortune. Up was the only way it could go until the values disappeared like a bursting bubble. Commercial property prices have now fallen by some 75% from their 1991 high."

"Where are those Japanese fat cats?" asked Bob. "I have a yen to talk to them."

"The Japanese regard failures as personal shortcomings so the fat cats are probably in the doghouse," Limbo replied. "American stock promoters also use demographics about baby boomers telling investors what will likely happen in the future. Dr. Root feels that such predictions do not properly take into account the role of emotions, which might provide future cracks in the Wall Street of confidence. She mentioned, for example, how people can instantly 'fall in love' with an expensive house with little or no research, but then spend weeks researching how to invest a few thousand dollars. She also mentioned how the same people who collect coupons to save pennies can blow money on big-ticket items like gas guzzling cars with barely a thought. Dr. Root likes to dig up the fact that a large segment of the population spends more time and effort planning a week's vacation than planning retirement, which can last decades. And when they do get serious about retirement they rely on some of the worst sources of information like TV financial news.

"Dr. Root has said that, time after time, investors are told all kinds of rational sounding conventional economic arguments by financial sales types and economists which end up being dead wrong: Japan being a prime example. She said that economists don't feel comfortable with a discipline that can't be put into numbers; and when they do factor in psychology they call upon learning psychologists like Dr. No who focus on intellectual logic and are disconnected from understanding emotional logic. Dr. Root thinks the refusal to recognize the unpredictable, irrational part of investors is itself irrational. She gets quite emotional about the subject shouting 'Zeese schvein don't understand zah role of zah unconscious oon zah power of fear. It's like teaching swimming after you read about it in a book. Zay haven't been analyzed.'"

"Dr. Root sounds like such a dog," exclaimed Bob.

"She looks like one too," commented Sir Real, "and is quite foxy and sarcastic as you would expect from a Queen's dog. Dr. Root even likes to make fun of the public's fascination with secret agent *Junk Bond* as an example of the triumph of emotions over intellectual logic. She said to me: 'The public thinks *Junk Bond* is the world's best secret agent. So vye does everyone know what he drinks, what he looks like, and that he works for Her Majesty's

Secret Service? What kind of a secret agent is zaht? Yet zay line up to see him and no one kvestions it.'"

"I never thought of that before," said Bob. "*Junk Bond* movies won't mean the same anymore."

"Mr. Catz," said Limbo, "you know that expression 'a little bird told me?' Let me tell you something that the public and Dr. Root don't know if I may join in: *Junk Bond* was once employed by 'The King' in America before his employment with Her Majesty."

"You mean Elvis?" said Bob, wide-eyed.

"No, silly, I'm talking about *Michael Milk'em*, the king of high stakes finance, the king of junk bonds. It was *Milk'em* who first popularized the use of junk bonds for financing high-risk companies that couldn't get conservative banks to loan to them. Some of these companies are household names today. *Milk'em* showed small companies how to access the capital markets by offering high risk, but high interest paying bonds. To some, he is regarded as a folk hero. Haven't you seen those 'Got *Milk'em*?' ads in business news with attractive corporate models demonstrating the rewards for milking the system?"

Keep Clam

> *If you're not inside, you're outside.*
> —Gordon Gekko in the movie *Wall Street*

"That name '*Milk'em*' does sound familiar," said Bob. "Isn't it a fact that he got into trouble of some kind?"

"Yes, he made millions in clams illegally," answered a barely audible voice from the moat. "I can talk now, but have kept clam for many years," said a gigantic Bent-nose clam, which broke the surface of the water. The clam named Clem had human-like, gray colored eyes, which never blinked, in its drab looking shell. It continued to talk as it floated on the liquid surface.

"*Milk'em* was imprisoned for violating insider trading laws and sent to what some call a federal tennis camp."

"Tennis is a great game," said Bob. "What are insider trading laws?"

"Inside information has to do with special privileged corporate information," Clem explained, all the while slowly opening and closing his clamshell. "This is information not yet available to the general public that can affect the value of a company's stock. You can't use such information to buy and sell securities because it gives an unfair advantage in the marketplace."

"Can you give me an example?" asked Bob.

"Yes," replied Clem. "Say a company officer in a pharmaceutical company tells you, a member of the public, in private, that a new drug has successfully passed trial tests. This information has not yet been released to the public. You would have an unfair advantage to profit. Insiders with special access to information include directors and officers of corporations and anyone who owns 10% or more of a corporation's stock.

"Those who provide such tips from the inside, 'the tippers,' as well as those who receive tips, 'the tippees,' can face big fines and prison sentences if found to have willfully violated these rules."

"Gee Clem, talk like that makes my hands feel clammy. Is there any way I can be in with the 'in crowd'; but be in with the out of trouble crowd, too?" asked Bob.

"Yes," answered Limbo. "There is legal insider information you can now access through the Internet. Insiders have to report their trades within ten days on a form called Form 4. There is also a year-end report called Form 5. By studying these forms, you can draw inferences about how insiders are reacting to the values placed on their company stock. For example, maybe the stock plunged in value because of bad news, but insiders are snapping it up.

"It could be because insiders have faith in the long-term prospects of the company and believe their company shares are at a bargain price. You should watch in particular what the CFO, or chief financial officer does. The CEO is often most familiar with day-to-day operations in the company. Sometimes insiders, like the president, will buy up shares to demonstrate confidence in the stock. So you have to be careful about assumptions. That's why you should pay more attention in many cases to insiders like the CFO. There is a subscription- based Web site called www.insidertrader.com which deals with this kind of information, which only large scale investors with big bucks could once readily access. You can also look at www.insiderscores.com for opinions about insider buys and sells. Once we all get in on the inside, then everything will be on the outside. That's why any clam worth his Kosher salt will advise you to not preach what you practice. Well, I think I've told you just about everything I can without revealing my sources. There really is nothing left to say, other than I'm happy as a clam at high tide."

Clem silently sank back into the moat.

Reversal of Fortune

"Just before I was openly interrupted by that clam, I was thinking of some further information on Japan that would be of cold comfort to you," said Limbo. "Tomorrow will be the 21st century when you wake up; and if you go back in time to 1989, the 21st century was supposed to be the Century of the Pacific. Actually, it was going to be the Japanese century. The Japanese still are the world's best private savers; it's just that millions of small investors don't trade in the stock market like before.

"While circling around and around, I have heard stock promoters in the U.S. say that the public really doesn't have a choice but to invest in the stock market to make sure there are adequate reserves for retirement. Japan is a wonderful example of how that's nonsense sales talk. People do have other choices there and in the U.S.: choices like the bond market, real estate, precious metals, bank certificates of deposit, money market and high yield floating rate bank loan funds. Beauty is in the eye of the market beholder.

"Twenty years ago, you could put money into a simple federally insured bank certificate of deposit and get a return of 12% in the U.S. Who's to say that kind of government backed return can't return? Who's to say that American baby boomers that are fueling this current market won't have a change of heart and decide to dump stocks when they retire? You just never know."

"Will I get a chance to meet anyone from Japan?" asked Bob.

"Later on in your travels with Sir Real you might come across Mr. Tsunami," said Limbo, "if he is well enough to talk to you. He is an emaciated stock market bull and best-selling author of *Of Mice And Yen*, which deals with the humbling of the Japanese economy despite a powerful currency, the world's best savers and record trade surpluses. The 1980s was their era of cheap capital, with money being tossed at Japanese companies left and right. Japanese companies seemingly could do no wrong. Mr. Tsunami told me they believed in the Yiddish folk saying: 'If you have money, you are wise, and good-looking, and can sing well, too.' They also believed in one of the great financial myths: that the stock market is a good predictor of what's to come. You don't have to be a bird to engage in flights of fancy. The stock markets in the U.S. are no more reliably forward looking than the Japan ones about economic conditions.

"Perhaps Mr. Tsunami can talk some more about the tsunami or tidal wave of bankruptcies, unemployment and suicides that have swept over the land of the rising public debt in recent years. Perhaps he can also talk about the disillusionment of millions of Japanese investors who saw their portfolios and raw profits of the 1980s turned into sushi as they were severely nicked by the Nikkei."

"How can you protect yourself so that you get out in the Nikkei of time?" asked Bob with a tone of concern.

"When it comes to stock, you can set it up so that when a price falls to a certain level the stock is automatically put up for sale in the marketplace," Limbo explained. "It's called a 'stop loss' order. Stop loss orders make breaking up easy to do. You can request a 'stop loss limit' order where the stock is only sold if you get a specified price, say $10 for a stock currently selling at $15. If only a general stop loss order is used, you get whatever price the stock sells for once the hair trigger price of say $10 in our example is reached. You may end up with a sales price far lower than $10 unless it is a limit order. Wealth Corgis like to limit their losses to small amounts because big losses often sap investor confidence.

"You can also request that a stock be purchased once a set price is reached. You make an offer that anyone can refuse. Unless you specify what you want to buy or sell a security for, then your purchase or sale price is based strictly on whatever goes on in the marketplace. *Kenneth Starling* told me that buying and selling securities is about contract law. In order to have a contract, you need an offer and an acceptance involving something of value. A limit order is what is called a conditional offer. You are placing a limit or conditions on your offer to buy or sell. You can place other conditions like a time limit on your offer, too. No one can accept your offer and create a contract relationship unless the conditions are met. Conditional offers give you a measure of control that you can't get from making a general offer."

"Does this meandering, stagnated, stuck in a rut, market movement have a name to it?" asked Bob.

"Yes, it's called 'sideways action,'" replied Limbo. "In this kind of situation, it becomes very important to learn how to squeeze out results and become a skilled stock picker. There is also a lesson from the Japanese experience. It's not what is commonly thought in America these days: that investing overseas is high risk. It's that the future is uncertain everywhere.

"The Japanese with their strong yen, massive savings and phenomenal exports (unlike the U.S.), still had a stock market that was leveled by way over 50%. Japanese in general didn't want to invest overseas because the best market was obviously Japan. Japan was the safe, logical and sensible choice. Americans may be now making the same mistake. After all, over half the world's stock market value is still outside the U.S.

"The Japanese market soared high and fast before making a steep dive and then floating midway year after year. Things seem to average out. As a marsh hawk, that's what I've learned while preying about." Limbo then flew away in a zig zag fashion.

"Attention To The Deficit Disorder"

Bob was just about to ask Sir Real to continue moving forward when he saw a big black and white colored female Corgi wearing a red cardigan sweater and a child's yellow-colored water wings swimming towards him singing, "I have the urge—the urge to splurge."

"Who in the heck is that?" asked Bob.

"I thought I told you about her," said Sir Real. "That's Lady Buy, the unsinkable American consumer from the state of Entitlement. Thanks to the current economic boom, she has been swimming in money and has been called 'the engine of world growth' by leading experts."

Lady Buy swam up to Bob and treaded water at the edge of the moat. She then said: "Hello, I look different from Sir Real because I'm what is known as a Cardigan Corgi. I'm on my way to another big red tag sale at La Costa Nostrums Department store. I want those great pick-of-the-litter deals. Retail sales and credit debt are the backbone of the U.S. economy. Itsah howah you say 'our thing.' Itsah bella . . . belladonna . . . kahpeesh?"

"I ah kahpeesh credit cards can have you drowning in debt and swimming with the fishes. I ah kapeesh that credit card interest charges are like asking to be fitted with cementah shoose. I ah kapeesh that revolving credit card agreements turn consumers into paysan' knows, financial serfs on a treadmill, joostah like in the oldah country. Where are the savings if you are paying high double-digit Nostrums' interest rates? Even in today's economy, you are probably paying around 20% interest. It's so profitable that Nostrums now has their own bank. I ah also kapeesh that when interests rates go up, the sky is the limit for credit card companies. However, when interest rates go down they do as they please. Credit card interest rates may have no ceiling but they certainly have a floor. Credit card advertising talks about tasting the sweet life, but it's really about getting more burden than a bigger slice of the economic pie."

"Just paying off credit cards would probably be far better than any returns I could make on average in investments with none of the risk," Lady Buy replied to Sir Real. "I am rather drenched in debt. However, Dr. Root assured me things don't have to make sense because emotions don't have to be rational.

"Even Mr. Spock of *Star Trek* has commented on how earthlings are often illogical. After all, does it really make sense to virtually wipe out the lean healthy buffalo so you can replace it with hormone and antibiotic fattened cattle? Why are Mafia guys who fleece the weak, commit horrendous crimes, and think honest hard-working people are morons considered to be romantic figures to a 'get tough on crime' public? If I had adopted thrifty conservative rational ways, the world would have gone into a deep economic downturn recently. The American consumer has been called an 'economic hero' in financial news. The business press often pats me on the head like a good dog praising me with phrases like 'resilient consumer' while I pile on more debt. According to establishment publications like *Business Weak*, only in America can you become a hero just by being a shopping mall addict. No wonder bankruptcy lawyers are starting to make house calls. If I'm forced by circumstances beyond my control to really cut back in the future, who knows what kind of impact that could have, aside from helping the environment?"

"Is that why you are called Lady Buy?" Bob asked.

"Her Majesty gave me the title of Lady Buy because I not only represent American consumer spending, which accounts for about two thirds of U.S. economic activity," explained Lady Buy, "but I also helped the world during the financial crisis of 1998 by going on a phenomenal shopping spree. I became 'the importer of last resort,' mopping up a flood of exports from emerging countries desperate for sales and facing financial collapse. I have many suitors because so much depends on my continued shopping, which is still going on with wild abandon. Exports to the U.S. are the engine driving the growth and recovery of these markets."

"What does Dr. Root have to say about your behavior, your Ladyshop?" Bob asked.

"Dr. Root says she sees things differently than the business media, which thrives on my purchases through advertisements.

The doctor also told me that financial consultants often don't recommend paying off credit cards because you will have less money to invest with the brokerage house. When in fact simply paying off credit cards may be the capo de capo of investment decisions. She likes to needle me that my behavior adds up to addiction; and that I'd be better off being a saver than some widget manufacturer's savior," Lady Buy responded. "I'm not going to see her again. I don't like to be around those who talk like that. Do you?"

"How can you afford to keep buying and buying?" Bob asked.

"I have been cashing in my gains on sales of homes and stocks, as well as refinancing homes with low interest rates and going into a lot of debt," replied Lady Buy. "Dr. No told me that low interest rates contribute to my higher risk taking behavior. Don't look at me that way. I'm not the only one living on borrowed dime. This year borrowers in general took on about $2.5 trillion in new debt including those corporations who gobble up one another in mergers and acquisitions.

"I'm so confident that next month I expect my confidence will be at an all time high as measured by the consumer confidence index. It's a monthly measure of my confidence in the economy. We're approaching the ninth year of what will soon be the greatest and longest economic expansion in our history. Of course, I'm delighted and am counting on everything just staying the same or getting better. Everything, including the stock market, is priced for perfection. My mind has no room for disappointment."

"What does someone like Dr. No have to say?" wondered Bob.

"Dr. No claims that, although consumer sentiment is considered a leading indicator for the economy, it can be a contra-indicator for a financial market like the stock market. Markets tend to reach their highest points or peak when confidence is at its highest. Both Dr. Root and Dr. No maintain that my compulsive shopping habits and attitude of spend first and save later, have contributed to record trade deficits which threatens the health of the U.S. economy. They call it 'shop til you flop.' However, those who benefit from shopping, including brokerage houses, often maintain the opposite—saying it's a sign of financial health that I'm not scared to spend. I actually heard that the other day from a brokerage house economist. They can be so funny without even trying.

"Thankfully, overseas investors have kept buying up U.S. assets in the form of securities, real estate and companies, pouring money back into the U.S. Right now, the U.S. is regarded as a safe haven for investing. I have been warned that this creates a dangerous situation if overseas investors get spooked one day and decide they can do better elsewhere."

"Why?" asked Bob. "And how does one keep track of your spending?"

"Foreign investors need to be persuaded to keep financing this trade deficit," Lady Buy explained. "If those investors lose faith, the dollar will get weaker and inflation will really rear its ugly head. High interest rates might be required to keep and attract foreign money to this country. In other words, we will have to buy confidence, which can be very costly for our stock and bond markets. You can track my trade gap through the Bureaus Of Economic Analysis and Census."

"How bad is your shopping spree?" asked Bob.

"It's no problem for me. However, according to Dr. Root, the situation is very bad. She told me that at the end of 1999 the broadest measure of foreign trade, the current account deficit, was a staggering $338.92 billion, 53.7% greater than the year before, which also set new records. In 1992, it was only $36 billion for the entire year. The U.S. current account deficit is a broad measure of trade in goods, services and various financial transfers. She says my appetite for imports far outstripped the ability of the U.S. to export goods in return. It's the worst trade performance since the Commerce Department started compiling the numbers. Dr. Root keeps telling me I can't just keep robbing Peter to pay the mall. It might eventually adversely influence interest rates."

"This global economy I read about seems so vast, advanced and complicated. I'm not sure I, like many others, can follow all this sophisticated information," Bob admitted.

"Don't worry," Lady Buy assured. "You mainly need to understand that I have an important job to do shopping at places like La Costa Nostrum's department store. The world has become increasingly dependent on my shopping habits. If I don't continue to take my work seriously, the system with its tighter-than-ever 'global interdependency' and weaknesses can start unraveling like it did in 1997-98, maybe even faster in the future. Troubled countries in Asia, for example, haven't really reformed and are even more dependent on the U.S. market. In other words, the health of the world economy largely rests on me, Lady Buy, demanding more and more imports and not turning into a real dog. Kind of surreal *n'est paw?*"

"Gee, I get it. It's really a lot like that Venus fly-trap plant in the play *Little Shop of Horrors* crying, 'feed me, feed me,'" Bob answered excitedly. Lady Buy then hurriedly swam away muttering that she was worried about being late for the sale. The little dog could be heard singing in the distance, "How much is that goody in the window?"

Money Talks

"I'm still not sure why a small investor like me should care about interest rates," Bob told Sir Real.

"There is nothing that affects the value of your investments more than interest rates," a deep booming voice from the black soupy moat shouted. "It is the chief factor in altering the moods of the financial markets. Falling interest rates are great for stocks because, for one thing, they make competing returns from fixed income securities like bank certificates of deposits look inferior to the potential of stocks. When interest rates are low, investors tend to place greater value on the earning possibilities of companies, so the values of stocks tend to rise. Low rates help companies to cut debt costs and encourage investment for greater returns. Bonds are helped, too, because lower rates in the future make present bonds with higher rates more valuable. Low rates, though, punish very conservative savers. Rising rates do the opposite by encouraging investments into cash positions like money market funds. Therefore, you need to understand as much as possible the role of money and debt in determining rates."

A great white shark with rows of razor sharp teeth and a cavernous mouth bobbed to the surface. It's white exterior was covered with numbers and the name SchNaws, written in that black soupy moat liquid, which quickly washed away.

"You have quite a big mouth Mr. SchNaws," Bob remarked.

"Not as big sometimes as that of the sarcastic mysterious Mr. Real, but big enough for my needs," answered SchNaws, who talked like someone who constantly gasps for air. "I have a voracious appetite for cash. It's the kind of appetite companies have when they are starving for capital, but now find that access to capital markets for selling their stocks and bonds has become very difficult due to changing economic circumstances; while commercial bankers at the same time tighten their loan requirements and refuse to renew lines of credit."

"I'm getting hungry just listening to you."

"You see, Bob," SchNaws said, "money is a symbol of buying power and a creature of thought. In circulation, it's called currency. On world exchanges, it's bought and sold like any commodity. It can be made of anything and not worth a single thing. It's only really worth what people will pay and not what any government has to say. I have been told that the only currencies that can't be bought are credibility and something called free thought."

"So what does a currency's value depend on?" Bob wondered.

"A currency's value depends on credibility and accessibility— not to mention demand and acceptability," explained SchNaws. The determining factor is trust. Money is a confidence game. Money acts like a mirror, reflecting the highest faith to the deepest fear. Money is about emotions, and flows around the world like oceans. It's always seeking to learn, where to find the safest and best rate of return."

"How can this have any impact on me?" asked Bob.

"A weak currency buys you less in addition to everything costing more," SchNaws said, "especially foreign goods on which the U.S. has become very dependent. Once prices start to go up for foreign goods, domestic manufacturers feel less pressure to hold down prices, too.

"Foreign investors in U.S. assets such as stocks, bonds and real estate may start looking elsewhere to invest if the money taken back home has less and less value. Unlike goods and services sold overseas, securities can be easily sold off if investment opportunities are better elsewhere. This can drive down financial markets. Weak currencies invite inflation, which raises the costs for goods and services while lowering the value of future company earnings. Inflation is why $6 won't buy a room any longer at Motel Six and why a first class stamp costs around ten times what it did thirty years ago."

"I don't quite understand how this impacts investments," said Bob.

"With high inflation, stocks are more inclined to go down in value," SchNaws explained, "because company profits don't have the same worth. If interest rates are raised to combat inflation, it also hurts profits because consumers have less money to spend and it costs more for companies to borrow. It's a double whammy. Overextended borrowers may no longer be able to just float by from month to month and end up drowning in debt. The higher interest rates rise, the more difficult it gets to predict what the results will be."

"What do you do besides swim around in the moat?" asked Bob.

"I hunt for bargains," said SchNaws. "Electronic currents are my seas as I sniff for overvalued currencies. There is no central location for exchanging money between countries. It's all done through electronics. Currency sharks, like regular sharks, have a phenomenal sense of smell for blood. We are able to sense a tiny drop of weakness in oceans of money. The currency market is the biggest financial market in existence. Our prey, worldwide money prices, has something in common with sharks: they are constantly in motion.

"Currencies float up and down in value relative to each other in a floating exchange rate system. It was a fixed system at one time until Nixon took the U.S. off the discipline of the gold standard in 1971. Country after country followed suit allowing their currencies to float away from the anchor of gold. A number of currencies, especially in poorer countries, have become floating casinos with widely fluctuating values and overvalued ships of fools gold. Elvis is 'dead money' but Nixon still lives in wild speculation. You can't manufacture gold the way you can manufacture money. More countries, especially dictatorships and pseudo-democracies, have been tempted to print extra money to monetize their way out of trouble. This opened the door to fluctuating exchange rates and currency speculators like me. It's about a constant worldwide vote where stateless money is free to undermine any country's currency. When a currency fluctuates a great deal I pay shark attention, especially when I smell blood. I like to feed on uncertainty, panic and currencies floating on rising tides of debt. It's true what they say about my kind of sharks never being able to rest or sleep: we can't stop seeing dead in the water currencies. To be honest, if it weren't for the money, we wouldn't be in this business."

"You have a killer sense of humor," Bob observed.

"Yes, I do," said SchNaws with an air of pride. "When the moment is right, I move in for the kill, selling the currency short and making bets against its stated value. I look for inefficiencies and like to draw the first blood hoping other currency sharks will join me in a feeding frenzy driving the value down even further. Who says money can't buy taste—for blood?"

"Can you give me examples?" asked Bob.

"This is what I did a while back when I smelled the blood of the English pound. Britain no longer rules the seas or the world's currencies. I am not one of those lone sharks. I like to work in packs. With other sharks and tens of billions of U.S. dollars at my disposal, including huge amounts of borrowed money for leverage, I pounded the heck out of the British pound—until it became my very own English patient. In the summer of '92, British currency met its Waterloo, as I snapped the back of the Bank of England.

"The U.S. dollar has now taken over the role as the dominant international currency; but the world is awash in U.S. dollars, which is backed more on faith than in the past. The Brits thought they were safe at one time, too. There is no such thing as safe when doubt sinks in about a currency's real value, followed by a sinking currency price, which can then be dragged deep underwater by sharks like me."

"What mischief have you been up to recently?" Bob asked.

"I found out in the early '90s that English cuisine is as bad as they say," SchNaws responded. "So recently, I made some more big bets, called macro-bets, starting with low on the food chain economies of Southeast Asia. I gorged on Asian food starting with the currency of Thailand called the *baht*. This helped kick off the start of the world financial crisis in 1997 and its blossoming in 1998. On 2 July 1997, I stormed into Bangkok like a Thai phoon creating a blood-*baht* with their *baht* currency. I then rang the neck of the Malaysian *ringgitt*. The Indonesian *rupiah* tasted the best resulting in devaluation close to 70% relative to the U.S. dollar. I was king of the ball on Bali. The most delicious aspect was how fast and sudden it could happen to these so-called 'tiger economies.' Overnight, they turned into financial pussycats—despite the near universal belief of economists and money managers that it couldn't happen."

"Is it because a bloody good optimistic outlook is not the same as knowledge?" asked Bob.

"Yes, that's what I learned at Shark Bait College," replied SchNaws. "With all their vast stores of information, they were caught by total surprise—a financial blitzkrieg. One not only has to have good data, which was lacking; it's also a matter of inference and interpretation. There was a lot of *Seoul* searching in Korea after I won against the won. Then, my attention turned to Russia. By the time I finished hammering and sickling their currency, it took a truckload of *rubles* to buy a piece of strudel. A large segment of Russia was reduced to a primitive barter system of exchanging goods and services, which still goes on today.

"I'm very thankful for the help of top corrupt officials of the Russian government in weakening the currency even further. Thanks to the Bullshevik artists at the Kremlin and master criminals, the country was looted. Fortunes were converted to foreign currencies and shipped to countries like Switzerland while the country starved. Meanwhile, the International Monetary Fund, the so-called international lender of last resort, backed in large part by U.S. taxpayers, was providing tens of billions in loans to support the currency. This gave the criminals and politicians plenty of time to convert their money and get it out of the country before the value fell even more. Any bets on whether it will be paid back? As *Dirty Haree* would say, 'Do you feel lucky, punk?'"

"How could this happen?" Bob asked.

"It is ironic that for decades hundreds of billions of dollars was spent trying to defeat the Russians in an arms buildup. Only when Western governments and banks loaned them tens of billions of dollars and sent over leading advisers to 'help' that Russia was finally brought to its economic knees—its currency turned into wastepaper. All it took was overly generous thoughtless loans, which became massive time debt bombs and free bad advice. The economic destruction to Russia was far worse than the Great Depression. No wonder many Russians consider the economic devastation the result of a devious CIA plot. I doubt it. Consider that their financial problems created havoc in the West, probably causing more financial damage than all the years of communism.

"Is it because the advisers and lenders didn't even know that they didn't know?"

"Yes," SchNaws answered, "and they made the Russians eat crow. South American food was great, too. It was *déjà chew* all over again. I focused on the Brazilian *real*, which was really out of touch with reality and still is. Vast sums of U.S. money were rushed in as loans to prevent a real crisis and spread of currency panic to the

U.S. It was so close; just like the Mexican *peso* crises of 1994 and 1997 in which I participated. The Mexican stock market was flattened like a tortilla as American investors rushed out; and I made even more money betting against their stocks as well as their currency.

"Sharks have always been able to move with breathtaking speed, but thanks to the double-edged sword of globalization and technology, I can move around like never before. What goes around comes around. Despite so many efforts to put obstacles in my path, it didn't take long for me to swim from Thailand to Malaysia, Indonesia, South Korea, Russia and Brazil to the doorsteps of the U.S. after the world's markets tanked. Minnows now have the capability of swallowing economic whales. Isn't that a whale of a cautionary tale?"

"How are things now?" asked Bob.

"Much of the economic surgery overseas has been through massive loans that need to be paid back," explained SchNaws. "Economic band-aids instead of serious changes, and rhetoric for public consumption won't do it. While I hear economists talk about so-called 'global healing,' I can still smell the blood from all the wounds that haven't healed. The symptoms may have healed, but the disease is still there not far from the surface. Disaster is supposed to help bring reform, but that remains to be seen. There is still hardly any of what accountants call 'transparency.' No one really knows what is going on any more than before: with the same corruption and family dynasty control and accounting books filled with financial land mines. They say that 'money talks but wealth whispers.'

"The major accomplishment so far is to tackle the problems by throwing more loans their way to pay back. It remains to be seen whether there will be quality life after debt for large segments of their populations. Sharks like me probably wouldn't be able to penetrate their economic waters so easily if they hadn't allowed so many cutthroat foreign investors in who easily turned tail when markets got choppy—swimming to safer waters with boatloads of money while throwing economies overboard in their wake. The locals bought into the new religion preached by the capitalist pigs and others about shareholder value and globalization. It turned out for many to be sharkholder value and globaloney."

"So what might happen next, Mr. SchNaws?" Bob then asked.

"If the U.S. has to raise interest rates to protect the dollar by lowering consumption, and keeping foreign capital headed this way, it will cause strain on the recovering countries who need to export goods and borrow on world markets. U.S. interest rates are the benchmark for interest rates all over the world. They can have a lot of interesting collateral damage when they rise in the U.S. forcing interest rates up elsewhere in response.

"In this recent financial crisis of 1998, *Dr. Green Spin* and the Federal Reserve quickly lowered interest rates to restore confidence and make money more easily available. Although widely praised for this action, many still do not realize that it was an admission that governments were paralyzed to do anything except to call in Lady Buy to shop like crazy, realizing that the alternatives were a lot worse. Rate adjustments, though, are often quick, easy and extremely powerful. The stock market recovered from earlier losses and soared upward from these artificially lowered rates."

"Why did you use the word artificial?" asked Bob.

"The reason the rates are artificial," explained SchNaws, "is because normally rates are lowered after an economy has cooled down. One of these days, there might be another crisis of some kind, but the U.S. might not have the same options to lower interest rates. Great white shark movie sequels have inspired me to think about returning for Asian Disaster Two. I have also been talking to Steven Spielberg about making a scary dinosaur economics movie."

"What do you plan to do in the meantime?" Bob asked.

"Currently," SchNaws replied, "I'm taking a second look at the new untested eleven-nation European currency created on 1 January 1999 and valued at $1.18 American, the fledgling Euro. I have this wonderful sinking feeling about Euroland and Euro value. So do European export companies that want to sell more to the U.S. At the least there should be short-term possibilities in betting against it while many wait to see whether Europe can really deal with its structural problems and become open for competitive business. Europe is filled with stubborn *burro-crats*. That's where some of those International Monetary Fund characters come from."

"Why was the Euro created?" asked Bob.

"It was created to be a common currency," explained SchNaws, "currently for eleven European nations. If it's successful in the long run, it will likely be a strong competitor against the U.S.

dollar for use as a reserve currency. Right now, it is a financial currency used in transactions like corporate bonds. There it is already a success. Interest rates have been kept lower in the European market. It's easier to raise money for international companies with Euro denominated debt. It won't be until January 1st of 2002 before coins and bills will be issued to the general public. Until mass acceptance comes along, you just never know. I suspect one reason our dollar continues to be strong is that Europeans are buying dollars to hedge their bets in case the Euro sinks like a lead weight. Also black market and Mafia money in European currencies is being converted to dollars.

"The public is trained by the financial companies to look for good times to make money. However, uncertainty and chaos are my friends. I feed on weakness, fear and those schooled to be economic fish. I especially like to go with the flow—the flow of money that is. So far, a great deal of money is still flowing into the U.S. from overseas and supporting the dollar. The Japanese, of course, all these years have recycled their massive trade surpluses by buying U.S. bonds. In the last three months of 1999, the net purchases of foreigners were $91.7 billion in stocks and bonds such as U.S. corporate bonds and Federal government bonds. I continually keep a close eye on the capital flowing into and out of the U.S., which I get from sources like the Securities Industry Association."

"Why did you say net purchases?" Bob asked.

"Foreigners sold stocks and bonds, too," said SchNaws, "in addition to buying them. The net result consists of total purchases minus sales. The Europeans have been among the heaviest buyers lately looking for good returns. Europeans have an enormous investment stake in America that can turn around and bite them, especially if there is a prolonged downturn in the U.S. economy. 'What goes around can come around.' Financial literature dealing with investments overseas warns a potential American investor about currency fluctuations and currency risk. What's comical is that there is great risk currently with American currency investments, too. All investments have risk. If there is ever a sharp reversal of confidence in the dollar, interest rates may have to go up dramatically to encourage investors to keep holdings in dollars or stay high. Rising interest rates are negative for both the stock and bond markets. Existing bonds offering lower interest lose more and more value as interest rates rise. Currency risk and interest rate risk can take a bite out of the safest investments."

"I guess there is no substitute for money," Bob noted.

"Yes there is," countered SchNaws. "Money isn't the only form of currency. One of the biggest currencies these days are shares of a company used to buy other companies—swapping paper for paper while keeping your cash. The public doesn't see company stock as a currency, but it is and can be over- and undervalued just like money. It is sometimes called 'funny money' or 'virtual money.' That's a big reason there have been so many mergers and acquisitions of other companies the past few years. Fat cats use their own company stock like money without having to borrow from anyone. Soaring share prices have helped companies seeking to acquire or merge with others because this high priced 'money' enables them to buy so much more.

"Smaller companies with sinking stock values and big potential often attract big fish companies. For investors owning shares in the acquisition target company, it can be a very profitable experience. Share values of target companies often rise considerably before being swallowed. Big fish companies may not even have the credit quality to borrow even if they wanted to borrow. In a rising stock market, though, stock, not cash, is king. Giant corporations like the telecommunications giant WorldBum, Inc. were built from the bottom up using stock as currency."

"Are these big company mergers successful?" asked Bob.

"Excuse me for interrupting," said Sir Real, bounding into the discussion. "I recently spoke to a corporate hog in charge of mergers named Hammond Bacon at an investment bank called *MoreGain Strangely Darn Wittier*. He told me they rake in huge fees from companies merging together—something like 4% or more of the entire amount involved. Think of what those fees must be for multi-billion dollar deals. It's mind-boggling. So investment banks thrive on mergers where companies pair up."

"That's a weird name for a bank," Bob noted. "It sounds more like a law firm."

"I like to deal with big Wall Street names," said Sir Real. "The investment bank, *MoreGain Strangely*, purchased the brokerage firm of *Darn Wittier*, which previously belonged to a huge department store, formed this one. The fat cats at the *Seers Road Block* store wrongly predicted that consumers would come in droves to buy stocks with their socks from *Darn Wittier*. So *Darn Wittier* was eventually sold to *MoreGain Strangely*, which wanted to connect with the small retail investors. There is a limit to how much the two businesses can cooperate because of the nature of their work."

"In what way?" asked Bob.

"They are separated by what is known as the Chinese Wall," said Sir Real. "It isn't a real wall. It's an expression. The investment side, which analyzes existing companies and brings new ones to the marketplace, has access to privileged information. It can't share this inside information with the selling side. It would give an unfair advantage to the exclusion of the general public. It's called trading on insider information, which you learned about from Clem the clam. There are severe penalties. Once in a while, you can read articles in the paper that firms on Wall Street still have leaks no matter how they try to plug them. Also when you talk to Lord Ha Ha you'll learn a funny thing or two about the fabled wall.

"Many acquisitions are labeled in the news as mergers or companies joining together as more or less equals. You often have one company, a suitor, acquiring another. Charities have been seeing the advantages of mergers lately, pooling their resources to cut costs and avoid competition for needed funds. Fast growing technology companies have used mergers and acquisitions to add talented employees, expand customer base and acquire important technology.

"Mergers and acquisitions of other companies often stem from weakness such as the need to keep growth from slowing, no viable future alone for one or both companies, the need for global alliances as a defensive posture, poor return on assets, the need to cut costs by eliminating a competitor and/or inability to deal with change. Studies indicate that approximately two-thirds of all mergers are not good value for the shareholders of acquiring companies. They can, however, run up the price of the weaker company joining the stronger one. In other words, stock owners of the prey end up doing better than those who own the predator. Movie and rock star marriages probably have a better success rate than most mergers. In other words, mergers are often about building expensive bridges to nowhere."

"Why is that so?" asked Bob.

"Increasing size also increases problems," explained Sir Real. "Merging of different business cultures can lead to the emergence of all kinds of unforeseen and / or papered over conflicts. However, the public hears mainly the 'bigger is better' hogwash from the capitalist pig bankers and fat cats who stand to profit and like to use expressions such as 'increasing synergies' and 'revenue enhancements combined with cost savings.' Although fat cats are very aware of these poor results, mergers can serve the purpose of hiding from the public their lack of imagination to grow the company. Mergers can be about big companies to satisfy even bigger egos. Fat cats also like to acquire and fire. They sometimes go after companies to fire employees quickly boosting profits because investors often focus short-term on the bottom line not the top line of financial reports, which deal with sales growth."

"Where can I find these fat cats I keep hearing about?" asked Bob.

"In Fat City of course," answered SchNaws. "It's somewhere on the other side of the moat, where it is supposed to be greener. I can see by the size of you that you are just a small fry investor. Nevertheless, if you don't learn to swim with the currencies, your portfolio may be eaten alive. It's important to appreciate the value of currency changes in order to shark proof your portfolio. Cash can be king at times, but just holding U.S. cash in an account can be a risky way to play it safe."

Deep Throat

"I just have a few more questions before you go," said Bob. "First of all, if this International Monetary Fund is so bad, why does the U.S. government continue to support it?"

"Because," explained SchNaws, "it indirectly is the U.S. government. The U.S. is the biggest shareholder in the 182 member bank. Without having to ask American taxpayers about money for specific purposes the government, through the IMF, can funnel money all over the world for pet projects, propping up corrupt, inefficient, bottom feeding dictatorships and setting the stage for future crises. There are complaints for public consumption now and then about the need for transparency in these countries, while knowing of course that dictatorships will never have transparency. Talk about the need for economic reform in countries that don't have real representative governments is utter rubbish. The best of ideas will never travel far as long as the cart comes before a hearse. Sharks getting loans are also loan sharks. The loans are like plugs for disintegrating ships. As they say in Greece, the birthplace of democracy, 'the fish rots from the head.' Now do you hear the music?"

"Yes. Dah Dah . . . Doo Doo Dah Dah," sang Bob. "Of course, that's the music created by Lalo Schifrin. It's the theme music from *Mission Impossible* and the IMF—the *Impossible Mission Force*. That's where both good guys and bad guys wear lifelike masks. You aren't sure who is who. The U.S. government funds the operation while denying any knowledge of involvement."

"Exactly," said SchNaws. "All that is missing from the Impossible Monetary Fund is the cool music, beautiful babes and Tom Cruise. The IMF was set up after World War II. Their original purpose doesn't even exist. Hook, line and sucker the American taxpayer gets fished in every year to act as the real banker of last resort to undemocratic regimes. The bailouts also aid foreign investors who want to get extra profit for taking high risk. Except a portion of the risk is passed on to the American taxpayer. When things go wrong, like the billions of U.S. tax dollars wasted on Russian thugs, the Secretary disallows all knowledge like with the real IMF and Tom Cruise. It just sets the stage for more and possibly much greater problems in the future.

"At any rate, the *burro crats* of this bailout organization are experts at stubbornly clinging to power. They have kept creating all kinds of ways to keep and enlarge their job positions with the monetary support of the U.S. government. They do some interesting economic studies of countries though, which you might want to look at as a source of information when investing overseas under www.imf.com. After all, you are paying for it."

"What does the IMF have to say about the U.S.?" asked Bob.

"That a slowdown soon is inevitable," SchNaws answered, "the only question being what it is going be like and its impact worldwide."

"Isn't the U.S. government committed to a strong dollar policy which will protect the dollar?" asked Bob. "That's what I read in the papers."

"It's a great white lie," SchNaws said. "Those verbal government assurances aren't worth the paper they are printed on. If the conditions are right, I may be able to eat the overpriced, diehard greenback for lunch one day. That's why I follow the money figures. All the policy means is that the U.S. government promises not to deliberately manipulate its currency to harm others in trade relationships. The upside of a cheaper dollar is that foreigners will find it more difficult to export goods to the U.S. and it will be easier for U.S. companies to export overseas.

"If holders of U.S. currency believe it is overvalued, government rhetoric won't mean a darn thing. They could bolt for the exits. Only something like really raising interest rates, action rather than words, would have an impact. The marketplace ultimately determines value. The strong dollar as a cornerstone of American policy has helped keep prices in check by making imports cheaper, attracted capital to the U.S. and helped dampen the price of exports needed to fuel consumer demand. However, the price has included record after record trade deficit that simply can't be sustained in the long run. Moreover, if the economy weakens but the dollar doesn't, American products can become more expensive overseas when the global economy slumps in response. The dollar lovers, the dollar bulls, are in charge now. When the time is right the dollar pessimists, the dollar bears, will come out of the woods. When they draw blood I'll smell it.

"Who knows how long Europeans and others will have a strong appetite for U.S. securities. It has been said that the U.S. dollar is overvalued by 25% or more. It's not only *Dr. Green Spin* who puts a spin on money figures. The U.S. government has put a positive spin on the trade imbalance saying it is a source of good news because the economy is so strong that it keeps sucking in foreign capital and goods—and sucking out American jobs. Even the masters of spin admit, though, that this imbalance can't last forever and has to be dealt with."

"I'm sorry to hear you sound so down on our buck," Bob commented.

"Deficits have to be financed somehow," said SchNaws, "and one day foreign investors might not be so willing to hold and reinvest dollars in the U.S. if they have better choices. Or they may have no choice. Japanese pension funds hold gobs of U.S. Treasury bonds and have to deal with a rapidly aging population and reportedly huge underfunded plans. Who knows when they can start selling off to pay their bills? Japan has the world's most rapidly aging population. If the U.S. economy should fumble, the U.S. dollar could tumble. That's why I think it's funny, to just hold onto dead president money."

"What do foreigner exporters do with U.S. money?" asked Bob.

"The foreigners take the dollars received to banks in their own countries, receiving their money in exchange," explained SchNaws. "These dollars are then sent to central banks like the one we have. Central banks can convert them to other currencies including their own or metals like gold, but often buy U.S. government bonds. The U.S. government borrows money and pays interest on short- and long-term securities. There are Treasury bills that mature in less than a year; Treasury notes that mature in one to ten years; and Treasury bonds that mature in up to thirty years. You can become a lender, too. With only $1,000, you can buy Treasuries directly from the government yourself with no fees or expenses at www.publicdebt.treas.gov; phone number 800-943-6864.

"Currently U.S. debt is considered the safest place to invest. Securities issued by the U.S. are one of the hottest export products. While Americans have had a buying spree for foreign goods, foreigners have been on a buying spree of their own, snapping up U.S. government debt. Foreigners now hold approximately one third of it. It is about twice as much as ten years ago. It is not the same as selling an industrial product. The 'sale' is about borrowing money and paying interest on it.

"In the short run, the U.S. has benefited from the 'flight to safety' of those seeking our dollars, especially from troubled countries overseas. The demand for U.S. debt has helped keep interest rates low, helping with mortgage payments and allowing extra money for other purchases. In the long run, we are more dependent than ever on foreigners not selling their dollars. Brokers sometimes talk about 'money in motion.' Smart money is always looking for the best place to go with the sunniest financial climate.

"Any major event that would cause foreign central banks to reallocate significant portions of their dollars and U.S. debt reserves into other currencies and government debt could have a disastrous result worldwide. I'm not even talking yet about all the money that could be pulled out of the stock market by individuals and corporations overseas. If the stock market sinks, it will very likely weaken the dollar. If the dollar sinks, it will very likely weaken the stock market. There is a very important relationship between the two. Any major event that shakes up confidence in the dollar is going to attract currency speculator sharks like me."

Read My Lips

"It's a good thing we have such a big government surplus, with more projected for the future," Bob commented.

"Projected domestic budget surpluses are just surplus talk like the strong dollar policy," SchNaws snapped. "A budget surplus means that the federal government takes in more money than it spends. A short time ago, government economists were claiming endless budget deficits—that went from here to the moon and back again. Now all of a sudden the debate is what to do with all the surplus money. It's really about politicians angling for votes while the public goes 'duh . . . bait,' not meaningful debate. I'm not the one who is really scary. What is scary is how wrong they can be about hundreds of billions of dollars. I am amazed how easily the American public can swallow almost anything fed to them from totally unreliable sources."

"Why do you think the projections are fishy?" asked Bob.

"The projected surplus is based on statistics such as life expectancies and cost reductions which are absurd," SchNaws began. "For one thing, with all the medical advances, people are more likely to live longer. Secondly, there are assumptions about future tax revenue built on very shaky optimism. The U.S. public has been accused of irrational exuberance in the stock market. However, government projections are now irrationally exuberant, to say the least. Both political parties know this, but don't want to rock the boat because it's a great campaign issue to argue back and forth about imagined future surpluses. Projections aren't predictions Mr. Catzfish. They are about numbers written in water that will wash away as easily as my name. You are too easily fished in by the latest school of thought. You remind me of those who are sold on the health benefits of shark without understanding the exposure to mercury poisoning. Great white sharks are not just in the sea. I'm not the only one with large crooked teeth."

"What would a big budget surplus have to do with a little fish investor anyway?" asked Bob.

"For one thing," said SchNaws, "it is allowing the government to buy back the king of bonds: the thirty-year Treasury bond.

These bonds have been used as benchmarks for safety all over the world and to set loan rates."

"You have to admit that we do now have a budget surplus," Bob noted, "and that this is still great unexpected good news, projections aside."

"Not necessarily," SchNaws cautioned. "There are those who say that the surplus is mostly a fiction because the government is using sleight of hand accounting techniques such as "borrowing' from Social Security and leaving IOUs in the account. Governments and corporations love to play shell games. The surplus in Social Security is added to the federal deficit to create a huge surplus. Even Social Security is only running a surplus because of the present baby boomer tax contributions, which will evaporate once they retire.

"Anyway, even if there really was a budget surplus, budget surpluses all the way back to the time of George Washington have a history of being closely followed in time by economic downturns. If the government in taxes is collecting so much unexpected extra money, and it's not from over taxation, then it probably means this economy is racing along way too fast. The central bank is going to have to slam on the brakes by raising interest rates making it more difficult to borrow and spend. Even surpluses can have their deficits.

"It may be delayed for a while longer because of the presidential election in November of 2000. Gobs of money will be spent before election time helping to stimulate the economy; and the central bank likes to avoid the appearance of supporting one party over the other. George Bush, Sr. has reportedly complained he lost the presidential election in part to Bill Clinton because of interest rate hikes. The central bank is likely to try to avoid all but the most necessary interest rate increases close to an election. After the election, it may be a different story. In the meantime, enjoy the party while it lasts. For over half a century, presidential election years have been good for the markets. I have to go. My owners are calling. Have a nice day."

"Who are your owners?" Bob asked.

"The hedgehogs," replied SchNaws. "I represent hedge funds and have worked with the some of the biggest, including the giant *TyranoSoros Wrecks* fund group—although it is a bit of a dinosaur now compared to its heyday."

"Who are these hedgehogs?" Bob wished to know, having heard so much about them. "And why is that TyranoSoros group a bit of a dinosaur? For some reason, that Soros part sounds familiar. It must be my imagination."

"The hedgehogs are experts at hedging their bets on the financial markets going up or down," SchNaws explained. "They take money from the wealthy and institutions like college endowment and pension funds to make higher profits than small investors make from conventional ways like highly regulated mutual funds. Their strategies involve higher risk, but at the same time they have much greater flexibility than conventional funds, using cutting hedge financial technology. Not that it always works. With a Nobel Prize winning formula, one group of hedgehogs nearly brought down the entire financial system in 1998 by betting the wrong ways. Even the TyranoSoros group got its hedge clipped in Russia; and lately has had problems wrongly betting that by now sky high technology stocks would be going down in price, when they are still going up. Making big bets on the movements of global stocks, bonds, currencies and commodities has become more and more difficult lately. Other styles of hedging involving smaller more nimble micro bets are proving more successful at the moment.

"The message for a small fish like you, Bob, is that even expert hedgers can get their portfolios trimmed. There are estimated to be over three thousand unregulated hedge funds. Maybe you will get to meet one of the hedgehogs if you are lucky. They are very secretive and usually spotted only once in awhile at Stonehedge. The Securities and Exchange Commission doesn't regulate them and they don't have to follow reporting rules like conventional funds."

SchNaws submerged shouting in his deep voice, "I'll be baaack, just like inflation," and disappeared into the moat.

"Bird Is The Word"

A group of American condors, with their bare heads and dull black plumage, circled above the wake left by SchNaws's departure. One of the condors had on a mini T-Shirt that read: "You Wouldn't Believe the Way We Carrion." It landed at the edge of the moat. "My name is Carrie," it said. "We're vulture capitalists, but we prefer to be called 'Reconstruction Experts.'"

"I've heard of venture capitalists—not vulture capitalists," Bob commented.

"We sometimes feed off the mistakes of venture capitalists, but mostly we look for delicious disasters. We follow characters like SchNaws all over the world making money off distressed companies and properties for those who invest in our Have Scavengers Will Travel Company," Carrie said with enthusiasm. "We pick the brains, talents and resources of terminally ill companies offering really stiff terms. I like to poke around getting the fat off the remains of dead and dying companies and extracting what I can from purchases of deadbeat loans. When you can buy loans for less than eighty cents on the dollar, it usually means companies are dying for my money and in lots of trouble. We're actually very understanding because Dr. No gave us sensitivity training. We tell such companies that even though they may no longer make sense to others, they can still make lots of cents with us—as long as they are willing to accept pennies on the dollar. I call them The Grateful Dead like the rock group—except their music is the kind you hear at a funeral. What can I say? It's a living."

"That's an interesting company name," Bob noted. It reminds me of 'Have Margin Call Will Travel' and 'Have Gun Will Travel.' Isn't there any original thought any more?"

"Maybe not with us, but the financial world is filled with imagination and creative thought. Wall Street can dream up securities based on anything, even the risk of rainfall in a given area. That's what makes it so exciting and downright scary," said Carrie.

"So who are you guys?" Bob inquired

"The company we represent is known as a vulture fund to our detractors," Carrie answered. Investors judge us by the companies we keep. All the vultures in our operation are members of *Waste Watchers International*. We look for companies that have been wasted financially. There are graveyards of opportunities everywhere. We consider the pros and cons of buying into companies experiencing very lean times, while weighed down by heavy debt, poor management, cash flow problems and/or excess manufacturing capacity. Even though we're no culture vultures, we're not such bad guys. There are many good companies desperate for injections of money to keep afloat as I fly around picking through the wreckage from the Asia crisis.

"My company is backed by millions of dollars from institutions like pension funds, major universities and U.S. corporations who expect me to provide them with high returns for investing money with us. Our logo contains the Chinese symbol for crisis, which is also the symbol for opportunity."

"How long does it take for you to make money?" Bob wished to know.

"Our time frame for return on investment is long," Carrie replied. "We find the bargains, make investments and then wait patiently, often getting involved in helping the companies get back on their feet. It's not as easy as some think or more companies would do it. Booty is more than skin deep. You have to be a really picky shopper and tough or your would-be bargain can turn into a money-sucking vampire. Some of these companies can reach out of the grave and pull you right in with them."

"That's so like the horror flick *Carrie* with a young *John Revolta*, that *Stayin' Alive* guy, before he became a star," Bob commented energetically.

"Well, I can assure you my team knows all about staying alive," said Carrie. "Vultures, of course, are naturally picky; and I am quite experienced after buying distressed properties from the U.S. Savings and Loans crisis. As in Japan, greatly overvalued real estate was used as collateral for loans by American 'thrift' institutions. When economic times became more demanding, they weren't able to cover depositors' savings based on these extreme valuations. A dog may be a man's best friend, but a greenhorn banker is a vulture capitalist's best friend.

"The federal government had to bail out and close hundreds of these savings and loan operations at a cost to taxpayers of around $150 billion spread over the next thirty years. Investment vultures landed on some incredible deals. It's that kind of overconfidence by bankers and investors that keep guys like us in business. It also guarantees government presses will keep working printing extra money to pay for these kinds of disasters: helping to maintain inflation by making money worth less over time."

A much younger vulture landed next to Carrie and interrupted the conversation. "Carrie didn't mention that we even go after still-born companies that never got off the ground, but have customer lists, copyrights, patents, et cetera for us to pick through," the vulture said. "We also love to go after companies facing collapse and set it up so that we are on top of the pecking order when they land in Bankruptcy Court. Some of the most attractive carrion to vultures are bankrupt companies. I'm planning to start my own fund soon called The Remains of The Day. Vulture capitalists are very entrepreneurial."

Carrie stared at the other vulture like she had X-ray eyes, then snapped, "I don't remember giving you permission to speak."

The young vulture slinked off.

"Are you planning to come back to North America?" Bob asked Carrie.

"I'll be returning to North America soon when the public starts souring on overvalued Internet companies," Carrie replied. "There should be some rich pickings when they become desperate for injections of capital and/or their initial backers, the venture capitalists, start getting impatient for their money."

"Is there a way I can invest in quality companies overseas without minimum hassle?" Bob asked.

"Yes," Carrie replied. "Many investors don't realize that the U.S. stock market has never been the world's number one performer in any year since 1970. The most successful stock market of the 20th century was Sweden followed by Australia. This year, the Helsinki stock market in Finland was Europe's best performing one gaining close to 150% in dollar terms. Markets around the world are more connected than ever before, but still often don't rise or fall in tandem. International diversification is not only a good risk reduction strategy, but it also offers many rewards. In a global economy, investors need a global approach. You don't need to be a vulture to take advantage of opportunities overseas."

"For small investors like you, Bob, I would take a look at what are called closed-end country funds. They are overseas versions of closed-end funds like Black Jack. These country funds have active money managers who screen stocks for investors. They help you zero in on different parts of the international market scene. As a closed-end fund, they don't have to redeem shares constantly, which can be very difficult in exotic markets. That's why open funds tend to avoid these kind of relatively non-liquid markets.

"India has the world's second largest pool of scientific workers. Israel is regarded as a second Silicon Valley, with more companies listed on Nasdaq than any other country outside of North America. Many of the forces that have driven the U.S. stock market upward such as deregulation and corporate restructuring are starting to take place in earnest overseas, especially in Europe. These investments can appear to be far away, but it's shortsighted not to take a look at the long-term possibilities.

"The fat cats see telecommunication costs dropping dramatically with great advances in computer networks. Information jobs are like liquid assets that can easily be transported elsewhere without the high visibility of shutting down so-called Old Economy manufacturing jobs. Not only jobs, but also even previously reliable assets, like the sacred cow home, can be made more vulnerable by giant technology leaps. Location for real estate might be somewhere far off. There is more than one way to get skinned by a fat cat. Speaking of technology, there is our neighbor to the north with some of the most advanced high technology companies in the world listed on the Toronto Stock Exchange. It may be good to get a little northern exposure if you want your portfolio to head north."

"Oh, Canada," said Bob.

"Yes," Carrie continued, "just like the national anthem. There are a number of sites on the Internet that deal with closed-end funds. You should also read a newspaper like the *Financial Times* of London, a favorite of mine, which you can find at http://news.ft.com/. You can take a look at intltrader.com for currency information, foreign stock quotes and global online investing as well as worldlyinvestor.com which has some experienced and interesting columnists. For world headlines, there is also ustrade.com/parts/news.html. Country funds can have seasonal trading patterns such as being more discounted, better bargains, at certain times of the year than others: like the last two months of the year. Of course, what happened in the past is no guarantee of the future."

Carrie and her companions then flew away, flying high over the bakery sign.

It . . . It . . . It's Alive.

Inflation is always in the wings because it's the most tempting way for governments to raise money.
—Milton Friedman, Nobel Laureate

"I rather enjoyed learning about how the value of money relates to inflation and interest rates," Bob commented. "I'm not sure yet how the parts work together; or what inflation really is. I need to know more."

"What do you mean you don't understand, eh?" asked a large bird with clipped wings and legs placed so far back on its body that it walked with a clumsy floundering gait. "I'm from Canada see, so like the moose, I talk about zed not zee. Americans call me a Coin'uck.

"Do you realize that for a period in the 1970s the American dollar did not receive a warm welcome in cold Canada, eh? It was worth far less than the Canadian dollar. You think I'm talking crazy, don't you, because an American dollar can buy approximately $1.50 Canadian these days? Or is it just because the Canadian dollar coin with my likeness is called a 'loony?'"

"You do act and look a little off," Bob said. "But these days, that's normal."

"I'm on my way to Florida," said Coin'uck, "but my retirement money doesn't go as far as I thought it would by the time I convert Canadian money to American. Who would have thought this would happen coming from one of the richest countries in the world, where our money was once worth more than yours? You just never know, eh? I guess you have to diversify."

Coin'uck suddenly flew away, pursued by a green colored bird of prey screeching that inflation is about too much money chasing too few goods leading to rising prices. The bird introduced itself as an inflation hawk named Hawk Talk and said it was a voting member of the Federal Open Market Committee.

"Why do you call yourself an inflation hawk?" Bob asked. "Aside from your green color, you look like an ordinary hawk to me."

"I may look green, but I'm not green," said Hawk Talk. "An inflation hawk is the opposite of an inflation dove. Both groups work for the Federal Reserve Bank and vote on whether or not to raise the cost of borrowing. Raising the cost of borrowing money is the main weapon the central bank has in the war on inflation."

"Why is it called a war on inflation?" Bob wished to know.

"It's politician and newspaper hype for the public," Hawk Talk explained. "That's why we have wars on drugs, wars on poverty, wars on disease, wars on illiteracy, et cetera. Every cause becomes a war. It's a good thing we're peaceful. Now may I continue?"

"Sure," Bob consented.

"Inflation hawks," Hawk Talk began, "believe in aggressively attacking with interest rate increases when their hawk eyes spot signs of inflation taking to the air. Hawks like me think that *Dr. Green Spin* is benefiting in large part from a series of lucky coincidences including the collapse of raw material prices in Asia, the communications and technology revolution, the foreign love affair with the U.S. dollar, budget surpluses and so on that can't continue indefinitely. Doves believe in a more 'wait and see' approach. If interest rate increases are necessary, doves prefer a more gradual hike by quarter points over more extended periods of time."

The Usual Suspects

"Is there any way I can check for myself, other than the cost of goods in the grocery store or waiting to hear from the government?" asked Bob.

"The annual rate of inflation is measured by an index published monthly called the Consumer Price Index or CPI," Hawk Talk explained. "Way back in 1967 it was arbitrarily fixed at 100 to measure the cost of over four hundred household expenses including clothing, medicine, rent and so on. Essentially, it is the price for a basket of goods and services. Inflation is about the change in the cost of this 'basket' from year to year. Get your notepad out."

"Okay," said Bob.

"To get a more advanced view than is mentioned in the daily news, I would check the first week of every month with www.dismalscientist.com on the Internet," Hawk Talk advised. "Columbia University's Center for International Business publishes a leading inflation index or LLI. It includes factors such as import-price changes and growth of the federal deficit. *Dr. Green Spin* seems to like it. If the index keeps creeping higher over a number of consecutive months, then chances are higher that we'll vote on an interest rate hike. Inflation can be seen as a price bubble that works its way through the system like a chain letter from importers and manufacturers to wholesalers and finally consumers.

"So, I would also check on www.napm.org, the first business day of each month. That site deals with the National Association of Purchasing Managers Price Index: a measurement of whether manufacturers from month to month are paying more or less for their goods from their suppliers in general. Manufacturing activity accounts for around one fifth of U.S. economic activity and jobs. The index is made up of nine subcategories like new orders and inventories and is a measure of the strength of U.S. Production. The index was lower not long ago because of the collapse in the price of raw materials due to the Asian crisis in 1998.

"Costs for raw materials and imports are no longer falling. In fact, they have been climbing again. You should also take a look at the Production Index for Purchasing Managers, which deals with the level of expansion or contraction for manufacturers, such as new orders. *Dr. Green Spin* starts spinning round and round anxiously like a whirling dervish when both production and price increases spike above sixty at the same time, especially when they continue to do so for several months. Fifty is the dividing line number for more or less activity. When the two major numbers hit sixty, alarm bells start going off in *Dr. Green Spin*'s head. They say he sometimes becomes so wound up that Dr. Root has to have him sedated.

"On the seventh day of the second month of each quarter, I would check the Bureau of labor statistics at http://stats.bls.gov to learn about productivity, which is also critical to keeping prices stable. Productivity growth these days has been unusually high, as Ms. Coward mentioned, due to the great technological changes or maybe not, as you learned from Madame Bifteck. Higher productivity enables companies to better absorb cost increases from labor, energy and raw materials. However, if the index drops back to a more average growth rate, chances are greater for passing on price increases to consumers. This last year of the twentieth century it was 3.6% for the entire year largely due to huge investments in new technology. For the last twenty years, the rate has been around 1.5%. This recent accelerated rate of growth will eventually moderate. Things tend to average out. That's what a lot of my hawk talk is about.

"Our Federal Reserve, like central banks the world over, has the same concerns about how much money is being pumped into the economy, the cost of borrowing or interest rates and inflation: how fast prices are rising for goods and services. I'm very hawkish these days on the need to raise interest rates much higher and reduce the amount of money flowing into the system by, for example, increasing borrowing requirements at financial institutions like brokerage houses. Right now, I spotted that disgusting cheap loony and felt I had to chase it away."

"I remember President Nixon was overheard saying in the Watergate tapes that he didn't give a flying duck about the value of the Italian *lira*," said Bob. So why should you get so worked up about some looney Coin'uck?"

"The president used a much stronger word than duck, Mr. Catz," Hawk Talk noted. "Of course, I don't talk like that, do you? Anyway, I hope you remember what I have to say a little better than your history lessons. My work includes protecting buying power, which gets eroded from inflation. Newspapers and magazines have mentioned lately that inflation is dead, but that's because they don't understand it's a hydra-head. For one thing, it's hiding in the stock market and real estate where the value of assets is expanding, creating more dollars for consumers to spend than goods and services are being created to purchase.

"My hawk eyes can tell you that those who say inflation is dead suffer from financial myopia. They can't see that what has been holding down prices in this soon-to-be record economic expansion has been the economic oversupply from overseas: wrecked and wretched economies that have extra factory capacity with which to supply us at rock bottom prices. This has also undercut the ability of non high tech labor to demand higher wages. One of our greatest exports has been jobs shipped overseas. The faster those economies recover, the faster we are going to have higher prices and inflation."

"So this inflation process is well understood," Bob observed.

"No, not at all," screeched Hawk Talk. "Those who have looked at summaries of our meetings can see that there are many differing opinions about what is going on. What you are hearing is the opinion of a number of hawks, including myself. What I can tell you for sure is that two of the biggest retirement planning mistakes are underestimating the impact of inflation and taxes. Hanging on to too much cash can be risky not only because money can be devalued, but also because of the insidious effects of inflation."

"Insidious?" Bob remarked. "That's too big a word for me."

"It's about what you don't know: the stealth loss of wealth," Hawk Talk remarked. "Inflation is not easy to spot, even by a hawk. Inflation has been quite low these past years. In fact, it has been about half the long-term average. However, even a low rate can erode your savings. A dollar received today is worth more than one received in the future as long as there is inflation. A dollar will lose half its value in twenty years at an inflation rate of just 3.5%. At an average 4% inflation rate, $1 would be worth only 96¢ one year later; and 67.5¢ in future purchasing power in ten years. $100,000 would be worth $67,556 in ten years. Or put another way, you would need $148,025.00 to equal the $100,000 in purchasing power you had ten years ago. Your investments have to keep pace with those kind of rising costs. Retiring happily in the financial world usually means after adjusting for inflation."

"I've been taking notes," Bob said. "Anything else?"

"You have to stay ahead of inflation," Hawk Talk advised. "Otherwise, you can end up being safe and sorry. The reason I'm so hawkish about preventing outbreaks of inflation is that once it takes root and stabilizes at a higher figure then the public begins to have inflation psychology, the expectation that prices will go up. The public starts planning for prices to rise; and it becomes very difficult to bring them down again as it becomes a self-fulfilling prophecy. When inflation starts rising higher and higher, investors start unloading paper assets like U.S. dollars, stocks, bonds, et cetera to convert to real assets like real estate and precious metals.

"I haven't even included what taxes can do to savings. I'll leave that for someone else. Right now, I have to see if I can hunt down any harbingers of inflation that could threaten investments. We inflation hawks don't look for just specific numbers as many think. We look for general trends. The Fed has an eighteen-year track record of dampening inflation expectations. We can't afford to lose our edge."

"Maybe you should just chill out," Bob suggested.

"Not since the 1920s has the economy been so dependent on the role of the stock market," Hawk Talk pointed out. "The public has a misperception that the Fed's role is to prop up stock market prices. The mind set is that if things go wrong, all *Dr. Green Spin* has to do is open the credit valves wide and a rising tide of new money will lift the market back up. It may not happen that way. Individuals and corporations in general borrow money when it pays to borrow. If you can't sell your goods for example, it doesn't pay to borrow. Interest rates coming down alone isn't good enough. That's a myth. In Japan recently, even borrowing at virtually zero interest rates has had little effect on their recession. That's with money for nothing and checks for free."

"Gee," exclaimed Bob. "It's like that rock song, except isn't it about getting chicks for free and money for nothing?"

"Be serious, Mr. Catz," Hawk Talk urged. "The Fed's role in part is to prevent major disruptions of the markets, not limit the losses of the public. If your retirement account bites the dust, it's not the Fed's responsibility. Even *Dr. Green Spin* has warned that this misperception has dangerous implications. The financial turmoil in 1998 involved extraordinary disruptions in financial markets. Even the safest and most liquid of markets were affected. A paralysis had set in where investors weren't sure whether to buy or sell. For a short time, many companies couldn't go to the public markets and get needed loans by issuing bonds. Interest rates were lowered because of serious economic weakness, not because inflation pressures had gone down as has happened in the past. There are no guarantees."

"Okay, okay, let me see if I have this straight," Bob said. "*Dr. Green Spin's* interest rate medicine may make the stock market larger or make it small, but one day it might not be able to do anything at all. Go ask Japanese brokers who once felt ten feet tall."

"That's much better, Mr. Catz. I see you have been studying up on your rhyme and reason and have been inspired by a Jefferson Airplane pill popping song," Hawk Talk replied. "Let me add that what has happened in Japan happened here in the 1930s when Treasury bills were offering close to 0% interest. The phenomenon is not just 'made in Japan.'"

"Where is *Dr. Green Spin?*" asked Bob.

"Normally central banking is considered just a number-crunching dry business," Hawk Talk remarked. "However, right now *Dr. Green Spin* is working to cool an economy he considers overheating and has been seen jumping off a diving board trying to figure out how to make the economy have what is called a 'soft landing' or mild economic downturn. This is where growth slows to a range of around 3%. The economy continues to expand without great wage or price pressures and avoiding a sharp rise in unemployment. There is a worry about draining too much liquidity from the economic system resulting in a 'hard landing' or even a crash landing. Many corporations and individuals are heavily over borrowed on loans, which have helped create the massive liquidity in the system. Once it starts getting more difficult to borrow, there is no telling for sure what the impact will be. The ideal soft landing would involve slowing down the economy to a sustainable pace—a point between 3.5% to 4% growth where there is a much lower chance of sparking inflation. It's not easy to deal with the descent of a multi-trillion dollar economy. *Green Spin* has to make interest rate adjustments in such a way that he factors in the possibilities of runaway inflation and a serious economic downturn, so that the landing is somewhere between a rock and a hard space."

"How do you raise or lower interest rates?" asked Bob.

"The central bank has a twelve member policymaking committee called the Federal Open Market Committee or FOMC. They make the key decisions, which determine the availability of money and credit and the cost of money to be borrowed in the economy. The direction of short-term interest rates depends on that panel. The chief policymaker is the chairman, *Dr. Green Spin*, who began his term August 11th 1987 just before the stock market crash. He didn't cause the crash, but he couldn't prevent it either.

"The central bank manipulates the fed-funds rate, which is what banks charge each other for overnight loans to balance their books. The last time this year that the fed funds rate was changed was in November when the rate was 5.5%. In August, the rate was 5.25% and in June, the rate was 5%. It's creeping upward. Some think that by next year the rate could be a full point higher or more. Even banks need to borrow from each other. This manipulation is done by a process involving buying and selling government securities. The Fed also lends directly to banks at a rate called the discount rate. Even when these benchmark interest rates are left unchanged, the FOMC traditionally makes a statement at the end of the meeting, called a directive, on where they believe interest rates may be heading for the near term. This 'bias,' which is the balance of opinion of the voting members, can be neutral or it can have a belief that interest rates will go up or down. This directive now seems to be causing added confusion in the marketplace. Fed watchers can interpret the comment, or lack of comment, differently. Before *Dr. Green Spin* there was no such directive."

"I think that's called the law of unintended consequences. What happens after a decision is made to alter interest rates in the marketplace?" asked Bob.

"Usually within hours of any decision to raise or lower interest rates," Hawk Talk explained, "banks respond by adjusting their prime rate: what they charge their best customers. This affects all kinds of bank loans from business to cars and home loans. World financial markets follow the Fed's moves because the U.S. is the main engine of growth for the world economy and influences worldwide interest rates. Remember, all but one major economic downturn in the U.S. since World War II was caused by rising prices, which then forced us to hike up interest rates in response. Lower interest rates have enabled companies to be more profitable by borrowing at cheaper rates to invest in new equipment among other things."

"Your name was on that invitation list to the FOMC," Bob observed. "How come *Dr. Green Spin*'s was listed four times in four different forms of handwriting?"

"*Green Spin* is our top inflation cop and doesn't even look or act like the rest of us," Hawk Talk explained. "He is an octopus with hands instead of tentacles. This way he can say on the one hand it could be this or on the other hand it could be that and do a lot of finger pointing when problems arise. He can hedge his answers better than any hedgehog. You can never get a straight answer from him, while he is either wringing his hands from worry or trying to wring every last drop of inflation risk from our economy. *Green Spin* at times needs to be heavy handed about interest rate increases or light handed without overplaying his hands. He also needs all these hands to keep juggling."

"Juggling what?" Bob asked.

"His job is a balancing act," Hawk Talk explained. "Monetary policy is all about juggling. One hand, for example, has to bring supply and demand back into balance through interest rate adjustments so that inflation doesn't rear its ugly head. Another hand has to juggle with the implications of a falling dollar. A third hand has to weigh the possibility that with the record private debt in certain sectors it may be far more difficult to restimulate an economy that will eventually go into a downturn. Another has to wave a jawbone at the public for unrealistic expectations warning that the Federal Reserve's job is to protect the economy not rescue the stock market, which is not an FDIC-insured checking or savings account. The public has yet to understand that inflation problems undermine the ability of the Fed to lower interest rates if the stock market goes down significantly. Still another hand has to juggle with all kinds of incomplete evidence of where the economy is going.

"Only a giant octopus could handle a job like that. Since he's a typical octopus, *Green Spin* has a venomous bite. That's why the markets fear him so much. Like Muhammad Ali, he can fly like a butterfly then sting like a bee with interest rate hikes."

"Where do you find someone like that?" Bob asked.

"It's easy," said Hawk Talk. "From a newspaper ad. We just advertised that we wanted someone with a lot of hands-on experience, multi-task oriented, extremely flexible and willing to work long demanding hours for relatively low pay while being surrounded by lots of other peoples' money. Jobs like that are in the paper all the time."

"Of course," Bob observed. "Where is this *Green Spin* fellow anyway?"

"I believe he is visiting Dr. No," said Hawk Talk. "Dr. No has been explaining to him that the good times have been going on so long that it is wrong for *Green Spin* to complain that investors are suffering from 'irrational exuberance.' As you might recall, Dr. No's specialty as a Border Collie psychologist is boundary issues. The problem, according to Dr. No, is that investors, after such a long period, won't be able to easily discriminate when markets have started reverting to the mean."

"I can see you have a mean attitude like Sir Real," said Bob. "I'm in shock that the entire central banking system depends on this single octopus creature."

"Yes it would be shocking, if it were true," observed Hawk Talk. "I'm just playing with your mind the way news writers do. Have you ever seen the movie called *The Birds*? There are not too many movies that cater to my hereditary interests, but that is one of them."

"Do you mean the movie directed by the late, great Alfred Hitchcock starring Tippi Hedren, mother of Melanie Griffith, the actress who was twice married to Don Johnson and is now wedded to Antonio Banderas? Yes, I think I may remember it," Bob replied.

"Well then," Hawk Talk continued, "you may also remember that Hitchcock was disgusted with film critics who failed to understand his work: seeing things that didn't exist and failing to see things in his movies that were intended. Economic critics can have the same batting average. Many news spinners give the impression that *Green Spin* is all-powerful and can help the economy swim through the most turbulent of waters even giving the impression that he can prevent a recession. Not only was *Green Spin* unable to prevent the last major economic downturn, he denied we were even in a recession at the time. Shortly after, I recommended he see Dr. Root for his denial problems. I have seen financial writers talk about *Green Spin* being an interest rate czar and the most powerful unelected official in the U.S. government et cetera. If he were so powerful, the public would pay more attention when he says that it is not the job of the Federal Reserve to prop up the stock market, and investors need to understand that the market is far from risk-free. The Federal Reserve is an institution. It doesn't depend on just *Green Spin*, and there are economic forces in the world that are increasingly beyond the influence of the Fed. For example, as inflation comes back interest rates cuts become less effective because the real rate of return is less.

"You would think everything depends on *Green Spin* judging by some of the stories in the media. He has his share of lesser-known critics, though, who think that he has underreacted to what they think is an astronomical rise in stock prices and trade deficit, which can lead to grief later. Around these parts I have heard him called a Dr. Dolittle who talks to the needs of the stock market animals. It's called pandering to Wall Street. *Green Spin* though is the embodiment of the Federal Reserve: a consensus builder among the voting members, and a public *spokescreature*. He just has a vote like everyone else. Hawks and doves have a say in what goes on, too. Every year the makeup of the voting committee changes—sort of like musical chairs. Four votes are changed every year and chosen from among eleven regional Federal bank presidents. The twelfth involves the New York Bank, which is given special treatment. He/she always has a vote."

"That's where Lowen is from," Bob noted. "It must have something to do with the wahtah."

"Seven members from the Federal Reserve Board of Governors also have a vote," Hawk Talk continued. "That's where you get your twelve votes, although presently there are two vacancies among them. Everyone can voice his or her opinion. It's why you see so many feathers all over the floor after some heated discussions at the FOMC. *Dr. Green Spin* waits until the end to size up the mood all around, gives his own speech and then calls for rates to be left alone, increased or decreased. Hawks and doves go at it again, followed by a vote. *Dr. Green Spin* tries to create compromise and a united approach. Neither hawk nor dove wants to rock the monetary policy boat. If there is too much division, the financial markets can get upset when they learn how the vote went at a later date. There is a Fed Hawk/Dove rating scale at www.bondtalk.com. You can see the votes of the hawks and doves as well as learn about bonds.

"Like a typical octopus, *Dr. Green Spin* is basically shy and reserved. He becomes whatever he needs to be depending on the demands of the situation. That is why he signed his name different ways. Octopuses are chameleons of the sea that can quickly alter their color, texture and the shape of their bodies in a matter of seconds. They can squirt ink for a quick getaway and contort themselves to get out of the most difficult situations. In the end, the only thing a central bank has is its credibility in the marketplace. The perception right now is that *Green Spin*, who represents the Federal Reserve, is in control with all the fingers of all his hands on the right buttons. That's why, in spite of the huge problems with the trade deficit, low savings and what some see as an overvalued stock market, the economy keeps roaring along."

"What does the financial community think of him?" asked Bob.

"He has what Dr. No and other psychologists call the 'halo effect,' where just about anything he does is seen as the right thing to do. *Dr. Green Spin* is very aware of this. His speeches make some uncomfortable when he tries to 'talk down' the market with phrases like 'irrational exuberance.'

"*Dr. Green Spin* believes it is extremely important not to tip any of his hands when giving a speech. This helps him maintain his octopus flexibility at all times. All I can tell you is this before I go:

> *Green Spin spins tales about money,*
> *Which flow from his lips like honey.*
>
> *No one knows in advance what he will say,*
> *Or ever understands it the following day.*
>
> *He packs complex language into tight spaces,*
> *And is listened to in all the right places.*
>
> *Newspaper articles praise him daily on all continents,*
> *So he rarely needs to go fishing for compliments.*

Hawk Talk picked up a book called the "Beige Book" with his talons. He said it was a report on economic prospects in the twelve major economic districts of the U.S. and that the Fed had to rely on interpreting secondhand information. And that it was published eight times a year before the Fed meetings to determine short-term interests rates. He then flew away saying he was on the lookout for statistics to help him hawk his opinions on the need for interest rate hikes at the next meeting.

"Shell Games"

When Bob next looked at the moat, he could see the form of a creature over seven feet in length occasionally breaking the surface and heading towards them. It had a shell of some kind made of what appeared to be tough tissue, ridges running the length of its back, and extremely long front flippers.

"What the heck is that?" asked Bob.

"That's the largest living marine turtle in the world," Sir Real said. "It weighs up to fifteen hundred pounds. It's Shelley the Leatherback Turtle, our expert on retirement shells."

"*Kenneth Starling* told me you want to know about trusts," said Shelley.

"Yes I do," Bob responded. "I heard that they can help prevent a nest egg from getting shell-shocked from taxes and lawsuits."

"Yes, they can," Shelley said. "Here it is in a nutshell: A trust is a legal arrangement. It is created when you transfer to someone else, a person or a corporation—which is a legal person, personal property and/or real estate interests to be held for the benefit of him or herself or others. There are all kinds of trusts. They can be created through a Will after you die (a Testamentary Trust) or while you are still alive (a Living Trust). If the person who created the trust, the trustor, retains the right to dissolve the trust, then it is called a Revocable Living Trust. Trusts are used in estate planning for purposes like minimizing taxes, protection from creditors (those who have money claims against you) and peace of mind: like seeing that proceeds from an estate are handled properly and not dissipated or squandered by heirs."

"What's an estate?" asked Bob.

"An estate has to do with everything an individual owns after all debts are deducted," explained Shelley. "However, I am here mainly to talk about your new upstart company, Two Catz Fabricating, and retirement plans."

"It's not an upstart yet," Bob remarked, "only a startup company. So what can you tell me?"

"What I can tell you is that you now have big opportunities to save and protect your money no matter what happens to your questionable little company," said Shelley. "Retirement accounts are trusts. It's not just about a tax sheltered-type savings plan where you can purchase securities and deduct contributions from taxes, but creditor protection. For creditor protection alone, it is important to set up as many retirement accounts as you can."

"Do I buy the securities first and then put them in this 'shell?' asked Bob. "How does it work? I can't imagine it."

"Good question," Shelley commented. "I talked to some teenage students once who asked the same question. When you are used to dealing with such accounts as I am, you can easily forget how mysterious these types of accounts may appear to others. It's really a simple process. You fill out and sign papers for various accounts and then deposit money like you would in a bank account. Once the money is inside the retirement account, you can purchase securities like stocks, bonds and mutual funds including just money market funds. Some accounts like the 401(k) may limit your choice to mutual funds. Think of them as a virtual shell."

"So if I do non 401(k) type accounts," observed Bob, "my choices may be better."

"Yes," Shelley replied. "That's the great advantage of small company plans these days. If I assume correctly, you cannot yet afford nor do you need a 401(k) plan. You can set up a Simple Independent Retirement Account, or Simple IRA, for your small company without any start up or administration costs and currently defer as much as $6,000 per year for each employee. Simple IRAs are good for companies that have fewer than one hundred employees. You can't deduct as much as with a 401(k), which will be over $10,000 by next year, but it doesn't have the costs or complications. The Simple IRA applies to the employer, self-employed individual, sole proprietor, a partnership or a corporation. An employer has only to make a very small contribution to any employee of 1% of pay in two out of five years and 3% in the other three years, which is tax deductible. With employee turnover, the amount can be less."

"Only my wife and I would be employees," Bob remarked.

"Close to ten million people work for themselves in the U.S. So, you are hardly alone. In that case, you might want to consider a Simplified Employee Pension or SEP-IRA where you can contribute up to 15% of your income, not to exceed $24,000 currently. An individual retirement account allows for only a maximum of $2,000 presently. You can set up a SEP right up until the day you file your tax return for the preceding year. It's a snap and can be opened at a bank, brokerage or mutual fund company. With a brokerage house, you are likely to have better choices for IRAs. Like other retirement accounts, there are penalties for withdrawal before the age of 59.5. You can still take advantage of non-company individual retirement plans or IRAs. You can download Internal Revenue Service Publication 590 from the Internet at www.irs.gov or order a copy by calling 1-800-829-3676."

"What if I use my personal and company retirement options to the max?" asked Bob. "Do I have any other choices?"

"Yes you do," Shelley answered. "You can purchase an annuity. It's been mentioned as one of the best tax sheltered options available thanks to the super powerful insurance industry, which created them. Insurance companies are so incredibly rich that they were able to keep up payments through the Great Depression while banks went bust."

"But I don't need any more insurance," Bob noted.

"It's an investment offered through an insurance company," Shelley explained, "but it's not like life insurance. Financial advisers and writers virtually always mention tax shelter benefits of annuities and debate costs and performance relative to mutual funds without talking about legal implications. They usually aren't trained to think in terms of legal benefits. The benefits of annuities may not lie so much in tax or performance results, but legal protection in many states. I like to focus on the ability of annuities to offer creditor protection for huge amounts of money—what I call the O.J strategy, named after the notorious *Jaybird* client of *Kenneth Starling*. The more money you have, the more vulnerable you may be to lawsuits that can take it away in this lawsuit prone country. Annuities are also not subject to the probate process. This means that inheritors can easily gain access to money held in such accounts."

"How does that work?" Bob asked.

"Somehow I knew you were going to ask," replied Shelley. "Annuities are the opposite of life insurance in that money is to be paid out to you the purchaser/investor while you are alive. It is a mixture of investing and insurance and is in the form of a retirement shell to shield you against taxes. A contract is made with the insurance company to start making payments to you immediately once money is deposited or at a future date. The insurance part has to do with guarantees by the insurance company to pay whoever is listed on the policy as beneficiary, if you the investor do not live long enough for a payout. That part is called a 'death benefit.' This benefit, though, doesn't go to you. It's what I call 'live and let die language' meaning the only way someone else can live to collect in this manner is if you die. Who says insurance guys don't have a sense of humor? Often the beneficiary gets at least what you paid into the annuity. The insurance part is also linked to the fact that you can arrange for a guaranteed stream of income, which you can't possibly outlive.

"Like other retirement accounts, you can invest in the stock and bond markets through mutual fund-like 'sub-accounts' without paying current taxes, as long as you reinvest all gains and dividends. You only pay taxes when you take the money out for current use and you pay no penalties if you wait until you are 59.5 years of age. *Unlike government set up retirement accounts or shells, there is no restriction on the amount of money that can be put into an annuity and it doesn't have to be earned income, that is income from work.* Money earned from the sale of a house or stocks is unearned income. You can put gobs of money in if you choose at any time. If you don't want to invest, keep it in money market funds."

"Isn't it true there are other differences, too?" demanded Sir Real.

"Yes, it's true," Shelley responded. "I will mention only a few. Unlike other retirement options, you can't deduct what you deposit in an annuity from your taxes. Annuities may also have a stiff 'surrender' charge, which declines over time to make it costly to change annuities or leave the plan entirely. There is a new competitive trend to reduce and eliminate such surrender charges and offer inducements to sign up. Also, with annuities you aren't forced to start withdrawing money after age 70.5 like other retirement plans. This may be important to you later on for tax purposes if you are still in a high tax bracket; and just because of the fact that you may not like the government being able to tell you to make withdrawals or face penalties. Like the hamburger joints the government gives you a good deal on one hand with the IRAs, then makes their money on the fries, frying you on taxes and penalties later.

"With one type of annuity called a fixed annuity you can arrange it so you can get income for life. The insurance company is betting that if the odds are in their favor, they will make a nice profit before your death. They probably will. Insurance guys are the best gamblers in the universe, never mind the world. However, for those concerned about outliving their money as medical advances continue to unfold at an astounding rate, it may be worthwhile considering. As Nancy Shrew mentioned, financial predictions are nothing more than pie in the sky. Furthermore, it may be a useful way to protect yourself from uncontrollable spending habits that can leave you broke later on. Financial articles typically parrot the same old stuff about tax shelter protection, fund performance, fees, et cetera, while missing the boat on how retirement accounts like annuities may help someone build a legal and psychological moat around their nest eggs to protect them from a financial shellacking. If you ever catch up with Noella, I think she would agree that this type of asset protection should be part of spreading your risks. Otherwise, you may be taking a gamble you are not even aware of. Check out what the SEC has to say about annuities at www.sec.gov/consumer/varannty.htm."

As Shelley finished his sentence, he started sinking back into the moat saying, "Remember, if you can't take it with you, don't go." Within a matter of seconds, he was totally submerged, vanishing from sight.

It's Aleatory My Dear Watson

"Did I hear someone talking about gambling?" asked a squeaky sounding voice from behind Bob. Bob turned Sir Real around with a tug on his velveteen ear to find himself facing a black, adult goat surrounded by legal bloodhounds with little sweaters that read, Department of Justice. The black colored goat had dazzling solid gold teeth, which reflected the sunlight as he spoke and he introduced himself as mega-billionaire *Billy Goats*. Before he could say another word, a legal beagle claiming to represent Billy approached Sir Real and said in a stern, protective voice, "Billy is my best paying client. Stubborn goats are never compliant. In order to keep your interview in line, please sign and initial documents one to ninety-nine. Remember to cross every t and dot every i, or I'll hound you 'til the day you die. Your interview is strictly conditional, conditioned on the fact that all of our conditions must be treated as unconditional."

"You must be able to charge a lot since you are able to talk like that," Bob commented. Bob signed and initialed all ninety-nine documents, which the legal beagle pulled from a steel reinforced briefcase.

Billy now moved closer to Bob and began to speak:

Those hounds say I am not a nice guy,
And what I can't crush, I will buy.

I'm supposed to have a monopoly you see,
Where you have little choice, but to buy from me.

Now I can't dance nor can I sing,
But I can buy just about anything.

Some now say I have a character flaw,
'Cause I'm such a big time gambler wit dah law.

Gambling and investing can be much the same,
Both can bring losses, fortune and fame.

Horse bettors do research and stock investors, too,
I hope that's help and a bit of a clue.

Both can be serious for it's not just a game,
But investing has ownership rights and more than a name.

How many bets on a horse doesn't have any effect,
But demand for a stock determines what price is correct.

Both are about playing the odds,
And hoping for the best from the gods.

"Your sense of rhyme isn't too bad for a rich old goat," Bob remarked.

"Listen to me, Bobo," Billy began. "All investments, no matter how conservative, involve some sort of gamble. For example, conservative-sounding insurance is a gamble. This is because you are paying premiums, never knowing for sure whether you will ever experience a loss. The insurance company gambles they won't have to pay you or they'll have to pay as little as possible while you as a consumer gamble that they will pay in the event of a loss, which may or may not ever occur. Insurance guys are probably the best scorekeepers and probability experts in the world and even they make mistakes. It's aleatory, a gamble, from the Latin dice game. I love to play games. My enemies would be the first ones to agree. I have to go and see if *Kenneth Starling* will help me with my legal case. I've heard rumors that he plans to work for my enemies. I thought I could win by now because I have so many billions. I forgot that the government has more—and it's even in the trillions."

To Jail A Mockingbird

Billy left with the legal hounds in hot pursuit nipping at his legs while Sir Real continued walking. Soon they came to another tropical tree filled with leaves made of money near the moat. The sound of fluttering wings could be heard. A lone gray and white mockingbird could be seen circling high above the tree. The bird then changed directions and flew towards Sir Real. As it came within a distance of twenty feet, Bob could see that it had black stripes painted on it.

The bird cried out, "I'm glad you are learning about tax shelters, little investor man. Personally, I don't need them. It's only the little people like you, Bob, who have to pay taxes." After laughing for several seconds in a mocking manner, it flew back into the tree.

"Who was that nasty bird?" Bob asked Sir Real. "Why did she say that?"

"Her name is *Leona Hotelsme* or something like that," Sir Real said. "Don't pay any attention," piped a disembodied voice from the tree. "She is a former jailbird, a wealthy socialite from New York who foolishly bragged about not paying taxes to a member of her staff. The IRS got the last laugh and flew her to jail. I believe it was Abe Lincoln who said that what gets a skunk caught is its insistence on giving itself publicity. You can get your own laughs, too, in a legal way and help your portfolio fly away from taxation." As Sir Real came closer to the tree with money growing on it, Bob could see that the creature talking to him was now busy eating the tree leaves with its long hook-like claws while hanging upside down from a branch. It was wearing a T-shirt with printing that read: "What Did I Forget To Do Today? G . . . G . . . Get A Job."

"That's Slobodan, a financial sloth," said Sir Real. "He has an Eastern European name, but hails from Central America, I understand."

"There is a way even little people like you, Bob, don't have to pay taxes legally. Before investing, you should always try to find the best tax structure to shelter your investments from taxes. It can make an incredible difference in the results. Too many times investors are first chasing after a hot investment, when they should be first chasing after a hot tax structure. The structure I'm talking about is quite new and may help you accumulate a lot of money tax-free whether you start when you are young or old. It is such a no-brainer and so easy to do that even a financial sloth like me takes advantage of it. It's a way to maximize your returns and make lots of money without lifting a finger."

"I'm excited," Bob exclaimed "How does this work?"

"Not so fast," said Slobodan. "Sloths like to take their time. Let me first give you a lazy, easy to understand example of what happens when you are taxed versus tax protected: If you average 10% return on a taxable investment, but are taxed at say a rate of 30% on your earnings, then you would be left with a 7% net rate of return after deducting 30% of the 10% return. If it is tax free or tax deferred, then on a 10% rate of return you would be left with 10% net rate."

"So?" asked Bob.

"A 7% rate of return for $100,000 doubles the amount invested to $200,000 in ten years," Slobodan explained further. "However, at a 10% rate of return, $100,000 grows to $200,000 in only seven years. At fifty years of age, $100,000 at 7% rate of return would be worth $428,000 by the time you are seventy-one years old, but it would be worth $800,000 if you were getting a 10% rate of return. According to the rule of seventy-two, you divide 7% into seventy-two to arrive at ten years for doubling. Divide seventy-two by 10% and you arrive at seven years. So the taxable investment at 7% starting at age fifty with $100,000 leads to $200,000 at age sixty, and leads to $400,000 at age seventy, and $428,000 at age seventy-one. On the other hand, a tax-free or tax-deferred investment at 10% starting at age fifty with $100,000 leads to $200,000 at age fifty-seven, $400,000 at age sixty-four and $800,000 difference in results just by using a good tax shelter. Why work for all that extra money when it's so easy to be a financial sloth?"

"It does pay to be a sloth," Bob remarked. "How is it possible to arrive at such big numbers though?"

"It's about getting interest upon interest, if that's of any interest. It's about the miracle of compounding your money, which even Einstein reportedly claimed to be one of the great wonders of the world. In a typical tax sheltered account, you only have to pay taxes on profits when you withdraw money at retirement age. In the account I'm talking about, the Roth, you don't pay any taxes even if you're a sloth. It also has other benefits in estate planning."

"How much can you deposit into this account?" asked Bob.

"I have to check my notes. Normally I just relax all day and then rest afterwards." Slobodan said, lazily sifting through his notes.

Sir Real sniffed the air as he always did when he felt the presence of another creature. "I hear someone singing. It's out of your hearing range, Bob," Sir Real said. "It's another one of those songs about *Green Spin* spun with an accent."

"What are the words you are hearing?" Bob asked.

Sir Real answered: "It sounds like 'Oh my dear Dr. Brain. Vohn't you let me explain? I'm in great financial pain. Long term saving seemed like soch a strain. Please prescribe a kvick shtockmarket gain.'"

"Who sings like that? It can't be Elvis, can it?" asked Bob.

"That's Klaws von Roth Wilier," Sir Real answered, "a wily German Rottweiler specially trained to make investors aware of the potential of the Roth IRA which Slobodan was going to speak to you about. Investors have been missing some important points. What the Rottweiler has to say is quite germane."

"Nein, nein, you lazy sloth shwein," barked a tall, black, vigorous, shorthaired male dog, which suddenly leapt from behind the tree scaring the wits out of Slobodan and Bob. Saliva steadily dripped from the corners of its mouth forming little effervescent pools at its feet. "It's a guht thing I have nerves of shteel to put up with that barbarian sloth. That schvein never understands the importance of prehparation," complained Roth Wilier. "You can use the Roth only if you follow zah rules, Herr Cahtz, vitch I vill gladly explain now, yes. It is for your own good, of course. That's vaht vee always say, even vehn it isn't."

"Please switch to normal sounding English," Sir Real requested of Roth Wilier. "You already sound more difficult to follow than Dr. Root."

"Mit pleasure, Sir Real, although it vohnt be easy," Roth Wilier said with a sneer. "The Roth individual retirement account, or IRA, allows for tax free savings. If you are able to deposit $2,000 a year in your twenties into this account and get a fair rate of return, the compounding effect is astounding—and all the money you withdraw later on is totally tax free. In the not too distant future, you probably will be able to deposit much more. The compounding effect is so great if you start off early enough, that even if you stop contributing after a short time you can have more in your account than someone who regularly contributes every year later on. Even Herr Einstein who couldn't get his socks put on right finally discovered that time is really about money."

"How about an example?" Bob requested.

"Okay, Herr Cahtz," Roth Wilier assented. "The example will deal with only $2,000 since that is the maximum that can currently be deposited and a healthy average rate of return of 12% per year. In the last sixty years, the shtock market has averaged around 10% growth per year. So this is not an unreasonable target, yes. Of course, if you learn more about stocks in your financial journey from Cecelia, then maybe you can buy the next *Macroschlock* and make so much more than just 12% on average."

"But it's *Microsock*, Herr Roth Wilier, isn't that true?" asked Bob.

"Silence you fool," insisted Roth Wilier. "Listen to me, Mr. Catzscan. Haven't you ever heard of German engineering? Vehr I come from, products that crash all the time and need frequent upgrades are big time schlock. You are just too forgiving in America. Now pay attention mein little friend. Say you open an account and deposit $2,000 at age twenty-two, then at ages twenty-three through twenty-seven, you deposit the same $2,000. In the meantime, your money has been making on average 12% rate of return. At the age of twenty-eight, you decide not to put any more money in ever again. All you have deposited is $12,000. Your money continues to make on average 12% interest per year until you return to close out the account at age sixty-five. Now schvein, how much money would be waiting for you?

"At least $200,000," Bob guessed.

"Nein, schvein!" Roth Wilier blasted. "Guess again. Oon don't fail. Don't you realize how easy it would be for me to have you shot? All it vood take is vuhn kvick bark and your financial career vood be kaput. In zah financial world, companies and careers live and die everyday by zah numbers. Everything is about producing zah right numbers at zah right time at zah right place, even if it's for zah wrong reasons."

"Yahvohl Hairy Rottweiler. Give me another chance," Bob pleaded. "At least $150,000."

"Nein, Nein, now you dropped zah numbers like a Herr Klutz," said Roth Wilier in disgust. "It vood be $1,348,440. So you can imagine how much better off you would be by continuing to deposit in the account year after year instead of shtopping and shtoopping."

"I'm surprised you left out the word shopping," said Bob. "Well, what if I decided to wait until age twenty-eight depositing year after year?"

"That vood be very unwise," said Roth Wilier, "but better than nothing. You really shouldn't disappoint me. If you deposited $2,000 a year from the age of twenty-eight onward until age sixty-five, still achieving an average 12% a year growth, you would have $1,363,780—not much more than if you had just started at age twenty-two and made your last deposit at age twenty-seven in this hypothetical. If only $2,000 was put into such an account at age fifteen with an average 10% rate of return, the amount would be $234,782 tax-free dollars at age sixty-five. There is no age restriction, so a child earning money mowing the lawn can qualify. Money has to come from earned income. The maximum contribution is currently $2,000 per investor. If earnings are less than $2,000, then the maximum is 100% of income. Slobodan likes to talk about the Roth, but has never held a job. Contributions are always available to withdraw without penalty or tax. Oon remember the tax filing due date is the contribution deadline. There are no extensions. Do I need to make myself any clearer, Herr Cahtz?"

"Nein," exclaimed Bob, "you Roth Wilier schwein. I can see there is a lot to be said about just average type performance if time is on your side."

"Time lowers your need to take risks for high return," explained Roth Wilier. "Time also provides an investor the ability to take greater risks and engage in more aggressive investing. You have more opportunity for recovery from any mistakes that may be made. Younger people shouldn't wait until later to set up these kinds of accounts and invest. Even if you just purchase money market funds, you can be way ahead over time. It's almost dumbkoff proof. You can withdraw your contribution anytime, tax-free. However, after sixty days you can't put the money back. It's especially attractive if you think you will be in a high tax bracket during retirement.

"Again, since this is a retirement account, it will most likely provide protection against creditor attack. For example, one day you could find out that you don't have enough insurance to cover an accident or medical bills and be wiped out except for your retirement accounts. Bank savings accounts don't have that protection, in addition to exposing any meager interest made to taxes."

"I heard earlier on that you know something about a Super Roth," said Bob.

"It has been called that by some in the insurance industry," said Roth Wilier. "It's not really a Roth, but a way that may provide tax-free withdrawals in the future for those who don't qualify for the Roth because they make too much money. It involves overpaying on a life insurance policy that has investment features, which allow you to make profits from zah mahrkets. You then withdraw money as loans in the future, which are never paid back. Loans aren't taxable."

"That's a little too exotic for me," Bob observed, "and I'm not in a super high income category."

"I know, Herr Cahtz," said Roth Wilier. "Vee know everything from vaht you do on zah Internet oon other sources. It's not a vuhn vay street. Trust me. Big brother is much more about big corporations than the government mein kindergarten size shtoodent."

"Yah, sure," said Bob.

"Don't be shmart wit me, yah?" exclaimed Roth Wilier. "Now listen. Presently you can qualify for the Roth account if on your tax return your adjusted gross income doesn't exceed $110,000 if you are single and $160,000 for married couples with a joint return. A couple can contribute up to $4,000 per year. If your income is above that amount, then your ability to contribute is phased out as your income level goes higher. Unlike a traditional IRA, you can't make any deductions from your taxes for contributions. The Roth is about paying your taxes going in rather than going out. However, anything you earn may qualify you to withdraw tax-free later on provided you follow zah rules. I love rules and order even when zay don't make sense and are counterproductive."

"Please stick to the subject," Sir Real demanded. "That's my rule."

"I forgot myself," said Roth Wilier. "If you have a Roth account for five years, all earnings can be withdrawn tax free if you are at least 59.5 years of age, are disabled, or need up to $10,000 in order to purchase your first home. Unlike a traditional IRA, you can leave your money in as long as you want. A traditional IRA requires mandatory withdrawals at age 70.5 or you face penalties."

"Sir Real mentioned that the Roth had value in estate planning," said Bob. "Isn't that true?"

"Older people often are under the mistaken impression that the Roth is mainly for younger people," explained Roth Wilier. "Those older people who have traditional IRAs with money that they don't need and plan to leave to heirs might be far better off transferring assets to a Roth if they are eligible—that is, if they have an adjusted gross income less than $100,000. This has immediate tax implications."

"What does that mean?" Bob asked.

"It means that you get a tax haircut Herr Cahtz, but zah tax consekvences can be spread out over time by a gradual transfer over a number of years," answered Roth Wilier. "It doesn't have to be all or nothing; and it's best to pay taxes from monies outside the IRA. If you have to dip into it, then it reduces what you can pass on to heirs tax-free. You don't vahnt to damage or kill zah golden goose. Always keep in mind zah heirs Herr Cahtz.

"Remember with a non-Roth IRA, you have to start withdrawing money at age 70.5 whether you want to or not. This forces people to withdraw money, which becomes subject to taxation and lowers the value of the IRA 'nest egg.' Inheritors also have to pay income taxes on what is withdrawn. Between forced withdrawals and taxes, much more may be given up over time than if a conversion had been made to a Roth."

"Why does the government do this?" asked Bob.

"Vee have our reasons," said Roth Wilier. "The government allows conversions because it helps create the present phoney baloney budget surplus by increasing the amount of taxes collected now. The government is selling tax exemptions to the wealthy to collect taxes in the present. It's a gravy train for many fat cats. It hasn't been done this way in a very long time."

"Since when?" Bob wished to know.

"Since the time of Marie Antoinette—just before the French Revolution," said Roth Wilier. "In many respects, it's a half baked idea. Haven't you noticed the name of the company who owns zah bakery, schvein? Robbing zah fuhture to support zah prehsent is an old nutsy trick. All it rekvires is the use of politically right sounding language like 'wealth oon job creation.'"

"Gee," exclaimed Bob. "I thought it was just a cool historical name linked to Marie Antoinette's liking for cake. I had no idea it was some kind of financial history lesson."

"Do you think vee have nothing better to do than come up with names for your amusement, Mr. Cool Catz? You have only so much dreamtime. Vee vaste nothing here. It vahs planned from zah very beginning," growled Roth Wilier impatiently. "Besides, in zah financial world, vee make it our business to know everything yet vee know nothing, so vee are always up to something."

"You sound like one of those active mutual fund managers that can't beat a passive index fund, which merely apes the market, or one of those economic fortune tellers Nancy Shrew talked about."

"Be kviet you fool. Zay hear everything you say," Roth Wilier shouted.

"Tell me then how is this tremendous loss of taxing power going to impact another generation," asked Bob anxiously. "Where is this missing dough going to come from? How can there be enough bread to go around for necessary public projects?"

"You of all people, Herr Cahtz, should know by now that my only loyalty is to the Roth savings plan and mein beloved fuhture," Roth Wilier answered stiffly. "As Marie Antoinette wisely remarked about zah mahsses, 'If there isn't enough bread, let them eat cake.' Zis is all part of a master world plan to create a super Hex generation—cursed for years to come. Anyway, it is time for me to leave. I have my ohrders, yes. Vee really must do lunch, yah?" Roth Wilier then walked back behind the tropical tree with leaves made of money and was no longer seen. Sir Real continued the journey around the moat.

Phantom of the Options

Bob now heard a loud barking sound. It didn't really sound like a dog; and it wasn't. Instead, a seal, whose lips were covered with thick red wax, jumped out of the moat and introduced herself as Cecelia, the corporate seal. She was a gray and beige elephant seal who moved by pulling with her flippers then heaving her body forward.

"Hello Bob," barked Cecelia. "I have just been bottom fishing and checking out some stocks that have gone underwater lately to see if there is anything worth picking up. I picked up some oil and natural gas stocks since energy prices are so low. You wouldn't believe all these options I also discovered underwater. I'm sorry I'm late for your educational instruction."

"I heard about options when Sir Real talked about the fat cats," said Bob. "I don't understand, though, what 'underwater option' means."

"It means that failure is always an option," explained Cecelia. "This isn't like the taut space movie *Apollo Thirteen* where the actor, Ed Harris, keeps repeating 'failure is not an option.' Here there is abundant space for failure. Something like nine out of ten new companies using options to attract and keep employees disappear in the murky waters below. The reason there are so many options around the bakery is because of the current widespread belief that options are an easy way for employees to have their cake and eat it too. Employees are supposed to have an easy way to make lots of extra money while their employers pay the lowest wages possible— maximizing their profits. However, this kind of cake can turn out to have been made with only sugar-coated promises having no financial value.

"An option is a derivative. Its value is derived from the worth of another security. A stock option's value depends on a stock rising in price so that you can buy it later at a fixed low price guaranteed in the option. It's not only for fat cats, but also a way of attracting talented employees and rewarding them. It's also a way of paying the lowest wages possible. If the stock falls in price below the fixed number of the option, it doesn't pay to exercise the option. The options at that point are worth zero, and are therefore 'underwater.' Even if the company stays in business, it can be demotivating to employees. Options are often mentioned in terms of wealth creation. However, there is plenty of wealth destruction. They don't have a waterproof seal. Honk, honk," barked Cecelia.

"But I've seen pictures in the paper about employees successfully cashing in on options and retiring," noted Bob.

"It's true," remarked Cecelia. "However, there is a downside option to options. Options have become a popular way for companies starting out and/or growing very fast to attract personnel as 'golden handcuffs.' There are opportunities for making a lot of money, but very few employees percentage-wise do. You hear frequently these days about people cashing in their options. What you don't hear as often is about all the losers whose numbers will increase if the market heads downward. Golden handcuffs can become silver handcuffs then brass and iron handcuffs. The majority of start up companies fail, so the options become worthless. Options are about risk. The stock can go down in value, also making it worthless to exercise the option. If you have the option of buying a stock at $100, which is now $80, there is no advantage. Unless new more attractive options at lower prices are created to substitute or options are repriced, your only real option might be to get another job.

"Stock options are often regarded like money, except it isn't money. By the way, there are quite a few companies these days that are not as profitable as they appear to be because stock options are not mentioned as an expense. They can appear as a mere footnote in an annual report. Without the stock options, employee salaries would be much higher and the company earnings, which I'm going to be talking about soon, would be much weaker."

"What if the stock goes up in price enough that it is worthwhile to exercise the option?" asked Bob.

"Even if the stock goes up in value and options can be exercised," explained Cecelia, "they can dilute the value of existing shares floating in the market place. The more shares that are created to pay these employees, the more there is to divide up and the smaller the piece of the earnings pie. You can end up with crumbs. This is one reason companies are buying back so many of their own shares from the market place these days—to keep the earnings looking good. The shares have to come from somewhere. It's not a great way to be spending corporate money.

"This also allows a company to influence its share price by buying back its own shares, often these days at high prices. Even worse situations occur when huge amounts of money are borrowed to buy these shares. It tends to weaken the credit rating of the company and hurt those who own corporate bonds from that company. It's giving with one hand and taking with the other. In a long market decline, this kind of corporate policy can lead to a further erosion in share value."

Seal of Approval

"So, tell me about your line of work, Miss Cecelia," Bob requested.

"My specialty is placing a corporate seal on new stock and bond certificates," said Cecelia, "although these days most buyers don't receive certificates anymore unless they make a special request and sometimes pay extra. When your securities are registered in your name and you have actual possession of certificates, it's called direct ownership.

"When you own the certificates, but they are with an institution-like a brokerage house, then it is called ownership in street name. In this situation, you receive a statement, often monthly, from your financial institution listing what you own. It just involves electronic record keeping—what is known as book entry. How boring. Honk! Certificates can be beautiful like works of art. They have all kinds of colors and pretty pictures on special paper to make it difficult to forge, in addition to registration numbers. However, ownership in street name does have some advantages. If you are selling the securities, there is no need for physical delivery, and payment is normally made within three business days after the sale. It cuts down on the risk of theft or loss, you can track gains and losses daily; and borrow on them."

"I have some old certificates that I inherited," said Bob, "and no one so far has been able to tell me if they are worth anything."

"The certificate may or may not have any monetary value," explained Cecelia. "However, it can be worth a lot as a collector's item. There are those who collect stock certificates for their history and beauty. You can check with a stockbroker and/or a search company. Even though the company may be nonexistent, the investment may still be good. Companies are acquired, go through mergers and go through name changes. You can check with the International Bond and Share Society. They have a Web site: www.scripophily.org. You can also check on the following Web site: www.stocksearchintl.com."

"Although I haven't met Black in the Box yet," said Bob, "I have a feeling I should know more about stocks rather than just relying on mutual funds. Can you tell me more?"

"A stock is a share of ownership in a corporation's assets," explained Cecelia. "Figuratively, it is a piece of the corporate pie, but it is more than that. It is also a claim on future earnings or profit, what the company is left with after paying its bills. Companies these days are not necessarily valued on what they own, but what they are expected to earn and what investors think those earnings are worth. Ultimately, stock prices boil down to how much investors are willing to pay for them—supply and demand. It's not only about hard numbers in the present, but also confidence in the future of that company to consistently grow their earnings and make more and more profits."

"It seems like there is great confidence these days," Bob remarked.

"Thanks to our Goldilocks economy," explained Cecelia, "with high productivity figures due in part to technology advances combined with a low inflation and a low interest rate climate, projected earnings growth has been excellent. It's been investment nirvana. High earnings possibilities make stocks worth more and lower the risk perception to investors who find equities more attractive than fixed income investments like bonds. Earnings are the lifeblood of the stock market. So investors look closely at earnings per share."

"How is that determined?" asked Bob.

"Earnings per share are determined by dividing the company profit for each quarterly period by the number of shares outstanding or floated in the marketplace," explained Cecelia. "A million dollars profit divided by a million shares gives you a dollar per share earnings.

"The earnings from the last four quarters are called 'trailing earnings' and are used to determine the P/E or price earnings ratio: the price investors are willing to pay for every dollar of a company's earnings. A company's stock divided by its twelve-month earnings per share provides the price-to-earnings ratio or P/E. Basically P/E is about what investors are willing to pay for a company's earning power. Comparing a company's price to its earnings power or P/E is the most common way to value a company because the key to stock ownership involves the owner's share of the company's profit stream. A $100 per share stock with $10 in earnings per share during the prior twelve months gives a P/E of one hundred/ten or ten. You can compare the ratio to other companies in the rest of the industry, as well as to the market in general, and historical levels."

"This example mentions price divided by earnings," Bob commented. "How is the price determined?"

"It's about confidence times expected earnings, even though all you have to go by is present or 'trailing earnings,'" said Cecelia. "The P/E is only useful as a general measurement. On a daily level, stocks trade on expected or forward earnings not on the P/Es listed in the paper. That measure of confidence I just talked about becomes some number multiplied by the expected earnings to give you a price for each share of stock. The number can be anything based on what investors think it should be. It's about confidence in future profits. If a company is expected to earn a dollar in profits, for example, the price can be any number times that dollar of expected earnings. If the multiple is twenty, then the stock is priced at $20. If the multiple is 100, then the same stock can be priced at $100. It depends on how investors view the potential for future profits."

"So in order for share prices to continue to rise either earnings continue to go up and/or the measure of confidence investors have in those earnings that they are ready to pay for goes up?" Bob summarized.

"That's right," exclaimed Cecelia, honking and clapping her fins. "And never in the history of the market has confidence ever been so high in general, especially for technology related companies."

"Since expectations change," Bob asked, "doesn't that mean that the multiple for a stock or the market in general can't keep expanding indefinitely?"

"Yes," said Cecelia, honking mournfully. "Profit expectations are the strongest force driving up the prices of stocks these days. In the past, assets or what the company owned, were given much more importance. Although confidence about future profits has reached undreamed of highs lately, the reverse is also quite possible. In recent years, the multiple for stocks in general has expanded greatly because of great expectations due to many factors like the peace dividend from the end of the cold war, the entry of millions of investors through company sponsored retirement plans, declining inflation from a previous high or disinflation and low interest rates. In order for these high values to continue, the pace of gains will have to continue. That remains to be seen."

"What do you mean?" Bob asked.

"Well," Cecelia began, "some think the multiple for the market as a whole has peaked and that further growth in stock prices are going to have to rely more and more on earnings. Investors, according to this line of thinking, are going to get more and more demanding in the future, as market conditions become more demanding, especially if interest rates start to rise. Earnings, though, have been historically quite high compared to the amount invested to achieve them. They have their limits, too. The question in general becomes how long will someone be willing to pay say seventy times future earnings on a stock that can only grow maybe 15% to 20% per year in the future? Although I don't have some of the musical talents of many of the characters around here, I like to think of stock prices expanding and contracting like an accordion. Confidence and earnings often operate in sync and can be thought of as handles of an accordion. As earnings expand or contract so may confidence, inflating or deflating the price."

"Thank you Cecelia. Now I feel I have a grip on the subject. When do you find out about earnings?" asked Bob.

"At the end of each quarter—at the end of March, June, September and December," Cecelia responded, "companies that have sold shares to the public announce their earnings. In the last two weeks of each quarter, companies often let investors know in advance, with warnings about expected disappointing profits and revenue shortfalls (translation: poor sales). For information about earnings, such as the change from year to year, expected growth over a five year period, earnings momentum, whispers about earnings, et cetera, you can check out some Web sites such as www.bloomberg.com, www.earningswhispers.com, zack.com, www.thomson invest.net/FirstCall, www.morningstar.com, www.marketguide.com and www.multex.com."

"Why let investors know in advance?" asked Bob. "They are going to find out anyway."

"It's been said to be a trust thing," Cecelia explained. "Investors surprised by negative news can get very upset, affecting the credibility of the company for future investing, hurting stock value even more. Maybe more importantly it's about trying to protect the company from lawsuits. Investors like positive surprises, so there is this game that goes on with stock market analysts who try and assess what earnings will be for a company.

"Often these analysts, who have relationships with the companies they are analyzing through their employers, the investment banks, give low ball estimates of coming earnings. This way the company can beat the earnings and have a 'surprise' for investors. It's about manipulating expectations. You've heard of hole-in-the-wall Chinese restaurants. Well this is about brokerage analysts cooking up numbers for the hole in the Chinese Wall that is supposed to divide banks from brokerage houses. This way analysts can help companies look good or not so bad thereby helping their employers maintain positive relationships with those they do business with. That's why so-called 'whisper numbers' about what the real earnings are likely to be have become quite popular especially thanks to the Internet. One way to look at the P/E is to consider whether it is equal to its long-term earnings growth. If a stock is trading at say a P/E of 20, with expected earnings growth every year of 20%; then, as a general rule, it may be fairly valued. Dividing the P/E by the projected earnings growth, 20/20, gives a ratio of 1. A ratio of 1 suggests to some professionals a fairly valued stock. A ratio lower than 1 suggests an undervalued stock. A ratio higher than 1 suggests the price is high. Faster earnings growth tends to be rewarded by higher P/Es.

"When looking at earnings surprises, keep in mind the cockroach theory: usually when you find one cockroach, there are more around. Good and bad earning surprises tend to be followed by more of the same. There are other valuation methods, of course, such as how the stock price compares to sales, the price/sales ratio, where again the lower the ratio the better. You're not the only one having a financial dream. The great financial dream is to find a sure fire method, but there isn't one. Investors are also living in a dream world if they think that you can just rely on P/E because earnings are so often manipulated these days. It's getting more and more difficult to figure out what a company really earns.

"Can you explain some of these other ratios in more detail," Bob requested.

"With the price/sales ratio, you take the annual sales of the company and divide it into the stock price," explained Cecelia. "It is sometimes used for companies, which have little profit to show in the beginning or maybe none at all. If sales are high per share, but the stock price is low resulting in a low ratio, it can help to target businesses that may be doing well with earnings only temporarily weak."

"What else?" Bob wished to know.

"Well, the price/cash ratio may be of interest," Cecelia offered. "The cash ratio refers to cash flowing through the company or what is known as earnings before interest, taxes and write-downs for tax purposes. It can give you an idea of whether companies with large write offs are making money compared to others in the industry. Media type companies, for example, have big deductions.

"Price/book value is another. Book value has to do with what the company would be worth if it was sold off or liquidated. It's about a company's assets minus its liabilities per share divided into the price. You want to look for a low figure. The ratio can help with determining whether a company is undervalued compared to its peers, especially when dealing with asset-wealthy companies. Buyout companies using borrowed money from institutions like pension funds and wealthy individuals look at such numbers to see whether a company is worth buying and breaking up.

"The P/E deals with past earnings. If you divide it by the expected rate of earnings growth in the future, you have what is called a PEG ratio. If the ratio is higher than two, it may mean an overvalued stock while below 1.5 might mean a worthwhile buy.

"Remember, buying and selling a stock or any other security is basically about two opinions: one says sell and the other says buy. The difference between a stock's buying and selling price at any moment, by the way, is called 'the spread.'"

"Isn't it true," Sir Real broke in contentiously, "that you left out an explanation of diluted earnings and made the process sound simpler than it really is?"

"Yes, it is true, Sir Real," Cecelia responded. "I thought I could get away with a dummy type explanation." Cecelia honked to signal that she was irritated. "When earnings reports come in, accounting rules require that every possibility be included, not just current shares in the market place. So stock options and convertible securities, which you have learned about, are also factored in. This dilutes the value of the shares, but is a more conservative reflection of real value. It is reported as earnings per diluted share. So you should look out for that earnings report too. Can I go now? Honk!"

"Not yet," said Bob. "If earnings are so important, how come there are companies worth billions in the Internet business like *Amazin'StockPrice.Com* that have never made a dime or have meager earnings at best with huge losses?"

Drop Red Gorgeous

> *Sometimes I have believed as many as six impossible*
> *things before breakfast.*
> —The Queen in *Alice in Wonderland*

Cecelia didn't answer. She just gave a stock certificate a red hot, waxy kiss before jumping back into the moat. Within a few minutes, she emerged with red lips and her entire fur was colored dark red. She wore a 1920s fuchsia colored sequined flapper dress and had a necklace watch with two different settings around her neck. Cecelia kept singing and honking to herself "It's my party and I'll buy what I want to. Buy what I want to."

"Tell me what I want to hear, Bob," said Cecelia in a lilting, honking tone. "Now, how do I look? Don't I look simply irresistible? Wouldn't you say my valuation is sky high?"

"Dahling," Bob exclaimed, "you look simply mahvelous. Your red color is fabulous. Absolutely fabulous. And that dress is just awesome. Is's totally hot. It's so *you*. Is it okay to stop now?"

"Of course I look good," said Cecelia, delighted. "My clothing, I will have you know, was custom-made by the well known Wall Street couturier 'Stop Making Sense,' a subsidiary of the Emperor Has No Clothes corporation. It was made from old-fashioned rip-off material, but given a new fashion look."

"Aren't those New York fashion houses expensive?"

"Yes, but I have to look good. My business now is to dress up company financials and attract naive investors. I now represent many high tech stocks that are priced for perfection with great expectations. Unfortunately, that also means there is no room for error in disappointing the growth expectations of investors. Yes Bob, I would stop with the compliments. It's important to know when to quit while you are ahead in the investing world—take big gains and small losses.

"Before, I talked about companies with established earnings and how earnings were the lifeblood of a company. Now I am here to talk about companies swimming in red ink and bleeding oodles of investor money or simply with stocks that are greatly outperforming the earnings worth of the business. Many of them are called glamour companies and are involved in the retail Internet sector. I call them 'concept' stocks—stocks with high hopes. These companies don't have to worry about real earnings because they don't have any. What counts are virtual earnings. We are supposed to be in a new economy where old ideas of value like present earnings don't really matter. Where I come from, only jellyfish are supposed to be able to float through life with no brains, no heart, no spine, no bones and no profits. Do you remember learning about snake oil salesmen in 'boiler rooms' heating up stock prices of companies that have nothing going for them—so called shell companies? Brokerage companies can use similar techniques like snake charming expert opinions about companies they do business with to pump up stock prices. Brokerage companies like *Morrall Stench* like to advertise how competent and worldly they are. Meanwhile, they have allowed their analysts to own shares in companies they are evaluating for the public. It makes you wonder if it's just the advertising that's really savvy."

"It sounds surreal," Bob remarked. "By the way, that dress looks so big on you I'm afraid to say. It's like those once stylish balloon dresses of long ago."

"This dress style is called 'overcapacity' in today's fashion world," Cecelia replied. "I'm sure you heard the term before. It makes me feel giddy and happens when you have lots of money funding many bad ideas creating all kinds of excess product and services. It's about the mindless pursuit of fast profits in the short term with inflated expectations. It's about large-scale misallocation of resources. Stretching the facts to accommodate unrealistic beliefs about future growth never goes out of fashion. I've been assured that the dress will shrink down in the long term to size once investment money and spending start to dry up as the cost of borrowing goes up. My big asset look will be gone, but I'll probably be sitting on painful piles of debt. For example, the telecommunications industry, cheered on by the commission happy capitalist pigs, have convinced investors to gorge on hundreds of billions of dollars worth of debt and equity to fund the new fiber-optic network highway. The investors are all wired up about the wired world but haven't yet connected with the fact that way over 90% of this new capacity is unneeded at present because the high tech network can't ring up the needed sales. So far these highly touted companies have mostly reached out and touched investor wallets. It's kind of funny wouldn't you say that those who preached about the Information Age didn't have this information before they went on a spending spree? Bullish forecasts are not the same as knowledge. This is what I learned from the Queen's dogs at Doggone It College."

"Do you really think you will go from high to dry?"

"Yes. Earnings are about real goods and services production. Instead of having a price based on a multiple of earnings, we have a price based on a multiple of fantasy—a P/F instead of a P/E. Investors are also buying in droves because they expect prices to rise. When the multiple or financial claims against future earnings are so high as to be disconnected from reality, then you may have the makings of what is called a financial bubble. Valuation is not necessarily the same as real value."

"So you can see a bubble taking place," said Bob.

"No," Cecelia responded. "No one really knows an investment bubble exists until after it bursts, as it did in Japan. The nature of bubbles is to get bigger and last longer than anyone expected. Eventually, even the skeptics give up. That's when you are least protected. All I can tell you for sure is that bubbles have always been a feature of capitalism. The public has been taught that *Dr. Green Spin* is so powerful that interest rate cuts will automatically give rise to a vibrant economy. It's part of that 'don't miss the boat' sales propaganda which encouraged investment in drop red gorgeous companies. Mountains of debt, personal and corporate, as well as excess production (How many more computers do you really need in your house?) may make a return to 'normality' much more difficult than is fashionably assumed. Any real return to 'normality' will have to take into account the law of the average, not the kind of normality the sales industry talks about."

"But aren't there logical explanations about drop red gorgeous companies?" Bob wished to know. "Isn't greater risk about greater possibility of reward?"

Eyes Wide Shut

"Sometimes risk is the only reward. You are talking about another Wall Street myth. Many of these money-losing companies are considered red 'hot' stocks because of their popularity. They are also red hot because they are burning through cash invested in them at a phenomenal rate. They have to keep investor confidence high to keep stock prices up. That's why you see so many press releases from them: we are doing this and we are doing that even though we still aren't making any money. It's for a good reason.

Sharp loss of confidence will stop cash coming in and employees will bolt to other companies. A risky investment can just be no different than buying air. In the meantime, they are like the bunny in that battery commercial going on and on long after critics thought they would have died."

"What may happen over time?" asked Bob.

"Benjamin Graham," replied Cecelia, "whom some have called the father of value investing, said that in the short run, the stock market is a voting machine. In the long run, it becomes a weighing machine. Investors in the Internet section of the economy have put up over $1 trillion for these companies so far. Some of them will do quite well. The great majority probably won't stay afloat. It has been estimated that at least three-quarters of these companies will be non-existent in the next five years. That's probably a very conservative estimate. Some of the sky-high share prices for companies with non-existent earnings reflect the astronomical growth rate of these companies as well as the fact that relatively small numbers of shares are released to great demand pushing up the prices.

"However, growth doesn't necessarily translate into profits, or profits that can justify the values placed on those companies. At some point, investors will tire of hearing about future possibilities and want to see actual hard earnings. They will start seeing red and screaming 'show me the money, show me the money.' At this time, there is the assumption that, since so many others are doing the same thing, it must be okay. There is a feeling of safety in numbers, until the loss numbers of the investments become overwhelmingly obvious. It's the same kind of assumption that was made throughout Asia before the lenders, borrowers and investors were badly burned.

"It will be interesting to see if this mass of investors who buy indiscriminately in these drop red companies will sell indiscriminately when times get tough. Past performance doesn't guarantee results. However, past process does. Companies have to come up with good earnings to plow back into research, employees, acquiring products, et cetera to grow the company. In the meantime, the party goes on and demonstrates the power of emotion in valuing stocks. It has been said that the central bank likes to take away the punchbowl just before the party gets going by raising the cost of borrowing. However, this party has been going on for many years and a large segment of investors at this time don't believe any significant threat is on the horizon—not understanding all the dynamics involved such as protecting the value of the U.S. dollar. The fact that *Dr. Green Spin* and the Fed came riding to the rescue after the stock market crash in 1987 and the financial crisis of 1998 has created what has been called by some a moral hazard: the belief that no matter what happens the Fed has the power to make things better. Maybe. Maybe not.

"The 1980s, up until the 1987 stock market crash, saw investors loading up with junk bonds involving loans to corporations with poor credit histories. This was not the only reason for the crash, but many investors were burned. These days, you have junk equity. Investors are loading up with the stock of companies that have no proven history of success with sky-high valuations. The stock market as a whole is now valued at a record 172% of U.S. economic output or GDP. This is more than double the level before the 1929 and 1987 crashes."

"I'm not sure I follow that," gasped Bob in perplexity.

"Stock prices, as you just learned," Cecelia began, "are based on a multiple times earnings real or expected one day. The multiple is about psychology: hopes and expectations. Stocks are about a claim of ownership on expected company earnings and the stock market as a whole is a claim on the value of the physical economy—annual gross production. The stock market is supposed to represent a significant portion of overall economic output and give an idea of how the economy is performing. This claim of value has never been so high in proportion to what is actually being produced. Profits have gone up a lot, but nothing like the astounding level of hope and confidence placed on them. Stock prices as a whole seem to be out of sync with the realities of economic production. Right now, altitude is everything. Don't go away, Bob. I have to change my outfit," Cecelia said, in a lilting, honking tone. "I'll be back, dahling."

"Just a second," Bob hastened to say. "You seem to be saying that this multiple has its limits, is that correct?"

"Everything has its limits," said Cecelia. "Higher values have been placed on earnings largely because of our present low inflation and our extremely low interest rate environment. The most common way of determining the value of a stock by analysts is by discounting what future earnings are expected to be. If a company is expected to grow by X% every year and is presently earning $1 per share per year, you can figure out five years away what the earnings will be based on that projected growth rate. However, a dollar five or seven years away is not going to be worth the same because of inflation.

"Future earnings are worth a lot more at this moment because inflation is only half what it has been over the long term on average. We haven't had low inflation like this since the early '60s. When the inflation picture changes, so likely will the multiple: shrinking instead of expanding. The multiple for the stock market in general is on average about double what it has been historically. It's difficult to believe that corporate earnings can simply grow far beyond what the economy itself can produce year after year. It doesn't make sense except perhaps to those who are cooking the accounting books. It's like the bakery: pie in the sky. It's time for me to plunge back into the unknown with my Wall Street darlings du jour and swim in creditor-infested waters. Just give me a few moments."

A Class By Itself

Cecelia plunged into the moat reemerging with her fur colored blue and commando weapons attached to her body. The words SEAL (Special Earnings Assets Losses) were written in white on her left side. She was now a Navy SEAL.

"I prefer to talk about something else now," Cecelia announced, "an elite class of stock: preferred stock. What we have been talking about is common stock. Preferred stock is a senior class of stock and considered more conservative. It is a 'hybrid' security with bond and stock characteristics like a convertible bond. Preferred stock has priority over common stock for investors getting paid for both dividends and getting one's principal back if the company is liquidated."

"Anything else?" asked Bob.

"Preferred stock pays a fixed dividend from earnings so one can take advantage of stock growth plus have a fixed income," Cecelia continued. "Dividends from common stock aren't fixed and at the time you purchase the preferred stock, the yield tends to be higher than whatever the dividend yield is on the common stock."

"Don't bonds provide fixed income and greater security?" asked Bob.

"Bonds and preferreds are both rated for their quality. Corporate bondholders, though, will be paid before preferreds if the company experiences what is called financial distress. However, preferreds with good companies have advantages over bonds. Traditional preferreds are issued as 'perpetual' securities, meaning they have no maturity date unlike a bond, which is for a set number of years. Newly issued bonds are $1,000 each, while new preferreds are available at $25 each. Like a bond, they may be 'callable.' This means that the issuer can call them back from investors. This can happen, for example, if interest rates fall enough to make it worthwhile for the company to buy back the stock or bond. The investor has the choice of selling it to the company, on the open market, or, in the case of the preferreds, converting the stock into common shares like a convertible bond."

"Why do you say traditional preferreds?" asked Bob. "Are there any others?"

"Yes," Cecelia explained, "financial instruments like dough at the Let Them Eat Fake Bakery can become synthetic. Synthetic preferreds have many of the same characteristics as the traditionals, but offer higher yields in return for set maturity dates of twenty to fifty years and are typically callable after five to ten years. They also pay monthly as well as quarterly. Preferreds in general should be considered for long-term investing. Although the dividend is fixed, the value goes up and down depending on interest rates like a bond, as you will learn.

"There is a see-saw relationship with the price. An owner of a preferred, like a bond, still gets the fixed amount promised, but if interest rates go higher the older preferreds with lower interest rates go down in value, while their interest rate climbs to compensate so that you still get paid what you were promised. However, if you were to sell at that particular time the twenty-five dollar preferred might have gone down to say $20, although its interest rate would have gone up to counter the loss in value the way a bond reacts.

"Preferreds in general can help keep a portfolio balanced, especially for those who like conservative bonds. They provide predictable monthly or quarterly income, but also may allow conversion to common stock. This flexibility allows a preferred holder with a conversion feature the right to participate if the common stock price goes up. If the common stock price falls, then the investor can choose not to convert. Your time is up with me, Bobby. I'm sure by now there are many more underwater options for me to look at. Honk!" Cecelia bid Bob and Sir Real adieu.

With a great splash, Cecelia dove back into the moat and disappeared. A heavy thumping sound could now be heard, but nothing could be seen. Sir Real continued walking with the heavy thumping sound getting louder and louder. Soon, the source of those sounds became obvious.

"Gorillas In Our Midst"

A King Kong-sized, blue colored gorilla approached and picked up Sir Real and Bob, raising them on the palm of its hand to eye level. He called himself Blue Chip and looked like a chip off a whole city block.

"You need to learn about market capitalization," said Blue Chip, boisterously.

"Well," said Bob, "I did learn that market capitalization refers to the value of a company determined by the number of shares a company has issued to the public times the price per share in the marketplace. See, I remember."

"Market capitalization means that size matters," spouted Blue Chip in a low rumbling tone. "Ten of the world's biggest corporations by market capitalization were in Japan in the 1980s, but are now reduced to three."

"So I heard," said Bob. "Why is that important to know?"

"It's part of learning how to spread your risk among different market cap categories when you invest in stocks. There are four general types of capitalization: large capitalization or large-cap (more than $6 billion in market value, middle capitalization or mid-cap ($2 to $6 billion), small capitalization or small-cap ($1.5 billion to $1 billion) and micro-cap ($3 hundred million or less). The amounts also cap what a company can be called. A small cap can grow into a mid-cap or large-cap; or the reverse can occur. Small cap stocks tend to have faster earnings growth potential than higher cap stocks. However, they are also more likely to be volatile.

"Micro-cap stocks are too small to be tracked by major tracking companies like the Russell 2000 Small Cap Index. They can sell for less than a dollar and have been known as penny stocks. If a stock goes from 50¢ in price to $1, it is no different percentage wise than a $100 stock that goes to $200. Money can be made in them, but you have to be extra careful because they are not as liquid as bigger company stocks. This means there are fewer buyers and sellers. These are approximate figures as opinions can differ slightly on what constitutes large, middle, small and micro-cap stocks.

"Large-cap companies have been referred to as blue chip companies in the U.S., red chip companies in Asia, and gorillas in the marketplace. They are the companies that dominate their industries and proudly proclaim that size matters. Usually in the past, they have given dividends to shareholders, which reflect a portion of their earnings so they tend to be favored by large conservative pension companies. In the 1970s, blue chips were called 'one decision stocks.' The reasoning was that all you had to do was buy a blue chip, then put it away for years while its value went up and collect dividends in the meantime. It turned out to be a fantasy just like the one about Bigfoot in the western U.S. Lately, some blue chips have lost a lot of value and red chips have been creamed in Asia. However, to Wealth Corgis, that is a sign of opportunity. They look for out of favor companies that have lots of potential in the future, which the herd now ignores, and position themselves to take advantage of a future turnaround.

"In the U.S., blue chips have been hurt by technology changes which have cut into their market share, as well as inability to raise prices in a low inflation environment, for example. They have to rethink their strategies. Many U.S. investors now think the stock market is a lot less risky than in the past and are investing in technology companies that they feel have more potential for fast growth. The less risk investors feel, the more the markets benefit. Small-cap, fast moving, nimble companies with high growth potential have been called gazelles and have become quite popular. In Japan, the hope is that the high tech gazelles will most likely lead the market out of their economic rabbit hole. Time for me to go."

Blue Chip gently placed Sir Real and Bob on the ground and then stomped away while the ground shook beneath them.

Foreign for an American

Sir Real was about to move on when Bob became aware of antlers moving back and forth behind the money tree which seemed to have moved. Someone shouted in a Boston accent, "Oh my God! It's one of those notorious, hair-losing Corgis. The Shed Coats are coming. The Shed Coats are coming."

After several more minutes, an exhausted looking reindeer poked its head out from behind the tree, trotted over and introduced himself as Paul Rain Deer.

"You look under the weather," Bob commented.

"Yes, but I can do something about the weather whereas others can only talk about it," Paul Rain Deer responded. "I come from a family of weather derivatives. Our specialty is hedging against the weather. My family is used by utilities, clothing manufacturers and even ice cream manufacturers. I like being involved with weather prediction because unlike Wall Street predictors, weather predictors learn from their errors."

"How does that work?" Bob asked.

"Contracts are made between parties to cover the cost of the weather hurting profits," explained Paul Rain Deer. "If the temperature, snowfall, rainfall or whatever weather index is used reaches a certain critical point covered by the contract, then the weather injured party has an option to get reimbursed. This way an ice cream company that experiences losses due to an unusually cool summer can be insured for losses and not have to pass them on to consumers. These contracts can be sold to others, like securities. I didn't want my value to be so derived from the performance of something else, which is what derivatives are about. Being a weather derivative is quite taxing so I became a turncoat. I opted out and chose to represent a more foreign line of work that may help investors weather a financial storm: ADRs."

"What are those, my foul weather friend?" asked Bob.

"Its about investing in foreign companies," said Paul Rain Deer. "First of all, consider all the consumer products in your home and see how many are directly or indirectly related to overseas companies. The percentage is usually very high. You are already investing in overseas companies. Companies around the world want to access American capital markets to sell stocks and bonds. They want the money and the visibility, reducing dependence on their home countries and ultimately lowering costs of operation. They do it through a process called American Depository Receipts or ADRs."

"How does that work?" Bob wished to know.

"ADRs represent shares of a foreign company," Paul Rain Deer began, "which are deposited in a bank overseas yet can be purchased and sold just like U.S. stocks. They are receipts for shares in the non-U.S. corporation. You are not really buying foreign company shares, but equivalents to them called depository receipts. A holder of an ADR can trade them in U.S. markets in dollar amounts and collect dividends paid in U.S. dollars. The U.S. listed foreign shares are issued by foreign branches of major commercial U.S. banks and have to answer to U.S. accounting standards called GAAP for Generally Accepted Accounting Principles, as well as the legal watchdogs of the Security and Exchange Commission. The great majority of institutional investors have holdings of foreign shares. It's regarded as an essential investment for growth and diversification. No sector is weatherproof from financial revolution. Remember how Bob Dylan once sang about how you don't have to be an expert on the weather to know which way the wind blows? In this business the experts often can't figure out which way the financial winds blow—even after they are blown away."

"What else can you tell me?" said Bob.

"You want to make sure that you pick a high quality company paying attention to the country and currency risk," said Paul Rain Deer. "An investor's ADR can be priced above or below what the underlying stock is selling for in the home country because it is a separate market. ADRs can be selling for a higher price than the same stock in the home country because of the ability to buy in the U.S. with U.S. dollars. However, to make sure you are not greatly overpaying, it is worth your while to check www.ADR.com. Excuse me, but I feel the temperature changing and the economic climate cooling. *Dr. Green Spin* and his buddies must be raising the cost of borrowing. I have to go. You should too. You are running out of dream time."

Paul Rain Deer ran behind the money tree.

Notell Inside

Bob and Sir Real continued to look for Noella, but she was still nowhere in sight. They were now on the other side of the moat from where they had begun their journey looking at the backside of the bakery. Black threatening clouds floated above them as they walked up a small hill. Beyond the hill they could hear someone saying, "You can shear a sheep many times, but you can only skin her once." On top they were able to look down and see a stout black sheep, the size of a Shetland pony.

"I told you," Sir Real remarked, "that you would be meeting the notorious Black in the Box. She has remained hidden most of the time because the mutual fund industry has a very powerful lobby group that's after her. They don't want little investors to think outside the box."

"Hello, Bob," said Black in the Box. "I don't have much time to talk to you. Those mutual fund guys are everywhere. They want me to run with the herd, baa. As *Dirty Haree* mentioned, investment companies breed funds like rabbits. So, I'll speak quickly. One of the most important determinants of how successful a fund will be over time is overall costs. The fund companies like to play around with the numbers. That's why they don't want to tell you what you are paying for a fund in plain dollars and cents. You would then realize how little competition there really is in the fund industry when it comes to prices. Although cost alone shouldn't be the sole determinant, you can get more information with calculators such as the one at www.personalfund.com.

"Since you can't shop properly when you aren't properly informed, the big focus is on performance. Investors aren't paying that much interest in fees because the general market has been doing so well. However, it will make a big difference when the overall market changes direction especially if it's for a long time. You may be continuing to pay high fees on a money-losing fund. Even in these good times money managers have tended to lag behind general market performance. That's why index funds have become so popular. However, they have their drawbacks too, as you learned. They are little giants. When the market does well they are giants. When the market does poorly they shrink."

"What else can you tell me?" Bob asked eagerly.

"My name comes from the fact that fund managers only have to notify investors twice a year of their top holdings," said Black in the Box. "Funds change their holdings frequently. It means that you have no real time connection with what you own. You never really get to see until much later what is under the hood so to speak and driving the returns forward or backward. You are putting your money into a black box which may turn into a black hole and trusting that it will turn out okay. State-of-the-art interaction with out-of-date information is another contradiction you can discuss with Barbi Q. It is a matter of trust, in a business that may not deserve your trust. This is one of the major reasons investors have been leaning towards index mutual funds and their cousins the ETFs (exchange traded funds). You know what the holdings are because of the index being followed."

"What else can you tell me before you have to run off?" asked Bob.

"It is very difficult to determine whether the fund is following what they promised in the prospectus," said Black in the Box. "Money managers these days are being forced by circumstances to meet high demands from investors, which may be unrealistic. So they can cut corners and speculate more than they should to drive up the numbers so that their days on the job aren't numbered. Most mutual funds operate on an old fashioned system of pricing at the end of the day. So you can't react quickly if you want to. You have no idea until the end of the day what your holdings are worth in this high technology age. In response, you usually get the self-serving 'buy and hold' advice from them."

"What about relying on the fund manager?" asked Bob.

"It can be a less reliable process than counting sheep at night to fall asleep," explained Black in the Box. "Fund managers change like bed sheets in many funds. It can be much easier to figure out the worth of stocks and bonds than to use a fund manager who may not be around for very long. Funds are not only bred like rabbits, they also go extinct merging into other funds and going out of business at a much higher rate than the public is aware. Each year during the 1990s, over 5% of these 'rabbit' funds have been killed off because they aren't successful. In a ten year period, you're looking at quite a change, especially for an industry which talks about holding on for the long term. You might want to check out www.fundalarm.com."

"What about taxes?" asked Bob.

"Mutual funds are not tax efficient," said Black in the Box. "They should be used, if used, in a retirement account where taxes are postponed until time of distribution. The performance returns the companies advertise don't include the impact of taxes, which can be really significant in funds that change their holdings frequently. If the fund sells securities that they have held for a long time, you can get capital gains taxes, which vary from 10% to 20% outside of a retirement account. The mutual fund owner has no control over when the fund manager decides to take profits. January is the time of the year when the fund owner receives IRS forms called 1099s notifying him or her of the taxable distributions created from the past year.

"The fund owner often just inherits someone else's tax bill. The shares could have been purchased a long time before one even bought into the fund. When the market goes down significantly, mutual funds are required to redeem shares for those investors who want to get out. As they sell off securities to pay for this, tax consequences are triggered from shares that have made gains. So you can be hit with a big tax bill while your fund is going down in value.

"Short-term sales and dividends are taxed at regular income rates, which can be as high as 39.5%. When the market slows so that double-digit gains are no longer the norm, then the tax bite can really show up. There are studies that claim taxes can cut into performance by 3% on average. That's a lot considering that stocks in general have outperformed bonds by around 6% on average. We're not even talking about fees. Funds not only don't want you to know about costs in simple language, they also don't want you to truly understand the tax situation."

"But isn't it true," demanded Sir Real, "there are tax efficient funds too."

"Yes it's true," bleated Black in the Box, "but an index fund may be still better for you. Tax efficient funds are new and relatively few, using techniques like avoiding stocks that pay dividends and holding onto stocks for longer periods of time. Some critics say that performance is being sacrificed to make the funds pay fewer taxes. It's too early to tell if it's a good deal. Index funds just hold stocks of the index being followed and are passively managed with low turnover. Therefore, there is far less change in holdings, which can trigger tax consequences. The problem, though, is that market tracking index funds with the big run up in stock prices can have significant gains that can be realized if the market goes down significantly as they sell off stock to pay investors. Nothing is black or white. Remember you still haven't left Grayland."

"Do you think I should avoid mutual funds?" asked Bob.

"Mutual funds have some good advantages," said Black in the Box, especially for small amounts of money. A major reason for the proliferation of so many funds is that they are increasingly concentrating on marketing rather than management. They deliberately give an incomplete picture of their billing methods and tax consequences. Thanks to abundant fees even from no-load funds, they have tremendous marketing resources to influence investors.

"You have to be very careful and pick funds very selectively if you use them at all. Their ads talk about diversification and professional management, et cetera, and America has had a love affair with mutual funds. However, if the markets get rough in the future, many mutual fund lovers might decide that the way they charge, the lack of control over taxes and real time information make mutual funds a rip off. You don't want to be caught in a backlash. It has been estimated that three quarters of mutual fund investors have never experienced a prolonged bear market. Who knows what the reaction will be. Investors are also starting to realize they have other choices."

"Like what?" Bob wished to know.

"If you want to have a money manager, the requirements for having your own managed account have changed thanks to technology. Brokers match you and your requirements to a professional money manager for an amount as low as $50,000. Unlike a mutual fund, you own the securities which are managed and don't have to deal with taxes until you sell. With the use of computers, accounts no longer require large sums of money to manage."

"But isn't it true," demanded Sir Real, "that this is largely a cookie cutter approach too?"

"Yes," responded Black in the Box, "especially if you have less than $1 million. You often hold the same portfolio that thousands of others do. Some brokers using snob appeal and telling investors that mutual funds are for poor people are promoting these managed accounts. What's amusing is that these accounts are often modeled after mutual funds and can have the same mutual fund managers. It's called a 'wrap account' because of the market wrapping. The broker provides the 'wrap' music. Salesman-type brokers like managed accounts for the same reason as mutual funds. You just lead the client to different managers and you don't have to really do that much or know that much. It's basically selling and schmoozing with the clients.

"An old style broker may offer much better flexibility and service than some money manager you will never get to talk to unless you have lots of money involved. The term, 'money manager' can also be loosely used like the words 'resort' and 'estate sale.' It's easy to call yourself a money manager. In some respects, it may be more difficult to become a bus driver. Big brokerage firms, though, tend to have a screening process to screen out the bad ones as well as follow up in what is called a due diligence process. Experienced investors can create their own fund portfolios at sites like www.foliofn.com."

"I think I hear sirens," said Bob. "Do you hear sirens?"

"It's the mutual fund police," said Black in the Box. "I have to go."

Black in the Box left hurriedly traveling in the opposite direction.

The Bad News Bears

Sir Real had walked no more than a few hundred yards further around the circular moat when Bob became aware of an awful smell.

"What's that horrible smell?" asked Bob. "It's worse than the dogs of the Dow."

"Bear repellent," said Sir Real. "Stock market bears aren't popular in many parts of the investment world, especially Grayland. However, there is more than one way to smell success."

Bob now noticed a little brown bear with a skullcap and prayer shawl printed with negative numbers bending back and forth like it was praying. Apparently, it had stepped from behind a nearby bush because nothing else was in sight. It had a teeny black lacquered violin in its paws and played this haunting, tearful, Russian music after it finished praying. The bear now turned and introduced himself cheerfully with a Russian accent as Bearly Legal.

"I like to play sad but inspiring music" said Bearly Legal. "That song is called 'Good Things Can Come in Bad Packages.' It's about how to make money from foolishness, fraud, and future fatalities— one of those f . . . f . . . fantasy and finance songs. Do you have a favorite time of the year, Bobalah?"

"Yes, October," said Bob.

"Me too," said Bearly Legal. "Some of the biggest drops in U.S. stock market history have occurred in that month. I love the Fall. Bears are those who see the bright side of bad news. I'm a little upset that Blackie is getting so much of the credit for being the black sheep of the mutual fund industry when I'm the real black sheep."

"You seem so cheerful," Bob observed. "Black in the Box talked like she was in a black mood compared to you."

"Black in the Box doesn't profit from her complaints," explained Bearly Legal. "I do. From Dr. Root I learned long ago that investors have a tendency to underestimate just how bad things can get. A major reason in my opinion is because they rely on a lot of half-baked information from financial institutions whose primary business is to market their paper dough products. It's a dream-selling business based on their fee-based perception of reality. I'm a real congenital bear and openly bearish, whereas Sir Real likes to look bullish in polite company, but is really a closet bear."

"Why do you have a prayer shawl?" asked Bob.

"I just had my bear mitzvah," announced Bearly Legal. "Even Roth Wilier attended. He isn't so bad. He is just another one of those stereotypical stiff overbearing humorless German Rottweilers. Right now I'm praying for what is called a bear market. I am what is known as a bear fund. The more a market goes down, the more money those who invest in my fund make. There are all kinds of bear funds like me with differing strategies. My fund specializes in shorting Internet stocks. There are bear funds that are the mirror image of Mimic. When a market like the *Down Jones* goes down, they benefit and become as big as grizzly bears.

"Excuse me, I meant to say Dow Jones. Must have been a Freudian slip. Now, my fund doesn't just wait for stocks or the stock market as a whole to go down. No. No. No. We like to sing the blues. All that bull from the marketing boys on Wall Street can be hard to bear. It is in our interest to be bearers of bad news: the real bad news bears."

"Could you give me an example or two?" asked Bob.

"Sure," said Bearly Legal, enthusiastically. "Recently, my little bear group has been publishing articles questioning the value of many Dumb-Idea.Com companies. The public is starting to get impatient with lack of results. You often have to wait until investors start getting in the mood to listen. As Dr. No told me, in order to have a proper communication, you need to have a message, a messenger and a listener. Now investors are starting to listen. Sometimes our articles focus attention on so-called aggressive accounting practices by companies. If others agree that a company is overvalued, then the stock can really tank making lots of profits for those who bet against the stock. You will see what I mean later on when you meet an accounting cheetah that specializes in lack of accountability. By investing in our type of funds, you don't have to be a pro like a Wealth Corgi to be involved in short sales. Our belief system is about profiting from the fact that so much of the information served to the public isn't kosher. The bull market is presently masking a lot of problems that we bears will feast on later."

"How come I haven't heard about you before?" asked Bob.

"I'm considered a heretic," said Bearly Legal, "and the market in general has been doing well these past years. I'm just a little bear fund up against a multi-trillion dollar fund industry. However, it is in your interest to be aware of guys like me and maybe have some bear insurance. Company retirement funds typically don't allow a choice of bear funds because it's contrary to conventional mutual fund religion that preaches 'buy and hold for the long term.' Everyone knows that securities such as stocks and bonds and the markets they trade in go down as well as up. To focus only on the long view is extremely shortsighted for investors. The financial industry likes to pretend, for the most part, that you can mainly make money by the market going up and to hold on in general for the long term. It's nonsense. You have choices. You can take my way and the high way. It's far better to play a violin than to be played like one. They like to play with emotions. And even though I look religious, they are the truly religious ones. The brokerage houses too with their holey predictions, high priest economists, and rain dance analysts.

"When tough times come the same characters that failed to properly warn of tough times will line up to give advice about what to do when the damage is already done. They have even hired me to write a book called *How To Make Your Investments Safe and Kosher Now That They Have Been Ritually Slaughtered*. Although it is too soon to publish it, the book has already been nominated for the No Bull prize. The Swedish Academy maintains that my work provides proof of the existence of Cold Confusion Economics and its ability to unleash unlimited amounts of investor anxiety. Freud was right: neurotic energy can be effortlessly manufactured at room temperature."

"You are a tough talking little bear," exclaimed Bob.

"Better tough talk than double talk," said Bearly Legal. "Financial companies often engage in double talk that it's too risky for the public to deal with markets going down; while at the same time they provide the investor margin loans to buy stocks so they can gamble about making a profit on the market going up. They are master hypocrites. It's in their interest to have you think this way because of self-serving reasons like all the management fees collected from investors holding onto long buy mutual funds; and the money made bringing new securities to the marketplace. My fund is a bugbear to the image that the financial industry projects of growth and stability.

"Funds that make money selling the market short may be an important strategy for hedging your bets when investing; otherwise, you may be selling yourself short. Biased investment literature typically omit bear funds as part of spreading your risk. How can you possibly spread your risk without considering this possiblity? A proper balance is essential when your retirement hangs in the balance. I know I'm kind of biased, but I've noticed that markets tend to peak when optimism or pessimism is at its highest. History does repeat itself, but never in the same way. It's more like a learning spiral. Maybe I'll explain it one day. I have free tickets to attend a rhythm for the investment blues festival put on by some of my bearish colleagues. It's called 'Let the Buyer be Bear.' Want to come?"

"No thank you," said Bob with anticipation of what was to come in his learning spiral. "I wish you wouldn't go. I would like to learn more about the upside of the downside. "

"Maybe I would stay if you had attended my bear mitzvah. It's okay—I know you're busy. I don't want you should feel guilty. I wasn't alone, thank God. In fact a great celebration was held in the state of Issurreal involving a great many of my bullish friends and acquaintances. The orthodox believers stayed on and on according to past custom. Finally the singing and dancing ended with prayers at the Wailing Wall Street, vows to refrain from pork financial products and renewed interest in chicken—the other white meat. You see, you don't have to be bearish to attend a bear mitzvah Bubbleah. A good bear mitzvah is not just about a big party but making a man out of as many bullish investors as possible. One day I'm sure you will read about it in the papers, if you have the time. I have to go now. Goodbye and good luck on Fall Street," he said with a downward wave of his right claw. Bearly Legal adjusted his negative numbered black skullcap then wandered off playing more tearful music, as Bob said, "Gee, I've come across kosher dogs and kosher chickens before, mostly in delicatessens, but never a kosher bear. That's the gospel truth."

No Bull Please, Just the Bear Facts

While Bearly Legal had been speaking, the bush had started to move closer and closer to Bob and Sir Real. After Bearly Legal had departed, it stopped moving. Heavy breathing could be heard. Someone said: "Every bull eventually spawns a bear. Some don't know and some don't care."

A booming voice then sang, "Oh what a difference a bear makes— just plenty more little howlers. Oh yah yah dee yah dah."

"Who is that? Speak to me."

A beautiful giant panda with woolly fur and distinct black and white markings stepped out from behind the bush and introduced herself as Panda Monium.

"Like every dog," said Panda Monium, "every bear has its day. We are about to have the longest upsurge of general market activity or bull market ever recorded. When a market like the Nasdaq or Dow Jones falls at least 20% from a previous peak, it is often arbitrarily defined as a bear market. There are all type of bears. Some have huge claws so that the market remains down for years like in Japan; and what happened in the U.S. from 1929 onward and the 1973-74 stock bear market. Those long grinding multi-year losses of at least 40% are defined as a secular bear market.

"Commodities and stocks relating to them have been going through a secular bear market as you learned from Goldie within a general bull market. It's the astounding success of technology related stocks that has boosted the overall market. At the same time, it should be kept in mind that the overall market is more dependent than ever on their continuing success."

"Give me some more of the bear facts," Bob requested of the beautiful Panda bear.

"Other bears have little or no claws with a market being down just a short time like a matter of months," explained Panda Monium. "This is called a cyclical bear market. Bear markets always start out as 'corrections' or drops of 10% or more. The idea is that the market has corrected for past excesses. It's only when the figure goes beyond 20%

correction that a bear market is created. It is more than a number, though. It's also about psychology. According to Dr. Root, textbook emotional reaction starts with denial and belief that the market has to go back up, followed by acceptance, and then 'zah fear.' Good news can be treated as an opportunity to sell rather than buy. Bad news can be overstated. There have been approximately two-dozen bear markets this past century depending on how a bear market is interpreted. Bear markets involve 'buyer strikes' and forced selling. The equity sellers like to give the impression that bear markets are just occasional interruptions to this wonderful bull party that goes on most of the time. The stock market did do very well from 1921-29, then again from 1948-66 and from 1982 to the present end of the century. The rest of the time though, investments in general were hibernating according to the Down Jones Average. In fact it took the Dow 25 years to recover from the 1929-33 bear market. Maybe that's what the bulls meant by investing for the 'long haul.' It was a beary good time for us—and that's no bull.

"Scientists have been studying bears to try and figure out how they can hibernate for such long periods of time and barely lose any muscle strength. Bear markets can act in a similar manner. Just because a big bear may have been hibernating for years in the stock market doesn't mean it can't have a grizzly awakening and adversely affect you and your portfolio when the markets go into bear territory. There is a whole new untested generation of investors ready to be bear tested; at a time when retirement accounts (translate: stock market) are now starting to replace the home as the chief financial asset. Bear markets wear down emotions and confidence and many investors may find that they don't have the personalities to allow their portfolios to hibernate even for short periods of time. Psychology studies indicate that investors remember even small losses better than a big gain. It's deep and emotional—and beyond the intellectual brain."

"Is there any other information on bear markets I can look into?" asked Bob.

"Try www.lowrisk.com/98crash.htm and www.markethistory.com," suggested Panda Monium. Do you know where I can find some good Chinese food? I'm getting so hungry since my last meal one hour ago."

"No I can't help you," Bob replied. "But if you find one of those old restaurants with 1950s red plastic seating, heavy white coffee cups and very limited lighting, please let me know. It's my favorite kind of restaurant."

"Just a moment Ms. Panda Monium," Sir Real broke in. "Isn't it true bears can lay financial traps too?"

"Yes, I confess," said Panda Monium. "Bears in the financial world sometimes lay traps, but not intentionally. Sometimes investors can become convinced a bear market is coming on, and pull back on their investments. But then things change and the market shoots upward. It's called a classic bear trap. Bulls lay traps too, especially the pros. They can 'talk up the market' filling the news with all kinds of positive-sounding statements so they can unload their shares on little investors before the market tanks. As we bears like to say 'Don't worry. The worst is yet to come.' It's time for me to go."

Panda Monium wandered off and Sir Real continued his walk around the moat. Soon, they reached an area that was thick with tall grass.

"For Your Lies Only"

The tall grass nearly covered Bob and Sir Real. Traveling through it, they could hear someone humming a Rolling Stones song, "Paint it Black" and singing about not wanting colored numbers anymore. It was a female voice with a strong South African accent. As they came closer to the singing, they spotted a wild cat with tawny fur in a black and white checkerboard pattern and claws. In its mouth was a paintbrush, which it was moving back and forth on a gray canvas covered with colored numbers, mostly red. As the paintbrush touched the numbers, they turned black. The jungle cat dropped the paintbrush from its mouth and introduced herself as Lubri Cat, the slipperiest accounting cheetah on the face of the earth, capable of removing spots from leopards as well as bad corporate report cards.

"Nice to meet you," said Bob by way of introducing himself. "I like numbers because numbers don't lie."

"That's very nice Bobby," said Lubri Cat with a smile. "Why don't you just pick a number, any number from my canvass? I like numbers too. Numbers don't lie—but my clients sure do. Creative accounting is like a paint-by-numbers picture in which I decide how to connect the financial dots. I'm a short-term fixer, a turn around artist who makes companies, institutions and governments look good—or at least a lot better than they should. I've been known to paint a healthy profit picture for many a company with profit margins not even as wide as the space between a wall and its wallpaper. Some call it cooking the books, but I call it improving the looks. I help companies like dot-coms paint attractive pictures of their companies for investors. I've had complaints that the work I do is not transparent. You'd think that should be quite apparent. It's true my paintings look opaque—but only because I make a better fake. Do you like my painting? I am thinking of calling it Black Magic or something French like Moolah Rouge—because the kind of accounting work I do is called 'putting lipstick on a pig.' This work of art was prepared for a giant highly recommended telecommunications company called Lucid. What isn't clear to many little investors is how Lucid has loaned massive amounts of money to financially weak customers to create sales and pump up earnings. I don't want you to see me in just a bad way. Using accepted accounting methods I've artfully helped companies to legally overstate earnings and help contribute to the belief in the productivity miracle."

"I got the picture. It's cool," Bob complimented Lubri Cat. "So you're mainly the artsy shmartsy type? I've never had the pleasure of meeting a good con artist before."

"No," Lubri Cat replied, "I'm not just a number painter and scam artist, but a wordsmith of sorts. For I know how to word financial reports. I'm not the king of beasts but lyin' is basically what I'm about. Hee-Hee. Generally accepted accounting principles allow for a lot of fictional accounting, but I like to go beyond that for true artistic expression. I am becoming so well known, by the way, that *Dr. Green Spin* asked me to do a portrait showing how the booming stock market has painted him into a corner. I'm very flattered the good doctor saw fit to choose me. He is quite an artist himself, although of a different school. Central banking probably has much more to do with art than any other discipline."

"What kind of catcalls does a cheetah like you make?" asked Bob.

"It's not just about my catcalls. My fat cat employers as well as those in the accounting cheetah profession believe that one is entitled to not only one's opinions, but also to one's own facts. Say a discovery is made that money is missing and a fund depleted," Lubri Cat said by way of example. "I can write that it was mistakenly overstated or inflated, so it doesn't sound like investors were 'cheetahed.' I deduct a little of this and a little of that to make an earnings report look nice and fat. If we don't have earnings I can write about revenue, and make projections about future earnings that may prove untrue. There is rhyme and reason to what I do, even though I may be a cheetah without a clue. Let me further explain:

My art is what some call abstract,
From different viewpoints, I make fiction look like fact.

In countries like Japan, my paintings sell for millions.
This isn't really costly when you realize I helped cover up banking
*   and pension losses in the billions.*

My employers have included politicians and the crime organization
called the Yakuza.
I think that's Japanese for lots and lots of chutzpah.
It's much like our own rip-offs from the 1980s crisis called Savings
and Loan.
Huge amounts of money are borrowed with no intention to pay back.
Then the public is told that taxpayer money is needed to convert the
numbers from red back to black.

"What happens to the money?" asked Bob. "Where does it go?"

"Don't worry," said Lubri Cat. "This money is often not squandered. It's merely laundered. It goes from bank to bank, until it draws a big blank. It's similar to a washing machine. Eventually, the dirty money comes out clean. The money often doesn't stay. It's sent to cuckoo clock efficiency Switzerland or offshore and not far away. By now, you must be aware that my work is in demand most everywhere. The public is often late to recognize how number manipulation makes such a wonderful disguise. I like to fudge and make it too. Would you like me to serve you some, before I say good-bye to you?"

"No thank you," said Bob. "You are giving me the impression that there are a lot of corrupt and unethical practices going on in the financial world."

"I don't like to talk like that. Do you?" Lubri Cat asked with a purring sound. "I prefer to say that there is plenty of wiggle room in accounting for earnings. If it were not for the likes of me companies would be at a loss to explain their losses. A good cheetah has more than nine lives and its days are rarely numbered. So you have to be very careful and look at factors like cash flow. It's absolutely foolish to go strictly by the earnings numbers. The SEC has stepped up investigations, but there is so much manipulation going on that it's actually scandalous. Many fat cats believe that stating earnings in the best light is their right. It's been called 'the earnings management culture.' In a sharp economic downturn, it will become much more obvious how companies cook the books when stocks start tanking. The only ones who will really benefit are the professional short sellers who make it their business to be skeptical. Unreliable accounting is another reason for learning to spread risk."

A strange looking housecat, with a see-through body loaded with cash, brushed against Lubri Cat and said, "You look startled, Bob. What's the matter . . . cat got your tongue?"

"I taught I taw . . . I taught I taw a puddy-cash," Bob stammered.

"You did. You did," Sir Real assured. "That's a cash kitty of the same name in reverse."

"I work sometimes with Lubri Cat," said Kitty Cash. "I'm a secret cash kitty. I have to keep a sharp-eyed alert for government accounting watchdogs. So I don't have much time to talk to you. They have been complaining a little more loudly lately about lack of accounting transparency. My job is to keep up appearances without proper disclosure. I not only cross ethical boundaries, but also legal ones. Although cats don't live in the future, management often does trying to satisfy the expectations of investors. Where I am employed, they are under constant pressure as a public company to boost earnings and demonstrate an even upward trajectory in their growth."

"Well don't just pussyfoot around the subject, tell me what you do exactly," Bob insisted.

"I help smooth out earnings and massage the numbers in a way that's less than legal," said Kitty Cash. "Occasionally we have a bad quarter or two for reporting purposes so the company dips into my secret numbered account and pulls out money to make the sales and profits look better than they really are. During good times, this money went unreported and was stashed away for a rainy day. Sometimes, I have operated as a fake or shell company buying goods from my employer with his money. It looks like the company is making all kinds of sales when all it is doing is selling to itself."

"So you're a really bad kitty," Bob criticized.

"Yes I am," said Kitty Cash. "But you're dog lover Mr. Catz, so I don't think we could be friends anyway. I want you to know though that accounting cheetahs and secret cash kitties are loved by professional short sellers. When they expose our deeds to the public they make handsome profits as stock values sink. In a way 'shorts' protect little investors. Wall Street is not really part casino as some have said. It's really part circus: with financial acrobatics, crystal ball readers, house of mirror accounting, tricksters, clowns, and lyin' kings."

Much Ado About Nothing

> *I'd compare stock pickers to astrologers, but I don't*
> *want to bad mouth astrologers.*
> —Eugene Fama, economist

Bob's conversation was interrupted by hysterical laughter coming from someone hidden in the tall grass. "I'll be your friend," said someone with a heavy English accent. "I'm everyone's friend." Sir Real went in the direction of the laughter with Bob on his back. They came upon a hyena wearing oversized rose-colored glasses and a black T-shirt with the words "Will Write for Food" printed on it. The hyena rolled back and forth in front of Sir Real as though it were writhing in pain. Around it were scraps of paper with writing.

Bob picked up and read each one of the scraps of paper. They had words and phrases like: Buy, Hold, Market Performer, Neutral, Accumulate, Strong Buy, Trading Buy, Market Outperformer, Long-Term Attractive and Top Pick. Beside many of them were the words Upgrade or Downgrade. This was obviously Lord Ha Ha, the stock market analyst Sir Real had mentioned earlier.

"Looks to me like you have a great job," Bob greeted the hyena.

"It's a dream job," cackled Lord Ha Ha. "Ha! Ha! I laugh all the way to the investment bank where I work every day making big bucks as a stock market analyst."

"That must take up an enormous amount of time," said Bob.

"It should, but it doesn't," Lord Ha Ha guffawed, turning almost pink with laughter. "I spend at least half my time marketing deals like IPOs and mergers to potential investors. One of the reasons I was hired was because, as a hyena, I like to look on the bright side of things. That's what my bosses want from analysts. I am generally very slow to say something bad about a company, but quick to say something good in my report. I analyze companies from the bottom on up in part to determine profits and sales. This type of work is supposed to be helpful to investors in trying to determine in advance a company's earnings and how those earnings fit into pricing a stock. Profits as you know by now, in large part, dictate share prices.

"Hyenas are excellent scavengers for information. I have to rely on whatever scraps of information I can find and come to conclusions about the financial health of the company I am examining. My real job is to diagnose what is truly going on. Companies can be evasive or at least less than forthcoming about the truth at times. Come to think of it, so can I. My point though is that it's not just like all the information is handed to me. I only get a snapshot, not an X-ray. It's when it comes to making recommendations about purchasing and selling securities that my job becomes quite amusing."

"In what way?" asked Bob.

"The majority of my recommendations, as with other analysts, are about buying the stock," said Lord Ha Ha, fit to burst into laughter. "My latest recommendations were 'Attractive Long-Term,' which really means that this stock can take a dive at any moment; 'Hold,' which really means hold the stock and you will likely get burned; and 'Near term cautious, but long-term optimistic,' which means I haven't got a clue what is going to happen next, but I'm covered."

"If you virtually never say anything really bad or meaningful about a company, your recommendations can't be very useful," observed Bob.

"Oh I wouldn't say that," Lord Ha Ha said mirthfully. "From a marketing point of view, they can be very useful. What analysts say can affect the price of a stock. However, in giving you a true picture of what's going on, the recommendations are often worse than worthless. We do business or solicit business from the very same companies that we make recommendations about. My employer wanted someone with class, like an English lord, because analysts have this genteel relationship with the companies we cover. We don't really probe, question, and challenge like the great TV lawyer Sir Real. I'm a party animal. Corporations have a cozy relationship with Wall Street that they don't enjoy with Main Street. We have two sets of clients: corporate issuers and investors in corporations or stockholders. When we issue these reports, it is corporate issuers that are most important to us, not the little investors. We want to help issuers sell their stock. There is no such thing as a free hunch. Ha! Ha!"

"What do you mean?" asked Bob.

"Do you really think for a moment," Lord Ha Ha explained, "that we would want to lose business from those we have an investment banking relationship with, like potential company mergers or divestitures or raising capital for companies through stock and bond underwriting? Mergers, by the way, have to do with the fat cats and their spin doctors running around claiming that one and one makes three: in other words, the sum is greater than the parts. Divestitures or company spin-offs have to do with the opposite approach: fat cats and their spin doctors running around claiming that breaking up a company into parts is going to be worth more than the whole. Often the purpose of mergers and divestitures is to divert investors' attention from the fact that the fat cats in charge aren't doing a great job. No matter what the math, it always adds up to fat profits for the capitalist pigs. The highest profit margins for investment banks are with mergers, acquisitions, and issuance of new stocks. Bonds, aside from junk bonds, are low margin profit.

"Do I, Lord Ha Ha, look like some kind of party pooper? Not on your investment life. What are our chances if I issue a negative report on a company that may bring us in a lot of money? We want to be on their good side. Not only might I face criticism from the client, but also my superiors and even other analysts including those at other firms who are trying to get the same business. I have to deal with peer pressure and job protection. Just because my stock recommendations are a joke doesn't mean I want to be made a laughing stock. If we analysts tend to give an average-type recommendation then it is safer, no matter what happens. It's a fact that hyenas never like to take chances, so we analysts have a strong herd mentality, taking refuge in a group or 'consensus opinion.' It's really about our safety but it also makes the public feel more comfortable that we seem to be in general agreement. We are when it comes to helping our employers sell equities and helping the companies our employers underwrite. That goes for brokerage economists who make forecasts, too. Did I neglect to mention that I could also get a percentage of investment business that comes our way?"

"That's kind of like the fox guarding the hen house," Bob commented.

"Ah, but the fox is the hen house," said Lord Ha Ha with a laugh, "because the investment banks own or are linked up one way or another with retail outfits or brokerage houses that market the securities. Analysts like me, who are supposed to just analyze, have been turned into extensions of the sales department—many quite willingly considering the size of those bonuses. There are true independent analysts who don't work for companies that do business with those they study, but they are very few in number often working for the benefit of large institutions who don't want to rely on biased information and can afford to pay for it.

"Rarely do analysts ever say 'sell.' The worst comment is usually 'neutral' or 'average.' We have to water down our comments to please the powers that be. That's why I'm a mere lord subject to the whims of the fat cat kings. Companies, in return, treat analysts as a favored class of citizen like they do giant institutional companies. Despite all you hear about the importance of the individual investor, the system is probably what some would call rigged—far less than 3% of stock recommendations say 'sell.' I'm basically a promoter for many of my company's important prospects and clients. I'm a cheerleader for the corporations and a press agent for the investment bank. We upgrade and downgrade the ratings of companies, but only to a certain point. Companies we want to do business with have their privileges. That's what you can really bank on. I can tell you with all honesty that the system is all about dishonesty. I do recommend you see Noella's latest play, the surprise sequel to *Days of Swine and Roses* called *Recessions 'R' Us*."

"What is wrong with you?" asked Bob. "You keep limping about as you talk to me. Is it because you lamely rely on corporate fat cats to feed you information instead of doing hard-nosed analysis?"

"Yes, that happens all the time. However, today I also got off on the wrong foot," said Lord Ha Ha. "When analysts make a bad call, and recommend a stock highly, which turns out to be a real turkey, they can trip over each other trying to defend their recommendation and the company they recommended. That's what happened on my last call. Another tactic we use is to say that management wasn't straight with us when we have a sense that investors are getting really ticked off. We become the talking wounded hopping around with lame excuses. By the way, I should mention these recommendations are not just directed at the public, but the sales force for the securities. Recommendations by analysts help protect the sales force. If a recommendation goes bad, then the sales representative can seek safety from an irate client in the fact that the analysts highly recommended it. One day there will be talk of major reform and we will go through the motions to appease the public; but snakes don't reform. They just know how to slither away from danger. Free advice from brokerage firms will always be expensive because they are free of objectivity. It's about getting you on the fries.

"Even though my research is laughable a joker can still be a wild card. There is power to this job that I enjoy particularly when I make a good call. Comments from analysts, even relatively unknown ones, can move stocks and entire markets, but it doesn't mean the information has any true objective worth because it comes from a biased source. You have to always consider how the source of information is being funded. You have to follow the money. Sometimes analysts make ridiculous positive recommendations, which cause the stock to go up quickly as the public snaps it up and confirms that they made a good call—a self-fulfilling prophecy. Later on, the stock can dramatically or even slowly drop in price, since it was possibly only held up by hot air in the first place, but it no longer matters. In the meantime, the analyst has made a name for him or herself because the 'target price' recommended by the analyst was reached. Once it becomes clear that a stock is going downhill, analysts then become Olympic class downhill racers trying to outdo each other in downgrading or lowering their recommendations. We cut and slash investment ratings more to protect us than to protect you. For those investors who are stuck with lower priced stock, they can usually be consoled with phrases like: 'it isn't a loss until you sell it,' 'the stock will come back, it's probably just temporarily oversold,' or/and 'you're in this for the long-term, aren't you?' Influence is not the same as knowledge. This is what I I learned at Laughs On You College."

"What do the Queen's dogs have to say?" asked Bob.

"You would have to mention them," replied Lord Ha Ha. "They enjoy calling my reviews of high tech companies 'high dreck.' I think it's Yiddish for 'trash.' My work never passes their smell test. Ratings reviews by equity analysts connected with brokerage houses and investment banks are of no importance to high-class investors like the Wealth Corgis. They're for the lower clawses. So if a broker tells you his company has rated such and such 'Best Buy' or 'Outperform,' just remember my name and say 'Ha Ha' to him."

"What are you recommending to me, if anything?"

"Just because something is newsworthy doesn't mean it's nose worthy," explained Lord Ha Ha. "To be successful at investing, it helps if you develop a nose for discriminating between worthwhile investing information or knowledge and company propaganda. According to Dr. Root, Freud suggested that humans feared and repressed the power of smell when they began walking on two legs. That's why even when brokerage recommendations are shown to stink to high heaven, little investors come back for more. Some investment experts mention how it is important to be selective in analyst recommendations. Why would you want to sift through garbage when 'time is money?' Unless of course you are a masochist. Then you would be speaking to Dr. Root, not me. Ha. Ha. Ha."

"You sound almost nasty," Bob remarked.

"Oh, you have the wrong impression about me, Bob. I'm sorry," Lord Ha Ha apologized. "You probably think I'm prejudiced, too. I can assure you that I don't have a prejudiced bone in my body. I've never met a stock I didn't like. Ha Ha Ha."

"So what do I do?" Bob nervously asked.

"You need to 'Accumulate' a nose for sense and sensibility when it comes to brokerage house recommendations and business 'news,'" Lord Ha Ha answered. "Investors of your size better get wise to how experts are often hungry salesmen in chic disguise. What should be clear to you by now is how little transparency there is in this business. Brokerage analysts and their economists are not pure bred. They have lots of sales blood in them. You may be able to save a lot just by discounting their importance. You would be much better off talking to a financial ferret than me, someone who specializes in analyzing financial gibberish. The information I have is homogenized and pasteurized. Gee, I hope I haven't upset you with unpleasant details about how corporate 'saw such' is processed for your consumption by the capitalist pigs, with artificial rosy coloring and lots of superlatives. If I may say so, it tastes best when used with a bottle of vintage *Whine* later. For your convenience, we have a large selection in stock. Ha Ha." The laughing analyst then quietly slipped back into the tall grass shaped like numbers and hid behind them.

Law and Odor

"It's a mystery to me how these companies can legally protect themselves when their analysts make these kinds of recommendations," Bob moaned.

"And pop goes the Internet Bubble," sang someone from under a nearby rock. The rock moved to reveal a small, slender, reddish brown animal with a white underpart that called himself Ulyssel Weasel and spoke with a lisp.

"It's so simple," said Ulyssel Weasel. "You just have to carefully phrase your wording so that Joe Public thinks 'this is all Greek to me' when it's read. I'm a legal weasel specializing in financial disclaimer language. My job is to make sure escapist weasel language the size of mouse print is added after recommendations are made. Haven't you heard of the Freedom of Misinformation Act? This language warns the reader that the information is not to be relied on in any way for making investment decisions. Things have to balance. This is a financial business for goodness sakes. Nothing plus nothing equals nothing."

"Thanks for nothing. I don't follow," said Bob.

"You're not supposed to follow, silly," said Ulyssel Weasel. "It means that recommendations are made, but no one can be held legally responsible if the reader relies on them to his or her detriment. It means that the information you just finished reading is as reliable and trustworthy as a street sign which reads 'Drug Free Zone.' It means that it can be 100% fact-free. If you don't mind my saying so, I think it's quite crafty the way I am able to defang laws and regulations. That's why they use guys like me who can suck the contents out of an egg while leaving the shell superficially intact. You see this disclaimer language is the equivalent of telling *you* to go suck on an egg. Someone has to draw a line in the information sand to help keep the brokerage world safe for hypocrisy. Hee. Hee. Hee. I think it's time you talked to a financial ferret if you want to avoid nest egg on your face. Or maybe you should talk to Dr. No about pushing the limits of hazy boundaries."

Ferret or Foul

Ulyssel Weasel then darted into a nearby hole and disappeared. Noises could be heard, like muffled talking, and another weasel-like creature emerged from the same hole, mostly colored white, but with black feet. It was a black-footed ferret with a raccoon-like mask that introduced itself as Inspector Cluefaux, a former member of the Commission des Operations de Bourse—the French stock-market regulator. He had a nasal sounding voice and spoke with a broken Parisian accent. The inspector was dragging a book behind him with the title *Financial Shenanigans: How to Detect*

Accounting Gimmicks and Fraud in Financial Reports, by Howard Schilit.

"I hope you have learned by now how untrustworthy information can be Monsieur Catz," said Cluefaux. "I wear a mask to remind me of how frequently information is masked. Trust no one my friend, not even me. Even so-called conservative banks have trillions of dollars of loans on the books that are valued only according to the time of the loan agreement, not current market value. That's why when times get tough they can come up with lots of ugly surprise announcements for investors. Earnings reports by themselves don't offer sufficient information. You have to look beneath the surface of corporate statements and reports. You have to learn how sales and profits were truly achieved.

"It's been called the earnings game, selective disclosure, aggressive accounting, creative accounting and cooking the books. The purpose is to hide from the public what's really happening in a company. It's about quality of earnings that's important, not quantity. On October 11th 1990, the Dow started heading upward, staying firmly in bull market territory. If it stays in bull market territory by October 11th 2000, it will mark ten years. This success has helped cover up the massive accounting irregularities that are going on. Bull markets don't just breed brilliance."

"I learned a little from Lubri Cat, the accounting cheetah and Kitty Cash. What else can you tell me?" asked Bob.

"I can't teach you all the tricks accountants use to paint a sunny picture," Cluefaux offered. "There are so many of them. Basically, what companies do is in one way or another exclude expenses to make their profits look better than they are and add earnings from other sources like venture capital investments in other companies, which have little or nothing to do with operations. They also use artificial stimulants such as buying back shares to boost earnings performance since the fewer shares that are in the marketplace the better earnings look. The accounting cheetahs reformulate the numbers so you are dealing with faux earnings, which don't give a clue to what is really true. That's why my job is to be Inspector Cluefaux. The worst cases are those that involve outright fraud where fictitious sales are created—so-called revenue recognition situations. You can't rely on stock market analysts from brokerage firms to help. As Lord Ha Ha informed you, independent research is as much an oxymoron as sales education."

"So, how can I learn to become an Inspector Cluefaux?" asked Bob.

"Forget about stock market analysts, Monsieur Catz," advised Cluefaux. "The only analysts that matter for the little investor like you and short traders are the bond analysts: the ones that look at the credit worthiness of a company and the ability to deal with debt. It wasn't until *Amazin'StockPrice.Com* floated a bond that investors started getting a better picture of what's going on with that company. Bond analysts get rewarded for being leader-of-the-pack worriers and pains in the assets. They like to ferret out weaknesses in company financials like profit and loss statements looking backward more than forward. With the common practice of smoke and mirror accounting real earnings can be a lot less than they appear to be—which means that stock values can be a lot higher than they should be. They specialize in tracking accounting cheetahs. Stock market analysts are, by and large, salesmen in disguise and spin doctors for investment banks and brokerage houses. The information is heavily tainted—'fruit of the poisoned tree.' You also want to look at information that companies have to supply the government.

"Companies have to file annual reports called 10K and quarterly reports within forty-five days after a quarter ends called 10Q with the SEC. There are also 8K forms that deal with amendments to 10Q when a material event occurs. You can access this information at the government's Web site www.sec.gov under the Edgar section as well as at Freedgar.com. Edgar stands for Electronic Data Gathering and Analysis. Through Edgar, you can now access SEC reports without charge and learn about pending lawsuits, S-1 or stock registration statements and other material information. Check out www.sec.gov/edaux/forms.htm regarding SEC forms description too and www.sec.gov/edaux/formlynx.htm for looking at companies."

"What other sites do you like?" asked Bob.

"Companysleuth.com, hoovers.com, and wsj.com may be helpful for information on companies," answered Cluefaux. "Value Line Investment Survey is available in libraries with easy to understand information on hundreds of companies in dozens of different industries. Sites such as www.newspage.com can help you track business news of interest. Charts can be helpful in my detective work, so I look at sites such as bigcharts.com. Information won't empower you. Only knowledge will. Doing your homework can be fun when you make money at it. You don't want to rely on so-called experts with a sales agenda. It's not only accounting that has lack of transparency. Now, I have to get back to my Ferret or Foul Detective Agency. It's my night job."

"What other kind of work do you do?" asked Bob.

"Right now I'm lookin' for rats," Cluefaux replied. "Ferrets are used to kill rats. The investment industry is filled with them. Newsletters are one of my favorite rat hunts. You have newsletters that own the very stocks they are promoting. That's illegal and called 'front running.' Newsletters can also be paid by companies to promote their stocks. If they don't announce the relationship, it's illegal. Famous people sometimes use their name in newsletters when they may be barely involved at all. Newsletters can also be used as a way to draw investors in for money management purposes. In fact, that is the main purpose of many newsletters, not to inform you monsieur. *Au revoir.*"

Inspector Cluefaux looked around and then darted back into the hole. Sir Real continued his walk around the moat with Bob firmly in the saddle.

What's Up Doc?

> *The 1990s have witnessed one of the great bull markets in American history. Whether that means an unstable bubble has developed in its wake is difficult to assess.*
>
> —Alan Greenspan
> Chairman of the Federal Reserve Bank, 1999

"Although I'm learning a lot," said Bob, "we seem to be just wandering around in a circle. Are we lost?"

"Not all who wander are lost or lost dogs, Mr. Catz," said Sir Real. "Now take a look upward."

There was an Olympic-class diving board perched about sixty feet above the moat. On it was a giant octopus with hands instead of tentacles and it was wearing dark glasses. The strange looking creature bounced up and down on the board singing the Rolling Stones' song about being stuck between a rock and a hard place. It dove off the board doing a somersault in the air before making an enormous splash in the moat.

"*Dr. Green Spin* comes out every day trying to determine whether the economy will experience a hard landing involving little growth such as only 1% or go underwater and tank: what is called a recession involving at least six months of negative growth or shrinking of the economy," explained Sir Real. "He keeps jumping into the moat trying to see whether he can figure out how to orchestrate a soft landing: healthy economic growth, but not high enough to trigger inflation. His critics maintain that all he does is go overboard loosening or overtightening on credit after he tests the waters. Financial writers have mentioned in the past how he can practically walk on water and guide the economy through the roughest and uncharted seas. I don't like the sound of that last dive. It sounded more like a thud than a splash. *Dr. Green Spin* is always diving into pools of ignorance. In spite of all the great advances in data gathering and technology, much of the Fed business is about giant leaps in faith. He doesn't operate on real time like I do. His reports can be as out of date as a mutual fund. I hope he isn't injured from that last dive into the unknown."

"He looks so much like the Federal Reserve Building and several of his hands appear to be deformed," said Bob.

"He looks that way because he is the embodiment of the Federal Reserve. Those hands aren't deformed. Two of his hands are definitely in the shape of buckets. One is used to throw cold water occasionally on Wall Street pundits who claim to know what he is going to do next or supposed to do next," said Sir Real. "The second hand is used to bail out the economy with interest rate cuts. The third hand is so tight fisted that it's hard to tell. Rumor has it that this hand is to be used as an emergency bucket to bail out small investors. *Green Spin* keeps denying this without revealing his hand while claiming that the public perceives an illusion based on a delusion, which will only lead to future pain and confusion."

Dr. Green Spin swam towards Bob and Sir Real using his hands like paddles and occasionally stopping to adjust his sunglasses. He was the size of a giant octopus, the type seen in Puget Sound, Washington. However, he had a deep almost hypnotic gray color, which glowed and reminded Bob that he still had not left Grayland. When he spoke, it sounded like an echo. One of his hands contained a short stick of some kind, which he waved about.

"*Dr. Green Spin* I presume," said Bob.

"Yes. That's me," said *Dr. Green Spin*. "You can call me by my first name if you like. My full name is *Dr. Alien Green Spin*."

"I understand from your invitation that I'll be able to attend the next meeting on interest rates," said Bob.

"That was a big mistake," said *Dr. Green Spin*. "We do make mistakes you know. People forget that hawks and doves at the Federal Reserve are only human. Key meetings of the Federal Reserve are held privately. Transcripts of these meetings are even kept secret for five years. There is no possible way you could be allowed into one of our meetings."

"But how could a mistake like that be made?" asked Bob. "You are the great *Dr. Alien Green Spin*, universally admired, an economic superstar with out-of-this-world monetary speeches."

"Okay. Enough already with the media exaggeration," said *Dr. Green Spin*. "My first term as Chairman began August 11th 1987. Before that, I was a Federal Reserve Board Governor. A couple of months after my appointment, we had the 1987 stock market crash. Why does that make me great? Since I have been Chairman the U.S. suffers repeatedly from the worst trade deficits on record and companies and individuals have set new borrowing records. In 1991, we not only experienced a recession, but it also took the Fed nearly half a year to realize we were even in a recession. We didn't foresee the global crisis of 1998 and barely avoided disaster. I'm just an orchestra leader, a consensus builder at the Fed, maybe a maestro of persuasion, but not a magician. That is an orchestra baton, you see, in one of my hands. It is not some monetary magic wand that will be able to automatically cushion the effects of years of monetary excess if things start to get out of control. The perception many investors have unfortunately is that interest rate cuts are the solution to all problems. It makes for interesting quick news, but is far more complicated than that. The public relies on a lot of ignorant reporting. Recycled information from brokerage houses and mutual fund companies isn't the same as knowledge. That's what I learned in Japan at Sashimi College."

"What do you mean?" Bob asked.

"You learned from Noella that the Fed has set a speed limit for economic growth of 3.5%. A higher growth rate than that is supposed to trigger inflation. Just two years ago, we were saying it was 2.5%. Some of the voting members think that it should be around 5% based on our fabled productivity gains, allowing for greater growth without triggering inflation problems. It's just a guessing game where I present the final figure agreed on for the time being. Although there is a lot I can handle even with all my hands full, it's easy to err and overplay a hand. There is a lot of psychology involved. Maintaining consumer confidence is critical. So even when the economy walks like a duck, quacks like a duck and looks like a sitting duck, I can spin upbeat language denying it's a duck. When times start to look tough I cushion my language and talk about prolonged subpar economic performance and continued weakness with the possibility of heightened risk. I like to talk like that. Don't you? Brokerage economists are often naturals at spinning positive sounding news because the business they are in is about selling investment vehicles. They are for the most part salespeople first and economists second—coming from the same working environment as Lord Ha Ha. They can see rainbows at the end of my soaking tub."

"Isn't a diving board a rather crude way to figure out whether the economy might tank?" Bob commented.

"That's my point. Aside from psychology, the major tools of the Fed are managing the growth of the money supply and controlling the costs of borrowing. Monetary policy of raising or lowering interest rates is a blunt instrument, like diving into the unknown. We could have a soft landing when interest rates rise, which involves the economy slowing down without much hardship, a hard landing involving negligible growth and increased hardship or an outright recession—where the economy shrinks for a minimum of two consecutive quarters. The recession can be mild, involving just a short time or severe going on month after month or even year after year. A soft landing would be good news. However, a slower economy still means in the best of situations, smaller profits for companies and growth.

"Then again, it could start out as a soft landing, but change into a hard landing because of the heavy debt loads of individuals and corporations and unprecedented dependence on the stock market. Some believe that what is driving a lot of this current economic expansion is the boom in lending from cheap and easy borrowing power. Some have dared to even call me Chairman of the Credit Bubble, who has allowed a situation to develop where the stock market now dictates policy instead of the Fed. Once the interest rate power is used, one can never tell for sure what the final result will be. My job, in part, is to engineer a landing without the economy going underwater, but my hands may be tied in the future by inflation concerns, maintaining confidence in the dollar, massive corporate and consumer debt burdens, et cetera. Whatever I do could look like the right decision at the moment, but turn out to be the wrong one in the long run. The financial crisis of 1998 was a symptom of serious global problems, which just keep getting papered over until the next crisis. At least in 1998, at the time rates were cut to stave off a disaster, inflation was only around 1.5%. The next time rates might be cut to avoid a serious downturn the extra liquidity could give a boost to inflation if it's a much higher rate than it was in the recent past making my rate cut less effective once inflation is factored in."

"Is there any way to tell in advance a recession is coming?" asked Bob.

"No sure way," said *Dr. Green Spin.* "However, there are two good indicators of the possibility of a recession. First, the stock market heads into bear territory for a while. Secondly, the interest rate structure changes. The government borrows money for short-term obligations like covering payroll and long-term ones. The long-term obligations of ten or more years tend to pay higher rates of interest than the short-term ones. Naturally, a lender expects to be paid higher rates for waiting longer for the financial instrument to mature."

"Naturally," said Bob.

"Sometimes the central bank boosts short-term interest rates on new obligations so fast that they end up being higher than the rates for new long-term obligations, which are set by the bond market. This can happen when the economy needs to be cooled quickly because of worries about the possibility of inflation. Instead of an upward sloping line on a graph showing interest rates going higher the longer you hold the obligations, the line starts out higher in the beginning. This is called an inverted yield curve and is a classic signal for recession."

"Both inflation and interest rate increases involve time lags. Collection of data can involve bad statistics and temporary factors. The same information can be interpreted many different ways. Although stock prices tend to fall before a recession, there is an old joke about the stock market having predicted nine of the last three recessions. The interest rate increases that started in June of this year, 1999, won't be felt until next year. It takes six months or more before the effects of higher borrowing costs filter through the economy; and a year or more before the full effects are seen. On the other hand, with the new economy, who knows for sure what will happen? A speeding economy now could end up looking like a slow motion movie later if things really do average out. In Japan, which has experienced over a decade of serious economic problems, the central bank was very slow to curb fast rising prices particularly in real estate and the stock market in the late 1980s. Then it was too slow to give the economy a break by easing interest rates when it went into a nosedive. Now they can't seem to come out of their economic rabbit hole. Can I tell you a little secret?"

"Yes," Bob answered swiftly.

"The public is told time and time again that a recession involves six months of economic contraction. However, that is just a convenient definition. It's the NBER, the National Bureau of Economic Research's Business Cycle Dating Committee that pros often look to. The non-profit NBER found at www.nber.org looks at factors such as depth and duration of an economic contraction. There are other definitions, too. Whatever the definition, guys like me avoid the R word in public so as not to spook investors. I don't like to talk like that. Do you?"

Doctor Doctor Give Me Some News

"Since I can't attend the Federal Open Market Committee meeting, could you tell me a little more about how this system works? There must be some rhyme and reason to it," asked Bob.

"Inflation will take a bite out of your purchasing power if it gets a chance," explained *Dr. Green Spin*. "So the Fed must be on the lookout for signals way in advance. Statistics are not necessarily reliable and since I live in an ocean of money, there is always a fishy smell. So I consider many statistics before I ring the interest rate bell."

"Like what?" asked Bob.

"I look at various indices such as the health of the dollar, productivity levels, consumer and wage price increases, purchases by industry and the price of gold and whether yields on Treasury bonds are running hot or cold. I'm not the financial physician many think I am. My focus is more on watching for and treating symptoms than disease. I'm more like a modern day wish doctor hoping for the best with limited treatment options."

"Why is the performance of the bond market or gold market important?" asked Bob. "It's kind of alien to me *Dr. Green Spin.*"

"Rising bond and/or gold prices reflect market expectations of growth and faster inflation. What they think is a very important indication. If, for example, there is continued sickness in the price of gold it might mean that inflation won't take hold or that price drops, deflation, will get hold and interest rate cuts will get weak and grow old. These signals are my canaries in a coalmine—alerting me to any future danger sign. The Fed controls short-term interest rates by loans directly to banks, but mostly from the fact that banks often need to borrow from each other. So the Fed determines the cost of their overnight loans to one another. The bond market reads my speeches closely and senses whether I plan or should raise short-term interest rates well in advance. New Treasury bond yields can start shooting upward like plants."

"It looks like your job is quite a handful," observed Bob.

"I need to have many a hand," said *Dr. Green Spin*, "because I have no idea where the economy will land. I like to say that on the one hand it could be this, while on the other hand it could be that—while I juggle priorities like a financial acrobat. Fortunately, most investors don't recall that shortly after I was hired, there was a stock market crash. However, I remember how value can disappear in a flash. Some think that the Fed raised interest rates too quickly and overtightened on credit. But now I'm being accused of doing the opposite, and might live to regret it.

"The Fed has to not only manage the economy, but investor expectation, which in this low inflation economy is suffering from high inflation. You see, inflation is not just about consumer prices going up like those in a grocery store. It's also about financial asset appreciation in stocks, real estate and a heck of a lot more. The stock price, when divided by earnings per share, creates a ratio you know called the P/E—a measurement of value on which many agree. For the past eighty years, it's been around 15.3 to 1. But recently, it's been around double that sum. Just going back to the average won't be that much fun. Inflation will force me to raise interest rates, which will then shrink the P/E. When it happens again, you might not like what you see. In a way, it's understandable that after so many years, investors are accustomed to double-digit gain. But will they still like me if I pull hard on the interest rate chain? A pendulum doesn't swing only one way. That's what the law of the average would say.

"If the stock market would continue to grow at a double digit rate, it would be worth more than the entire economy—if you contemplate. One recent survey found that the average investor now expects around an 18.6% annual return. This shows that the average investor has a lot to learn. With just $100,000, that yearly yield would be worth in the year 2065 many billions, if the investor was still alive."

"Can you give me any tips before you go back to your diving board?" Bob asked.

"When the thirty-year Treasury bond," *Dr. Green Spin* began, "which the government uses to borrow, offers a steady yield greater than 6.2, I would keep a closer eye on my stocks, if I were you."

"Why is that?" asked Bob.

"The bond market has quite a few pros—who know a lot more than the general public knows," said *Dr. Green Spin*. "Also, stock owners are willing to take on greater risk, hoping to be better compensated. But many will move to higher safety when bond yields are inflated. As the Treasury bond yield rises, money will start flowing away in larger amounts from the stock market planet—drawn to the relatively higher safety and improving yields of the bond market magnet. Remember, a bubble is created when prices and true values become very disconnected. The nature of bubbles is to get bigger and last longer than anyone expected. Eventually even the skeptics give up—that's when you're least protected. The public is fickle and now sees me as a winner. But should I fail, they'll have octopus for dinner. The biggest bubble of all is probably my reputation, but like all bubbles we won't know for sure until much later the true situation. In spite of what you have been hearing about how everything has changed with the Internet highway I would be careful to observe all Fed yield signs—because ours have to do with the cost borrowing. It has been said that you can't fight the Fed."

"Can't you give me a teenie weenie prediction about the future?" Bob asked. "I've heard you are a master at hedging your statement."

"Okay, but this is strictly off the record. In 2001 the U.S. economy will have its head to a gun. By 2002 a global slowdown will ensue which will be obvious to all but a few. In 2003 Wall

Street blind will again claim they can see. But in 2004 stock market returns will not be anywhere as good as before."

Without another word, *Dr. Green Spin* sank into the moat leaving nothing but a trail of bubbles on the surface. The bubbles, though, formed a pattern of letters and Bob took out his note pad. It was information on the Federal Reserve Website (www.federalreserve.gov/) where you could find information on the speeches of *Dr. Green Spin*, meeting notes of the Fed, as well as Beige Book summaries, the kind Hawk Talk carried.

Hedge or Tales

Bob and Sir Real continued to wind around the moat on their final leg of the journey. In the distance, Bob could see large structures jutting out of the moat cylindrical in shape and gray in color. As they came closer and closer, Bob realized that they were like fossilized hedges arranged in a semicircle. On each of the dozen gigantic hedges was a small animal of some kind. Its back was covered with dense, erectile spines and occasionally some of them would roll into the shape of a ball for protection. A few of them wore tiny cowboy hats.

A voice cried out, "Don't scare them off." It was Noella floating by on a green colored nest egg the size of a mini-bus. A menu from the Mercury Theatre and Delicatessen was printed on it with white lettering. The selections ranged from chopped liver to lox—to bonds, precious metals, real estate and stocks. "All the non-food items are called securities," it further said. "But the only real security lies within your head."

"We've been looking all over for you," said Bob, by way of greeting.

"I came to Stonehedge to seek the advice of the hedgehogs," said Noella. "Some of the leading hedge fund managers are here. They won't talk to you because you are just a small investor."

"What do you mean?" asked Bob. "They aren't exactly big themselves."

"As you can see, the hedges are arranged in a certain pattern in the moat," said Noella. "The hedgehogs control a very private pool of funds. They can use all kinds of techniques not permitted by mutual funds, such as selling short and borrowing large amounts of money for leverage. This flexibility allows the hedgehogs to hedge their bets in many ways and take advantage of opportunities not available with other kinds of funds. They are non-directional and not dependent on markets going up. Hedge funds in theory can hedge against falling markets.

"Hedge funds don't have to follow any particular formula. They can hedge their bets numerous ways including the use of what are called put options, which give the holder the right to sell stock at a higher price when it's value drops. It doesn't have the risks of short selling because you can either exercise the option or not. The most you can lose is what you paid for the option. Simply put, the put option provides insurance against a stock dropping in price, allowing you to put any loss on the other party to the contract. There is a joke going around about the 'put.'"

"Are you putting me on?" Bob asked.

"No," assured Sir Real. "It has to do with the belief that *Dr. Green Spin*'s future willingness to supply interest rate medicine will be insurance against a sick stock market becoming deathly ill. It's not a real put option, of course. It's a bet, a multi-trillion dollar question, and the mother of all assumptions: that despite what *Green Spin* says, if the stock market gets into serious trouble, he will have to swim to the rescue of drowning investors and save their monetary skins by cutting interest rates so that they can sell their stock at a higher price.

"Even though investors put no value on past performance of equities, they are putting great value on what the good doctor is likely to do. Hiding inside that assumption is another assumption that such cuts, if they do occur, will work like they did in the recent past, even though the circumstances are likely to be different. Factors like banks tightening upon loans to corporations, corporations stuck with too many goods, and an overvalued dollar limiting exports could dilute the effectiveness of interest rate cuts. Who knows? They may work or prove to be just another part of the great American financial myth tree, leaving many an investor out on a limb. To bailout or not to bailout. That is supposed to be the great American shakes-experience question. However, it may be the wrong question."

"I guess the proof will be in the putting," said Bob. "How can these hedgehogs do what they do? It looks like more fun than being a fat cat."

"Nothing is as fun as being a huge fat cat, except maybe being a rock star like *Mick Jaguar*," said Noella with a serious tone. "However, hedge fund managers can make big bucks: like 20% or more of profits. Furthermore, they don't draw a salary. There are thousands of these hedge funds controlling hundreds of billions in assets. The SEC doesn't regulate them because they don't deal with small investors. You have to be an 'accredited investor.' It means you have a net worth of $1 million or more or an annual income of $200,000 or more in each of the two most recent years, or $300,000 jointly with a spouse; and have a reasonable expectation of reaching the same level of income in the present year. Let's not beat around the hedges. It's for the rich and institutions. The super rich use hedging strategies and don't just 'buy and hold.' That's sales propaganda for little investors. If 'buy and hold' was really that good, they wouldn't need hedgehogs."

"I have one more question," said Bob. "Why do a few of those hedgehogs wear cowboy hats?"

"Hedge funds have a few cowboys," said Noella, "who take incredible risks with the funds to try and achieve spectacular returns like the jokers who nearly brought down the financial system in 1998. By and large, hedge funds tend to use their financial tools conservatively to cover assets while making a decent return. Heavy Treasury bond purchases by hedge funds have helped keep mortgage rates down. So the general population may feel their presence indirectly at times in beneficial ways, too. It's their lack of regulation and secrecy which poses a threat to the financial system. They live in the dark and so does the public when it comes to their darkside. It is amusing and ironic that so many of the billions used to speculate and possibly destabilize the financial system come from pension and endowment funds of conservative institutions."

What . . . Me Worry?

> *A four year old child could understand this. Get me a four year old child.*
>
> —Groucho Marx

"Since I don't meet the minimum requirements to deal with a hedgehog, what am I to do?" asked Bob, dismayed.

"Even if you did meet the minimum requirements," Noella explained, "it doesn't necessarily mean you should deal with them. It's their way of doing business that is important. An all-seasons strategy for investing is about hedging your bets. Financial advisers often mention the importance of spreading your assets. They will tell you how studies suggest that the way you structure your portfolio or how you arrange your assets among the three basic asset classes of stocks, bonds and cash or cash equivalents, like money market funds, is far more important than picking specific stocks, bonds or mutual funds."

"But isn't it true," Sir Real asked, "that such asset allocation may be a myth, too?"

"Yes, it's true, you sly dog," responded Noella. "Spreading your assets is typically geared to what is being marketed by the brokerage firm in the form of securities of one kind or another. It's not true asset allocation because hard assets like real estate, art, coins, insurance, et cetera are often not included. Moreover, as Nancy Shrew mentioned, computer models for asset allocation are far from perfect. Additionally, these asset allocation studies promoted by the financial industry are subject to criticism not mentioned by your typical adviser. There are articles with titles like 'The Myth of Asset Allocation' also in the literature."

"Isn't it true that financial myths are nothing new?" Sir Real grilled Noella.

"Yes, yes, it's true," Noella answered. "The financial world is filled with myth through and through. Japan is now the land of the rising debt with a stock market cut by over 50% for over a decade. With the worldwide crisis of 1998, gold should have shot up in value. Instead, it sank in value as foreign interests decided that the U.S. dollar and bonds were better bets. Conventional wisdom has to do with a particular moment in time, which often is irrelevant at another point in time. Internet investment enthusiasts have mentioned how prospects are so great that the normal business cycle involving a slackening of demand doesn't apply. Even earnings aren't really important. Such beliefs have helped to fuel the current market boom. The biggest myth of all may one day prove to be the current popular belief that proper financial and investing education can come from non academic sales oriented brokerage firms, mutual fund companies and TV programs. It may prove to be just a wild fantasy, a bad retirement dream, or a lawsuit nightmare. The future will determine how much is hit or myth. All I know is that the market makes fools of fools."

"No fooling?" Bob responded

"Asset allocation rests on the belief that you just never know for sure what is going to happen next," Noella continued. "Asset allocation was quite popular for awhile after the 1987 stock market crash. It's been said that asset allocation tends to become popular when portfolios go up in smoke and investors become smoked financial chickens. Asset allocation has performed poorly if you just look at short-term performance. It's not designed for a particular moment in time. It's designed to work over time. I spoke to Woody Allen the other day and he told me, '90% of success is just showing up.' Woody is an egghead comedian but a serious chicken. Asset allocation is about showing up in all kinds of different asset categories to hedge your bets. Different asset classes don't often march to the beat of the same drummer.

"Diversification is sometimes confused with asset allocation. Diversification has to do with spreading your bets within an asset class. In the case of equities, you should look at international as well as domestic stocks, for example. You should look at large cap, mid cap, and small cap stocks, et cetera. Today's winners can be tomorrow's turkeys. In 1988, for example, the best performing stocks overall were international according to some standard measurements. The worst performing stocks were large cap growth. In 1989, the reverse was true with international at the bottom and large cap growth at the top of the performance charts. Equity diversification helps smooth out overall performance. I have to leave now. I'm going to see a chick flick called *Chicken Soup for Your Portfolio*. It's the thirtieth sequel of that over-marketed *Chicken Soup for Anything We Can Sell* series. It goes to show you that there is a lot of money to be made on even a chicken sure subject with very little diversification. However, when it comes to investing you sure better be chicken and diversified."

Noella floated away on her nest egg. Bob patted Sir Real on the side and he started walking again. The scenery kept getting greener and greener as they wandered into pastureland.

Cow Tales

"It's true what they say about greener pastures elsewhere," observed Bob. "The grass is a dazzling emerald green. Why even that cow over there is green."

"That's a cash cow belonging to *Warren Bassett* the world famous investor who they say can milk profits out of stone," Sir Real told Bob.

"A $10,000 investment in his company in 1980 would be worth a small fortune by now. Her name is Moolah. Let's go see if we can get some information."

Sir Real approached Moolah, nipping at her hoofs in the Corgi herding fashion. She kicked backwards well over Sir Real's head, but only narrowly missing Bob's. Soon Moolah was herded next to the side of the moat.

"Okay, I confess. I'm one of *Warren Bassett's* cash cows. Warren won't speak to you. He doesn't like to give interviews. That's why you don't see him on television financial news like *See 'N Be Seen*. Television business news to him is for entertaining small investors like you, Bob. Besides, you came unprepared to give him any treats. *Warren Bassett* regularly consumes cherry colas, hamburgers, T-bone steaks and Dairy Queen Blizzards. Why do you think he still looks so good after just turning seventy?"

"It must be some sort of a contrarian health diet. Well," Bob began, "tell us what you can. Next time I'll bring him something."

"Good," said Moolah. "First of all, you have to understand that Warren talks in a classy manner, but he acts like a junkyard dog. Contrary to popular opinion, he is not just a stock market guy. He loves all kinds of junk as long as he can find value in it, including good junk bonds. He likes to buy them 'pre-owned' on the secondary market from investors who sell them to him at bargain prices like sixty cents in the dollar. Warren also likes to buy stock in companies with strong franchise operations, great brand names and excellent cash flow at bargain prices. He wants investments that have long-lasting potential for superior profits and then he buys these good, but weakened companies, at a low enough price to provide a wide margin of safety. Warren likes his companies to be good to the bone. *Warren Bassett* has been called the most successful investor of all time, the sage of Omaha, the seer of Nebraska, the Oracle from the Midwest and at least twenty other titles in thirty-six languages including Latin. I'm just kidding— about the languages. It's forty-six."

"What else can you tell us?" asked Bob.

"Warren has had problems lately," said Moolah. "Maybe it's age, but he can't seem to get his profits up like before. He was a student of the great value investor Benjamin Graham. Bassets, like Corgis, are low to the ground value investors; and Warren loves to read newspapers like the Wealth Corgis. He is a newspaper junkie too."

"The value approach, as you know, is based on buying stocks at low prices with good earnings prospects. Four out of five stocks that are beaten down probably deserve to be beaten up. Warren can tell the difference between a diamond in the rough and a lump of coal. The skill is to figure out the one out of five that is worthwhile; and Warren has been phenomenal at wandering through the maze of stocks to hunt down the best values. In fact, the word warren means maze from an old French word for game farm, *garenne*. I bet you knew that already."

"Sure," Bob said, "just like I knew about the Riksbank in Sweden. Please go on."

"Despite Warren's phenomenal successes over the years, his investment company has been buffeted by the sea of change of the new economy stock market and has lost a considerable amount of value lately. This year it had its worst performance ever with some disgruntled shareholders saying he should call it the Warren Buffeted Company. Sometimes having a lot of smarts and a great track record aren't enough especially during these dot com times. So what if he is still worth tens of billions of dollars. There have even been bad jokes circulating that he should be put to sleep like an old dog, except he has already been asleep at the technology switch for years.

"Warren hasn't invested in the new technology companies because he has considered them to be outside his area of competence. Bassets are really slow moving dogs. Warren likes to use detailed projections based on a long history of past performance and the type of competitive environment to be faced in the future. Using traditional valuation methods, he has had a problem trying to make sense of many these technology company valuations; and figuring out which ones will succeed and which ones will fail in a fast changing industry. Moreover, he has been concerned about how the market seems to be so heavily focused on a narrow group of technology stocks. According to his critics, he therefore missed many of the big opportunities of late, which have powered the U.S. stock market to all-time highs. Warren doesn't care about his critics. As an old cash cow lover he remains typically uncowed by criticism from new technology loving commentators. He is only concerned about protecting shareholders in his company and finding what he considers worthwhile value. *Bassett* likes to buy when he feels that investments are selling for a lot less than they are worth. Value and growth distinctions touted by the Wall Street marketeers are meaningless distinctions to him because it's always about value and the relationship to price. Whatever you learned about growth vs. value from Sir Real reflects Wall Street's perception of reality, not the beliefs of *Mr. Bassett*. As far as he is concerned growth and value are sacred cows that need to be slaughtered by wise investors. There has been too much growth in ignorance and too little value placed on fundamentals."

"Isn't there any way I can find out more about the slow moving legendary *Warren Bassett*?" Bob asked.

"Since so much of the financial world is about theatre," replied Moolah, "Warren has adopted a stage name: Warren Buffett. You can find copies of his annual reports to shareholders at www.berkshirehathaway.com. *Warren Bassett* mentioned in an annual meeting in 1998 that probably the best book to read on his investing style is one by a professor Lawrence A. Cunningham at Cardozo Law School in New York, called *The Essays of Warren Buffett*. You can probably order it through *Amazin'StockPrice.Com*. It's certainly no cash cow, but an incredible bookstore."

"One more question," Bob insisted. "Can you tell us what he's up to lately?"

"He is being his usual contrarian heretical self," said Moolah.

"What do you mean?" asked Bob.

"One of things he is doing is buying entire insurance companies— lox, stock and bagel as Noella would say," Moolah mooed.

"Aside from selling insurance, what do they do?" asked Bob.

"Invest in bonds," exclaimed Moolah.

"Bonds?" asked Bob. "Why that's udderly amazing. What about stocks for the long run? What about buy and hold? Isn't that what he is known for?"

"Remember, I just told you he is a big buyer of junk bonds," said Moolah. "So that's just another part of the huge myth tree."

"*Warren Bassett* likes to buy and hold after blood is in the streets and he has picked up super bargains," said Sir Real. "He likes to buy when the stock market starts acting like it has Mad Dow disease, and good times no longer provide advice givers from big brokerage firms immunity from foot in the mouth symptoms. He doesn't just buy and hold. Speaking of bonds, we better get back to the drawbridge and go into the bakery if you want to see some of our bond movies. You are running out of dream time. And the economic skyline is getting cloudy even though you may not see it yet. Bolts of lightning never come out of the blue. There is always a cloud although it may not be visible. Hot air from New Era pipe dreams is beginning to collide with cold reality. Hot air in contact with cold usually leads to thunderstorms that can rain on the parades of little investors."

Buy Buy Bye Miss American Pie

Sir Real allowed Moolah to move on and he picked up speed running as fast as he could on his little legs. The liquid in the moat sloshed back and forth making louder and louder noises. When they reached the point at which they began, the drawbridge was gone with a few wooden rowboats attached by rope to a rotted piling. There was a notice that read: "To Our Valued Customers And Friends. The recent overpriced acquisition of Marie Antoinette Corporation by Guillotine Brothers Bankcorp has necessitated a broad restructuring effort resulting in the sale of the bridge used by common pedestrian traffic. A lot of expensively purchased goodwill has gone bad. Although financial waters appear to be very choppy, with daily market volatility for stocks approaching the highest levels since just before the 1929-32 bear market, economists in general continue to provide fair weather forecasts mixed with sunny predictions. There is no need for concern. Feel free to come and visit us any time. Transportation is available. Our research analysts miss the boat on a regular basis. As for our institutional and ultra-affluent clients, may we invite your attention to our state of the art private entrance built underneath the moat. There is no need for our 'white shoe' clientele to be on the same boat as small investors. For your added comfort we provide *Lattesbucks* coffee with cream of the crop information. We trust this will meet with your satisfaction. The Management."

"C'mon, Bob," suggested Sir Real. "Let's get going. You already missed the boat before by not buying at the high end of the technology boom according to many popular financial articles. Seriously speaking, the song never remains the same in the financial world despite what you heard from Simon and Garfunkel in their 'Bridge Over Troubled Water' song. That's why there is no longer is a bridge over these troubled waters. Remember how that popular song "Take This Job and Shove It" was followed some time later by the song "I Wish I Had A Job To Shove?" That's the change in economic tune I'm talking about. Okay, I'll push from behind and herd the boat across the moat. I'm great at doing the dog paddle."

Bob jumped in with Sir Real pushing the boat toward the front of the bakery with his nose. The liquid composed of semi-solid numbers was not only rough to paddle through; some of it was becoming hardened and illiquid. With great effort, they crossed the moat and jumped up to the landing, which was above ground like the rest of the bakery. The doors of the "Let Them Eat Fake Bakery" were shaped and colored to look like slices of white bread soaked with butter. Graffiti had been scrawled on them: phrases like "underwriting is our bread and butter" and "our analysts know how to butter up to companies," "home of the famous *Junk Bond*, often the most profitable product in the investment dough making business" and "our junk bonds sell like hot cakes."

The doors opened automatically as the pair approached. Bob once again mounted Sir Real as they entered the pie shaped bakery. Squeals of delight and laughter could be heard coming from somewhere in the building. The pair came into a bare anteroom with walls, ceiling and floor covered entirely with smoke-colored mirrors. Bob was unable to see himself in the mirrors, which he found disturbing. A young female deer came through one of two mirrored doors and greeted them. She said in a sweet charming voice:

> *The mirrors will only reflect what you fear,*
> *Your repressed emotions are not ready to appear.*
>
> *Moods and reality depend largely on self-view,*
> *I see you're not ready to see that it's true.*

"Is this a fancy way of telling me that I'm still refusing to see that I may be my own worst enemy as an investor? Are you in charge of the bakery?" Bob asked with a sense of excitement. The deer answered:

> *Hello, Hello,*
> *My name is Jane Doe*
>
> *I make lots of bread,*
> *And am rolling in dough.*

I was trained in Osaka where they greet you and say:
'Good morning, have you made any money today?'

I want it all, and I want it now,
I want it fast, and I don't care how.

My expectations are a source of excitement,
Consumption is my path to enlightenment.

I can buy anything except class,
If you find me attractive, please make a pass.

"Gee, I always thought the only thing money couldn't buy was poverty. You're quite a little deer, aren't you?" Bob exclaimed.

"Yes, but I'm certainly not shy about going after the really big bucks," Jane said with a sexy laugh. "But of course I don't really talk like that, do you?"

"Oh no," Bob protested as his cheeks turned slightly pink and his forehead muscles tightened. "You know, I was wondering if you could tell me something about the bakery? Your name is quite familiar to me. I've seen it mentioned in lawsuits and wanted posters."

"Yes, of course my dear. Welcome. Make yourself at home. Our casha is you casha as we bankers like to say in Español. This fine bakery is a small section of a minor subdivision of a major subsidiary of a mammoth corporation, which has more power than many a nation. Buying into other businesses is how it grew, which it controls from the city of Deja Vu. Bigger is supposed to be better, and is now all the rage—except if you've been downsized at the wrong time and age."

"Cool. Where can I also find the location for the bond movies?"

"If you take the second mirrored door to your right, you will find our restroom and the theatre. Please be quiet as the capitalist pigs are in the next room creating enormous amounts of synthetic bread derived from relatively small amounts of dough. The process is getting more and more artificial. They call these goodies complex derivatives. The amount of such bread consumed by the financial system is simply amazing. The same dough keeps getting stretched further and further, likah bigah pizza pie. That's amore, eh?"

"Maybe that's a morto, eh?" Bob responded. "I have a question Jane."

"Go ahead, shoot. Oops, wrong wording," Jane Doe replied with a giggle. "How will this bread hold up if the financial system one day drastically cools, like it nearly did in the recent past?" Bob asked.

"The pinstripe bread makers have absolutely no idea. They don't know because a serious downturn has never tested the quality of this new type of bread. They just keep repeating the New Era music like an old broken record. However, sooner or later, human nature being what it is, there's always a return to classic rock and roll over economics. One day the roll over may be much more than the system can handle. Jane Doe says that this may cost you dearly. If you want to save your bacon I wouldn't recommend just relying on the assurances of the Capitalist pigs about the security of securities. This is the same mentality behind bringing profitless 'hot' internet companies to market in order to get enormous commissions. Investment vehicles can appear to be a lot safer when they are test crashed from a low hill as opposed to a drop off from a high cliff. The public relies on the sales industry for much information. Sales types like to talk about how history shows this and history shows that. History shows that lowering interest rates can boost the stock market. However, history also shows that oil spikes tend to be followed by recessions, that budget surpluses tend to be followed by recessions and that great investment booms tend to be followed by great investment busts. History shows that the sales industry has a natural tendency to choose the history that helps make sales. Let's not forget too that past performance is not a reliable indicator of future performance. That's why investment literature has legal disclaimers. The same may apply to theories about the monetary system."

Bob wailed, "I don't understand. What are you saying? What do you think might happen to little old me and my nest egg?"

Jane stared intently at Bob and started singing as she left the room, "You will have a hard day's night, and you will be whimpering like a dog. But if we get through to you, and you do the things you should do, you should be alright."

Debt And Alive

Bob dismounted Sir Real and opened the second mirrored door. He walked in with Sir Real by his side. Voices could be heard arguing in a room that was totally in the dark. The voices sounded familiar. Bob felt his way to a seat and sat down. Within a few minutes, lights went on. The room was like a small cinema. Someone was singing a financial version of the Johnny Rivers' secret agent song: "Secret agent plan. Secret agent plan. We've given you an undercover rating and taken away your investment grade name." On the stage were a variety of animals all with tuxedos and black bowties arguing about who is the real bond with voices of famous actors like Pierce Brosnan, Roger Moore, Timothy Dalton and even George Lazenby who lasted for only one very forgettable Bond movie. There was a Chinese bond represented by a Pug named Pang from China, as well as a state bond from the government of North Carolina. A mongrel dog named David Bowie sang about how he borrowed money directly from the public for his rock and roll show so as not to have to deal with a bank. While a Dachshund wiener dog bragged it was a corporate bond for a hot dog manufacturer named Frank. There was a guide dog representing a bond to provide funds for education—and one from a former communist nation. A Komodor dog represented the world benchmark for safety, liquidity, and interest rates, the thirty-year Treasury bond with hair like a blond who called himself "Komodor Bond."

Suddenly there was silence. The theatre darkened until it was pitch black. Everyone scattered and a circle of light started moving from left to right across the stage. Inside was a spiral and the profile of a white Scottie dog with a bow tie. The sharp exciting Bond music was playing. The Scottie jumped out of the spiral and said with the voice of Sean Connery, "My name is Bond. *Junk Bond*." It was the real Bond, but was the smallest adult Scottie dog Bob had ever seen.

Bob and Sir Real moved close to the stage to speak to the famous *Junk Bond* who had a tattoo of Scotland Forever on his body, just like Sean Connery.

> *Even strangers know my drinks are shaken, and not stirred,*
>   *said Junk Bond.*
> *Isn't that truly absurd?*
>
> *That's why I've been rated as junk,*
> *The opposite of an investment grade hunk.*
>
> *It's all determined by a rating agency,*
> *Based on safety and transparency.*

You may ask, why loan to me?
Especially when I offer such a weak guarantee.

It's not just because I'm so great you see,
And females want to bond with me.

It's because I have a very attractive yield,
One of the best in the bond market field.

It's about balancing your risk tolerance against desire for
*   higher reward,*
My risk and yield are so high, I was given a double zero rating
*   award.*

Right now the junk bond default rate is the highest since the
*   end of the Second World War,*
As corporations with weak balance sheets take advantage of
*   low interest rates like never before.*

"Tell me, Mr. *Junk Bond*, how this rating of yours is determined as well as anything else you consider relevant," said Bob with great anticipation.

"Credit ratings are used to assess the likelihood of timely payment of interest and principal payments on corporate and government bonds," *Junk Bond* began. "They are about a credit agency's opinions at a particular time. Ratings can change upwards or downwards. There are two main categories: investment grade bonds and below investment grade or junk. The reason there are so many different characters playing *Junk Bond* with super low ratings, like double naught seven, is because any bond from a government or corporation can qualify as junk if its investment ratings fall low enough. Investors sometimes think investment grade bonds mean low risk—not necessarily. Investment grade can one day turn into junk if the credit rating falls far enough. Even conservative sounding insurance companies are big buyers of junk bonds. You should know by now that appearances are rarely what they seem in the financial world.

"Junk bonds, commonly called high yield bonds, have to pay extra because of added risk of default on payments of interest and/or principal. Historically, the fourth year after a junk bond has been issued is often the most critical year for determining likelihood of consistent payments. What is very worrisome, though, is that lately defaults on high yield or junk bonds are happening more and more frequently after only two to three years.

If corporate bond defaults scare off more and more investors, even the very good ones will suffer and liquidity will start drying up in the moat. This will have a broad impact on the economy since companies have become so dependent on investors for loans to expand, hire workers, buy inventory, et cetera.

"The king of bonds is the thirty-year Treasury bond, also known as the long bond. It is regarded as a risk-free investment because of its full faith and credit backing by the U.S. government. Approximately $14 trillion in such bonds is currently outstanding. The long bond has been used for many years as a benchmark or guidepost to compare performance of both stocks and bonds against something that is considered risk free. Junk bonds, on average, have yielded 4% more than Treasuries. Lately, it has been higher and some think the difference could double or go even higher by next year as investors demand higher yield for taking more risk—the so-called risk premium. Remember, the greater the difference or spread, the greater the market's fear of what lies ahead. Markets, though, can be stupid about what lies ahead. Before the financial crisis of '97-'98, there were many junk bonds that were offering yields not that much different from U.S. government bonds. Unsophisticated investors were snapping them up, indicating great overconfidence and misperception of risk.

"As the government continues a policy of trying to reduce its long-term debt, the ten year Treasury note has become more popular as a guide with many including *Dr. Green Spin*. A loan to the U.S. government that involves ten years or less is called a 'note.'"

Not once did Sir Real cross-examine the great Sean Connery-sounding *Junk Bond* as he normally questioned others Bob had met on his journey. As *Junk Bond* was finishing his sentence, Bob could feel him slipping away. Sir Real was getting more difficult to see.

"Why didn't you cross-examine *Junk Bond*?" Bob asked in a disappointed manner. "I would have enjoyed seeing a top dog attorney like you, Sir Real, fire question after question at *Mr. Bond*. He didn't look like that much of a challenge either. I am surprised how small he is in real life. Is it because both of you are in the service of the Queen, and it is difficult to try and serve my needs and the Queen's at the same time? Isn't it true that even a Queen's dog can't serve two masters?"

"Although conflicts of interest are quite common in the investing advice world, I can assure you that this had little influence on my decision not to cross examine secret agent *Junk Bond*. You really don't want to upset these bond fellows, especially that one. He is a 'distressed' bond, the most dangerous one of all."

"I don't understand."

"First, there are so many of them. The bond market dwarfs the stock market. In fact, the stock market is like a Corgi in some respects: a full sized dog standing on really short legs. Secondly, my tough cross-examination style based on real television might create fear. Bonds price in fear, shooting up their yields at a moment's notice while shooting down their values. Remember, a bond price moves in the opposite direction of yield. If they don't like what's going on with the economy, for example, their new higher yields and lowered values can start blowing away company after company that needs to borrow at reasonable rates, and can't afford to pay the increased interest required to satisfy buyers. Even presidents have to learn to respect what the bond market has to say when they work on budget proposals. Otherwise, they can have their programs shot out from under them. Even the great *Dr. Green Spin* has to worry about the bond market. He can cut rates all he wants to but the bond guys can still keep borrowing rates high by not going along if they are worried about inflation on the horizon. The bond market can start dumping U.S. government bonds at the slightest whiff of inflation, causing interest rates to shoot up, killing off recovery. Banks loan on the basis of long-term bond yields. Surely you remember how Woody Allen once remarked that he wanted to be reincarnated as actor/lover Warren Beatty's hands?"

"Yes, of course," Bob answered in a puzzled manner feeling that a trap was about to be sprung.

"Ah but you probably didn't know," Sir Real continued with relish "that James Carville, the Democratic campaign consultant, once said he wanted to be reincarnated as the bond market because of its tremendous power in Washington. That's why bond guys have been called the 'masters of the universe.' Green Spin and company control short term borrowing costs. Long term borrowing costs can be shot upwards by the bond guys any time they expect inflation."

"No, I didn't know," Bob admitted meekly.

"That's okay, Mr. Catz, you're still learning," Sir Real said. "Anyway, Mr. *Junk Bond* is so small in size because his investment rating and value have plummeted. Please understand his rating is no longer just below investment grade where he was often called a high yield bond, too. It's now been downgraded to highly speculative—pure junk. His yield had risen to a level where he was offering interest 10% higher than benchmark risk free U.S. thirty-year Treasury bonds to attract buyers. Investors are starting to demand big premiums for taking on added risk. They want to pay less for these bonds while demanding a higher and higher yield. This last year junk bond issuers have defaulted on some twenty-four billion in debt, a new record, and these are the good times. I felt he may have been dangerously close to default and suspending future interest payments, maybe even putting a permanent silencer on them."

"Thanks for your explanation. I feel highly indebted. Imagine what kind of trouble these junk bond guys can cause when economic times get really rough. No wonder *Junk Bond* movies are so popular."

"With the heavy corporate debt burden these days, I imagine there are quite a few bonds like him and lots of fireworks to come: between 1997 and 1999, $373 billion in junk bonds were issued according to credit rating agencies. I would like to talk more, but your time is just about over. You have had a long nap, Mr. Catz. And I've made a big investment in you, which I can't stay around to protect. The reality is that you have to wake up soon and pursue your financial dreams. As for me, I'm just like one of those high flying stocks with a great past but no future."

"But I'm not finished asking questions," said Bob anxiously. "When will I see you next my furry friend?"

"Only in your dreams, Bob. Only in your dreams," Sir Real answered warmly. "It's getting early and I'm so dog-tired. Besides we must have 'closure' because that's what they say. It's no use trying to call us. We'll . . . call you."

As Bob gave him a big good-bye hug, Sir Real started barking in protest, "Objection, move to strike, motion for reconsideration, appealable error, request permission to approach the bench, paw favor *Hehnayral* Custer Iyah dohn really wahna go," as he slowly vanished. Bob awakened on a leather sofa alone in his library surrounded by piles and piles of mind numbing, sleep inducing, financial material with one of his Corgis licking his face. He felt as if he had been asleep for days. Bob noticed a verse he had read just before falling asleep. It was by Bernard Barton:

As I walk'd by myself, I talk'd to myself,
And myself replied to me;
And the questions myself then put to myself,
With their answers, I give to thee.

Bob then sat down at his desk and began to make notes of his dream, hoping he would have another one like it soon.

The End